Lessons in Nature

Malcolm Beck

Lessons in Nature

Malcolm Beck

Fourth Edition, Revised

Acres U.S.A.
Austin, Texas

Lessons in Nature

Acres U.S.A.
P.O. Box 91299
Austin, Texas 78709 U.S.A.
(512) 892-4400 • fax (512) 892-4448
info@acresusa.com • www.acresusa.com

Printed in the United States of America

Publisher's Cataloging-in-Publication

Beck, Malcolm, 1936-
Lessons in nature / Malcolm Beck. Austin, TX, ACRES U.S.A., 2005
xxvi, 334 pp., 23 cm.
Includes Index
Includes Bibliography
ISBN 0-911311-80-7

1. Soil management. 2. Organic farming. 3. Agricultural ecology.
I. Beck, Malcolm, 1936- II. Title.

SF91.G45 631.4

Dedication

There have been many people who have touched my life from early childhood on. My parents, grandparents, aunts and uncles, school teachers, and even some good cops influenced and helped mold me into the person I finally became. In my adult life there are many friends and associates who made my life much richer and fuller by just knowing them. There are too many of these important people to mention them all by name.

There is one person, however, I have to mention. I have spent the past 47 years with this person, and she has always stood with me as a partner, giving encouragement regardless of the risk, hardships, and problems we faced. With her support, I knew I could accomplish every goal I set for myself. This woman cheerfully helped me with my challenges, put my needs above her own, and bore me five healthy, beautiful children. She is the perfect mother and mate. I dedicate this book to my wife Delphine.

Contents

Critters: Friend & Foe

Appendix

Preface

As you read Malcolm Beck's book, you'll discover quickly that he is a well-educated fellow — no, not from formal schooling — from personal experience, trial and error, and experimentation. Malcolm has taken the time to watch and understand Nature.

He learned the secrets of soil management by reading the books of soils experts like Sir Alfred Howard and William A. Albrecht, and by working the soil with his own hands during his 40-plus years as an organic truck farmer and compost manufacturer. It's not been an easy road. Some called him crazy. Others just ignored him, but he never gave up. He never gave up because he knew he was right. He understood Nature's laws and learned to work within those laws.

Although powerful organizations are still a big challenge to independent-thinking people like Malcolm Beck, battles are being won, and the overall victory is in sight. Mainstream, chemical-rescue farming and horticulture is coming unglued. At the same time, organic, ecological agriculture and horticulture is taking over. Why? Because managing soil health works and because people like Malcolm Beck have proven that it works.

Malcolm is a very special naturalist and teacher in that he is completely open with his knowledge and skills, and he will help anyone. His philosophy is that God doesn't help those who keep secrets. Knowledge is the property of Nature, not the property of man, and certainly not the property of any one man. Malcolm also accepts the fact that we will make mistakes, and that we must continue to learn, adjust, and adapt.

I know of his willingness to share and teach and to continue to learn because, you see, I am his pupil.

— J. Howard Garrett,
author of Plants of the Metroplex, Organic Landscaping Manual,
Landscape Designs: Texas Style, *and* Texas Organic Gardening Book

Foreword

That mushroom cloud over Hiroshima had hardly dissipated when Sir Albert Howard's words went forth to the effect that two false premises had swept the republics of learning: partial and imbalanced fertilization and toxic rescue chemistry.

Clearly, earlier values needed to be recaptured, this in the face of the establishment of Poison Control Centers. The modern approach was designed to make the biological procedure called agriculture into an industrial procedure, the last relying on salt fertilizers and toxic rescue chemistry.

Fifty years ago there were few professionals who could defend biologically correct agriculture — except with lip service — against the "settled" science offered by the United States Department of Agriculture and the land grant colleges. There were plenty of talented amateurs who often didn't know the questions, much less the answers. All were appalled by the effects of radiation, but few were aware of the fact that the same effect was being delivered to human cells and protoplasm by farm chemicals used recklessly in the environment.

The most educated people in the world are self-educated. This one fact emerges from Malcolm Beck's *Lessons in Nature* with the clarity of a glass bell. Here are the finely tuned rationales for crop production without the obscene presence of poisons in, around and on the food supply. It all starts by seeing what you look at — soils, insects, crops. It gathers speed when harvest comes into view, and everything translates into human beings capable of thought and reason.

The "method" is nature's method, forever forgiving, forever tantalizing with her rewards.

Malcolm Beck developed his organic techniques — ultimately taking form in his Garden-Ville composting yard and farm/garden supply stores — on the job, first creating soil worthy of the seeds the Creator had bestowed. This led him to compost and a fine-tuned understanding of the natural nitrogen cycle and the natural carbon cycle. Insect control, he found, was seated in fertility management. Weed control depended on hormone and enzyme systems in equilibrium. Beck's method deals in common sense, not in academic language. His words have the easy cadence of Mark Twain, who had Huck Finn decide "I guess I'll just have to go to hell," this or turn in his friend Jim to the slavers. Beck shrugged off all the warnings of perdition, the "known" consequence of disobeying Extension and the purveyors of toxicity. Instead of hell, Beck learned how to produce the best-looking and most nutritious crops imaginable. The lawn, the greenhouse, the mulch bed, the garden, dozens of topics flow like a river of life's own fluid through these pages. Go to page one and enjoy a gardener's finest.

— *Charles Walters*
founder, executive editor of Acres U.S.A., *author of*
numerous books on ecological agriculture and economics

Introduction

Herein lies a collection of articles and stories I have written over the years. Many were written for various publications, some were not. Some were an attempt to relate a few of my discoveries and experiences, and others to explain the wisdom and beauty of nature to my children and grandchildren.

Besides the three Rs through the 12th grade, I have no formal education in biology, botany, or other sciences. My teachers were many good books and some learned friends who developed a deep understanding of ecology. But most importantly, my teacher has been Nature herself. I was blessed with a great curiosity about the out-of-doors from early childhood on. Luckily that curiosity continued through life, except for the time between when I discovered girls until I got married, but that's Nature also.

Nature is easily understood, but for a lot of people Nature is too obvious. They look right past the clues. To understand Nature, walk into the woods and meadows and allow your five senses to feed your brain. Then you must use your brain to think. A good thought to start with is "Nature is perfectly designed and everything is designed for a purpose, and that purpose is to be of service and aid to us." When studying Nature with this approach, you make discoveries that would otherwise be blocked from view.

— *Malcolm Beck*

My First Garden

As a very young toddler I always wanted to help my mother in the garden. My help mostly was stepping on or pulling up Mom's young transplants. Paddling didn't faze me; I was still always in her way. To solve that problem Mom gave me some large white seeds then chose a spot a few steps away and told me I should plant my own garden. I took Mom's hoe and chopped around until I had the soil in some resemblance of Mom's beds, then I planted my four seeds. Every morning early I would be out looking for my little plants. The suspense was really getting to me. Finally, the miracle happened, all four of my seeds were up sprouting — two big green leaves each. Now the suspense was waiting for my plants to do something other than grow green and big.

Mom always let me go in the pen with her to feed the chickens and gather the eggs. I was always barefooted and would step in the chicken mess, and of course I got a scolding or paddling. Later, Mom was getting baskets full of dried chicken mess and putting it in her garden. Curiously, I ask Mom why she was putting chicken mess around her plants. She responded, "It's food for the plants." Now I was really puzzled, plants eat chicken mess! This I had to watch. After some time I noticed the mess beginning to fade away; soon it was all gone. The plants must have eaten it.

I decided my four plants would need something to eat also but I sure wasn't going to give my plants chicken mess. One of my chores as a child was to take the kitchen scraps and throw them to the chickens. If that were chicken feed why wouldn't my plants also eat it? I would take the potato, apple and banana peelings and put them around my plants and they too disappeared into the soil, but not as fast as Mom's chicken mess did.

It seemed like a really long time before it happened, but my plants finally got some really big, pretty yellow flowers. I wanted to pick them, but she said don't, because in a few days we would have squash to eat.

My mother must have known what she was doing. By telling me I could have my own garden and giving me those big white seeds that can easily emerge through hard soil, grow fast, have big yellow flowers, and quickly make big and beautiful yellow fruit, she got me hooked on gardening forever. She even got me to love and eat squash.

Squash Pest Outflanked

Summer squash, yellow squash, zucchini, and white scallops were always part of our garden and one of our main vegetables on our truck farm — squash were next only to tomatoes in sales. On a farm with large plantings of squash the squash vine borer doesn't exist. For some unknown reason the squash vine borer will not attack large plantings. But they will get every plant in a home garden and shorten its lifespan. Squash bugs are another big problem for the home gardener; on the farm squash bugs are there, but so scattered that they do little damage. Powdery mildew is another problem the gardener and farmer have to contend with after humid, rainy and cloudy conditions. On our organic farm the good, fertile, healthy soil helps overcome all of these conditions, removing the need for controls.

There is one squash variety for the gardener and farmer that is delicious to eat and immune to all of the problems that plague the other varieties: Tatume, a perfectly round green squash that is best harvested when about the size of a baseball or little larger. If left on the vine it will turn into a 6 to 8 inch golden pumpkin.

Plant this squash, using plenty of compost, early in the spring and if kept watered you will still be eating squash until it gets too cold in the fall. Tatume is a veining squash that is not bothered by the squash vine borer, the squash bug or mildew; in fact I have never had any pest problems with it.

There is one problem with this squash: it grows and grows and grows. We have had one plant cover an area 29 ft. by 29 ft.! We ate all we could, gave away what we could, and fed the rest to the goats until they tired of it.

The Garden-Ville Story

Garden-Ville was founded by Malcolm and Delphine Beck as a family farm in 1957. The Becks had strong beliefs that farming should be done in a natural, or organic, fashion. They operated the farm without using any toxic pesticides or chemicals of any type. At the time, this practice was considered faddish and even foolish, but the Becks persisted in their beliefs and made the farm a success.

Their critics finally admitted that the Becks had proven their point on their small farm, but still contended that organic farming on a large acreage was not practical. In this criticism, the Becks saw a new challenge. They sold the eight-acre farm and moved the family to a hundred-acre place.

The new location required more study and research, but it did eventually prove successful — even more successful than the smaller farm since a larger environment was involved. Their success at growing fruits and vegetables organically became widely known. They were featured on television, in newspapers, and in many magazine publications. Soon people not only wanted the organic produce but they also wanted the compost Beck was making and using on the farm.

Thus a new business was started, and Garden-Ville became well known as a maker of compost. In 1980, Garden-Ville Fertilizer Company was incorporated. In 1984, John Dromgoole, another organic growing enthusiast, joined the company. By 1988, with the help of loyal employees, Garden-Ville grew into a two million dollar operation.

By 1998 the company was grossing $4 million a year. The Becks recognized the potential of their business and sold controlling interest to a company that wanted to take the Garden-Ville business and philophy national. But the new owners abandoned family values, and in less than two years the

Malcolm and Del's first farmhouse.

business was broke and on the verge of being lost forever. Then, in an answer to a prayer, Delphine ran into Jim Doersam, a family friend, and suggested that his employer — Texas Organic Products, whose parent company is TDS Inc., a family business — should buy Garden-Ville. The Gregorys, owners of TDS, are well-respected, good business people and grew to be fast friends. After studying the benefits, the Gregorys agreed to buy out the failing owners, but only if the Beck family came with the deal. Within two years after the purchase, Garden-Ville grew in reputation and sales way beyond the family's wildest dreams.

Garden-Ville is now a leader in composting and recycling and has innovated and produced many new products for the horticulture industry. Many of these products that never existed before Garden-Ville introduced them are made by using waste or by-products that would otherwise be thrown away. A good many of those raw materials come from the agriculture industry.

Although the composting operation forms the foundation of Garden-Ville, many other services are available. Garden-Ville is headquarters for the organic grower and distributes many natural products, such as bat guano from the Bracken Cave (the largest active bat cave in the world), colloidal phosphate clay (a natural phosphate), other rock mineral products, microbial active products, and other natural soil conditioners. Garden-Ville has also developed its own all-purpose fertilizer, called Soil Food, that nourishes the soil as well as providing needed elements for plants.

Garden-Ville sells and distributes products from most manufacturers of non-toxic garden chemicals. Garden-Ville also manufactures a full line of environmentally safe agricultural products and fertilizers.

In addition, Garden-Ville carries a full line of gardening and landscaping supplies, such as drip irrigation systems, mulching materials, gardening books, and tools. There is also a wide selection of bed edging material, including one that Malcolm Beck invented and patented.

Garden-Ville and Texas Organic Products now has three large composting operations, including the large biosolids composting plant taken over from the City of San Antonio. There are seven retail outlets from San Antonio to Austin with distributors in Texas and other states.

But Garden-Ville takes greatest pride in the dissemination of information about organic gardening and farming through public appearances, radio talk shows, slide presentations, and the publication of their own printed material. Particularly gratifying are the daily personal and phone requests for information about natural gardening and farming methods. Garden-Ville strives to continue as a leader in making this Earth a better place to live by studying, practicing, and teaching recycling and natural, safe methods of growing and living.

The TDS Story

Bob Gregory and his brother Jim grew up working in the family's metal scrapyard business in the west Texas town of San Angelo.

As a young man Bob attended the University of Texas at Austin, paying his way in part by working nights and some weekends in an Austin scrapyard. In 1971, Gregory began his own scrap metal business.

In 1974, Gregory graduated from UT with a degree in business and married his high school sweetheart. He borrowed $120,000, bought a truck, leased a larger warehouse and installed machinery designed to enlarge his ability to recover precious metals from old telephone and computer equipment. He called his company Texas Alloys, which he continues to operate today as part of his scrap metal operation in San Angelo.

After a few years in the metal recovery business, Gregory decided to diversify. Rising and falling international metal markets led to unpredictable revenues, and Gregory wanted a hedge against down years.

He investigated the garbage business by attending National Solid Wastes Management Association conventions in 1976 and 1977. By November 1977, Gregory began hauling garbage. The business looked like it could be profitable, and he asked his brother to join him as a co-owner. Jim agreed and moved to Austin.

Bob and Jim incorporated the company as Texas Disposal Systems, Inc. in January 1978. In those early years, the company grew slowly, one small account at a time, Bob Gregory says. By 1985, he was bidding on the downtown hauling contract for the City of Austin.

As the family learned more about waste disposal, they also learned more about the benefits of recycling and reusing materials. They offered their customers the option of recycling metals, plastics, papers and glass. This knowledge of recycling led to further interest is keeping organic material out of the waste stream.

And that's where Garden-Ville came in. It was a perfect fit. Garden-Ville had experience composting and reusing material that often went into the landfill. TDS was interested in keeping material out of the landfill and in use as long as possible. So Texas Disposal Systems and its branch, Texas Organic Products, became the parent companies of Garden-Ville.

Bob Gregory's experience taught him the value of information and knowledge and the willingness to try new approaches to old problems. As a result, Garden-Ville continues to develop new products and new ways to keep the Earth healthy and alive.

Kitchen waste being poured into windrow of compost.

Compost blended into windrows at the TDS yard in Austin, Texas.

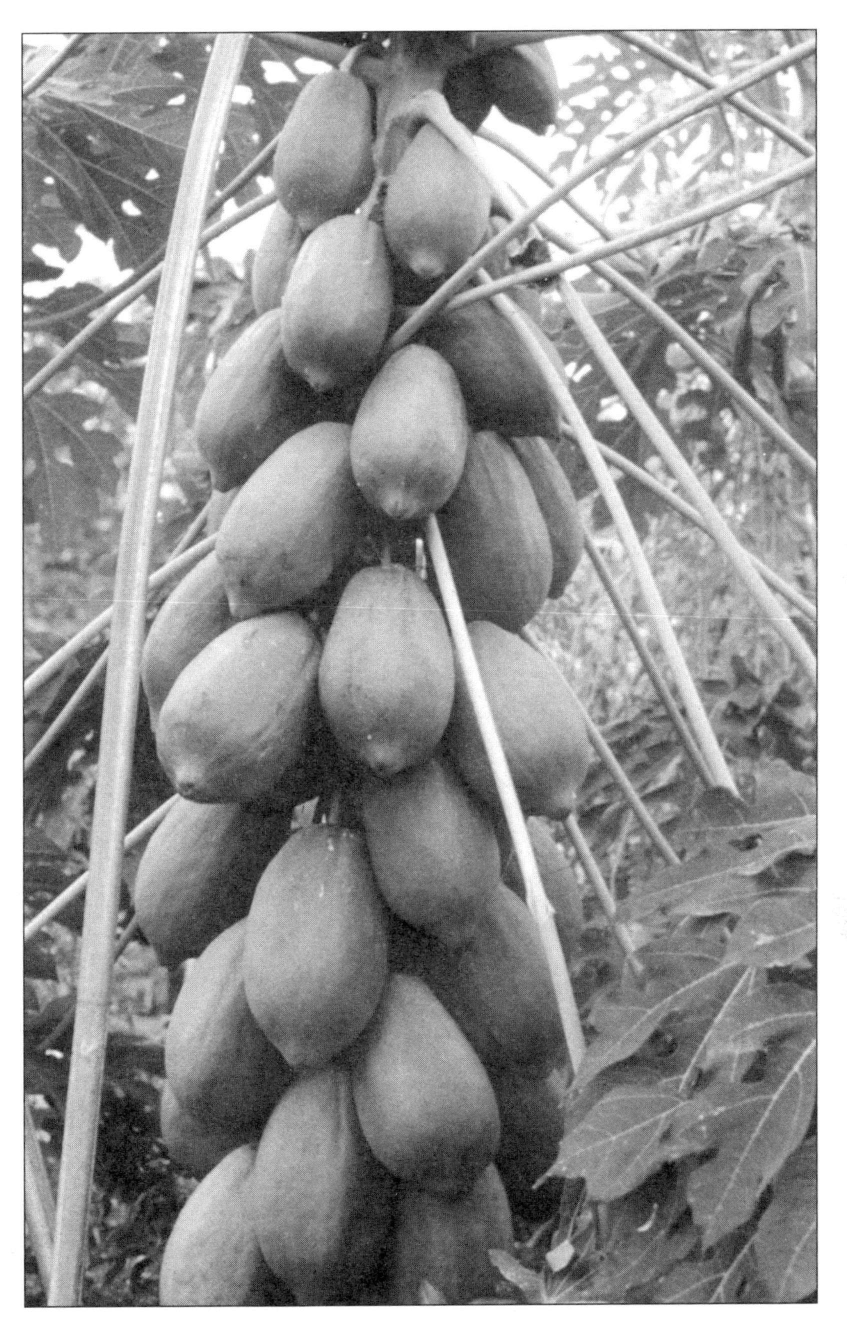

Organic papayas grown at Garden-Ville from the sprig of a plant developed at a botanical center. My papayas, fertilized with compost and mulched with local native tree trimmings, always got bigger and produced more than those grown by the specialists that developed them.

Why Organic Gardening?

What Is Organic Gardening?

Some of the proponents of chemical agriculture say that the growing interest in organic gardening is being generated by a few facts and a lot of fiction, and the term "organically grown" cannot be precisely defined. These people either haven't bothered to research the subject or they are getting it mixed up with the term "health food." They do not mean exactly the same thing.

More than 50 years ago, J.I. Rodale started the organic movement in this country as a crusade against eroding farmland and a polluted environment which he believed caused human health to degenerate. His inspiration came from studying the work of Sir Albert Howard of England and William A. Albrecht of the University of Missouri. After compiling and studying scientific papers from the world over, Rodale was confirmed in his beliefs. He went on to edit and publish *Organic Gardening and Farming* magazine, where he defined the term "organically grown" as "food grown without poisonous pesticides, grown without artificial fertilizers, grown in soil whose humus content is increased by the addition of organic matter, and grown in soil whose mineral content is increased with applications of natural mineral fertilizers."

Home gardeners and even many farmers soon learned to follow Rodale's advice, persuaded by the logic that poor soil can only produce poor plants, and poor plants produce poor animal and human bodies.

Many growers have learned that artificial fertilizers are only good to grow plants; artificial fertilizers do nothing to build soil fertility or even sustain soil fertility. With time, the soil begins to degenerate, as evidenced by the many worn-out farms around the country.

Gardeners and farmers discovered that with the natural or organic methods of soil building such as composting, cover cropping, and adding natural rock minerals, soil fertility would increase each year and artificial fertilizers would become unnecessary. As they continued to follow these organic methods, their plants seemed to develop immunity to the pests and diseases they were having before, and their farm animals, if left to natural selections, even preferred to eat the plants grown on the organically enriched soils. With decreased pest and disease problems, the organic growers didn't need strong poisonous pesticides but could maintain production

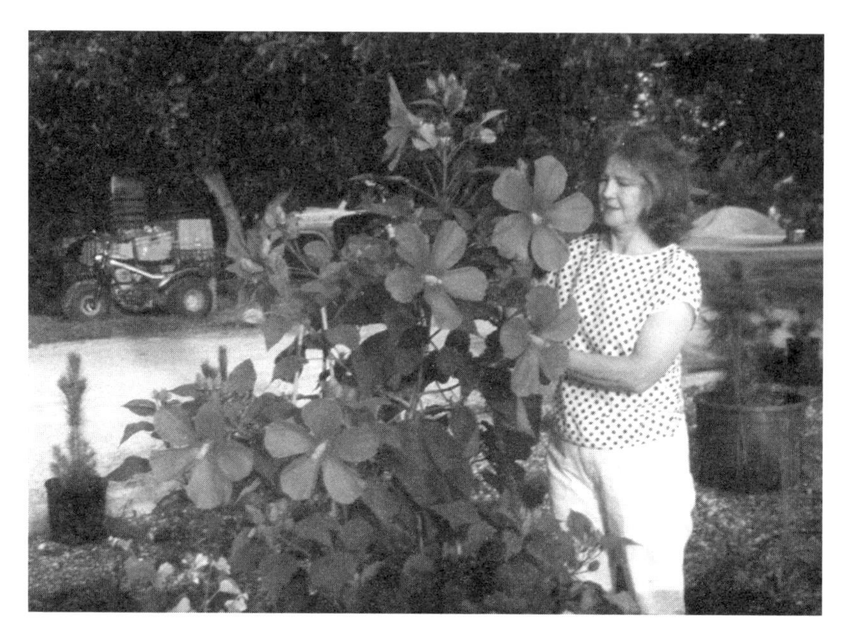

Delphine with organically grown hibiscus.

by using the safer non-polluting methods of pest control, such as liberating beneficial insects, changing cultural practices, or just planting better adapted varieties.

Research has shown that pests become immune to man-made pesticides which leads to stronger or more poisonous pesticide development. Many natural checks and controls of pests are provided by Nature that are safe and to which the pests don't become immune. We can work with Nature to use these controls and safeguard ourselves in the process. There are several fine books written on this subject, telling many ways to grow without poisonous pesticides, including two I co-authored with Howard Garrett: *The Texas Bug Book* and *Texas Organic Vegetable Gardening.*

Throughout the country, a growing number of farmers, small and large operations alike, are abandoning the heavy use of pesticides. They no longer try to eradicate pests with poison, which they not only found impossible, but also damaging to man's health and the environment and also costly. Instead, they are using what they call "natural pest management techniques." (Just a fancy name for organic methods.)

You can't yet call these farmers "organic growers," but they, along with many gardeners turning organic, are beginning to realize the answer to pest problems is not in a bag of poisonous chemicals, but in a better understanding of the laws of Nature and a desire to work with these laws.

I have compiled the following guidelines to help assist the organic grower.

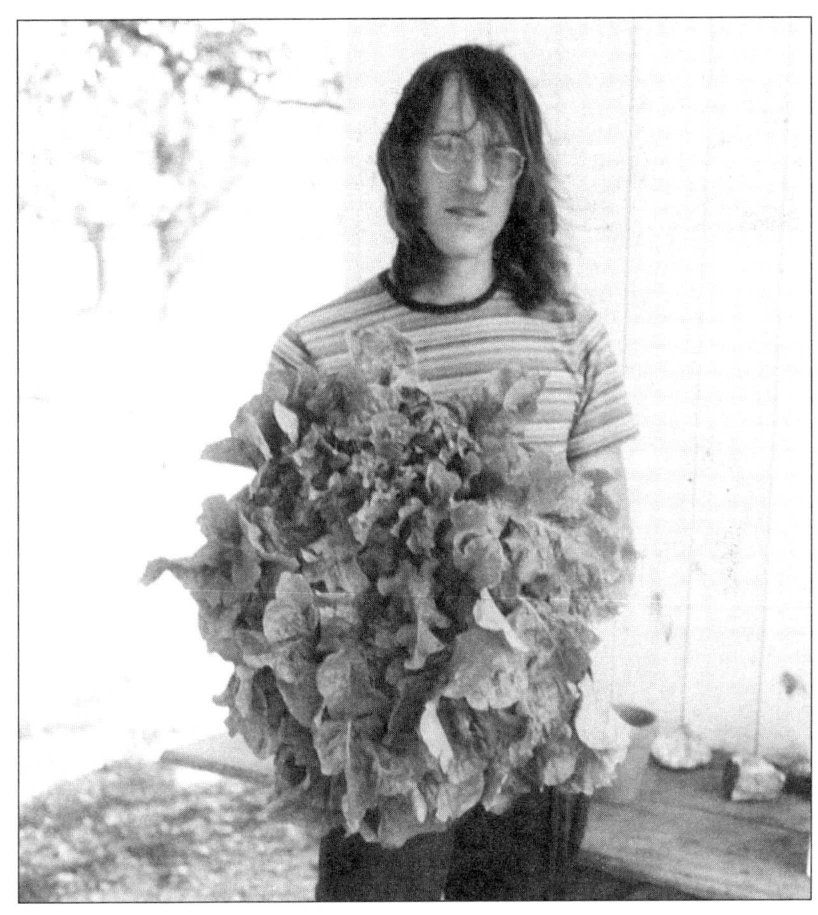

A leaf lettuce plant grown organically at Garden-Ville Farm.

Seven Organic Rules

1. Always use the best adapted varieties for each environment.
2. Plant in the preferred season.
3. Balance the mineral content of the soil.
4. Build and maintain the soil organic content — humus.
5. Do nothing to harm the beneficial soil life.
6. Consider troublesome insects and diseases as symptoms of one of the above rules having been violated.
7. Be patient. Mother Nature gives birth, but Father Time controls the cycles.

Our Future

Huge environmental problems face our species today. However, if we study to understand Nature and her positive laws, we can perform a critical role in attacking these problems. Anyone who loves Nature soon learns to see her deeper beauty and greater fascination. You learn to observe and understand the cycles of life-death-decay and rebirth. No living thing, plant or animal, escapes death. In Nature, every dead thing is usually deposited in the very place it dies. There it serves as mulch protecting the soil until it finally decays. In due time, it is covered and replaced by still later deposits of expired life.

In a natural environment, there is no waste. Everything is reused and is usually made into something of still greater value for the sustenance of life on Earth. Dead things furnish the organic matter to supply energy, food and structure for the beneficial soil life. The beneficial soil life creates the conditions for healthy, abundant plant life to feed the animal life. And the life cycle continues. In a natural environment the life cycles add to the past and build a future. Without continued death and decay, future life species and systems would degenerate, eventually to extinction.

Earth is covered mostly by water, only 20 percent is dry land. In the beginning the dry land consisted of lava, basalt, granite or other hardened, once-molten material. There was no soil on earth. Only life forces can make soil. But, there was no life because it takes soil to support life.

Our biggest problem worldwide is that most of our farmland no longer has the organic matter for life and energy it once had. As little as 200 years ago, all of the farmlands across the United States had an organic content of 3 to 8 percent. The once-fertile Rio Grande Valley is wasting away with a soil organic content that tests at 0.2 percent to 0.8 percent. Now most farmland everywhere is down to 20 percent or less of what it should be. As recently as the 1940s, the organic content was *all above* 3 percent and closer to 5 percent. This represents a drop in organic content of between 70 to 90 percent in 60 years.

Topsoil lost to erosion is an increasing problem today. As the soil loses its organic matter, it becomes unable to hold and trap water. Any water allowed to run off carries the topsoil with it. It goes into the rivers and streams and is lost forever. Then we are left with barren unproductive subsoil.

Freshwater shortages are worldwide and are increasing daily. Seventy-four percent of the Earth is covered by water. All of it is salty except for about 3 percent. Between 80 percent and 90 percent of that small amount of fresh water is used in irrigation. Irrigation needs could be cut 30 percent or more if only proper soil organic matter was maintained. Storing water also helps prevent shortages. The safest and most efficient place to store our annual rainfall is in the soil under a mulch cover.

A mulch layer of leaves, twigs, grass, compost, or any organic material from man's waste stream will protect the soil from the baking sun and drying winds. The mulch holds heavy rains in place until they soak in. This prevents floods and soil erosion.

Water amounts greater than the soil can hold filter on down and slowly drip into our aquifers to keep them at a constant level during dry spells. Water allowed to run off carries topsoil with it, then both end up in the salty sea. Or, if trapped in lakes, we lose 4 to 6 feet of water each year to evaporation and the soil carried with it silts up the lake.

At soil level, under the mulch, the grubs, earthworms, termites and numerous other forms of soil life chew up the mulch and churn up the soil. Then the microbes take over and compost it. The composting activity creates mild organic acids that dissolve minerals from rock in the soil, and then it all becomes healthy, rich fertile soil. Decaying organic material on the soil surface saves water and builds fertile soil.

How Nature Saves Water

Because of the increased carbon dioxide release under plants from mulch, compost and organic-rich soil, the pores on plant leaves stay open less and shut longer. This causes plants to transpire less, allowing them to draw less moisture from the soil while growing. Even though organic-rich soil can absorb and hold more water, plants grown in organic-rich soil actually require less water to grow.

Air Pollution

Carbon dioxide is admitted to the atmosphere from burning fossil fuels in our factories, power plants and automobiles. Carbon dioxide is believed to be changing our weather patterns. Soil scientists have calculated that excess carbon dioxide now found in the atmosphere is nearly equal to the carbon lost from our farmlands.

Scientists have also calculated that all we have to do to offset the carbon dioxide in the atmosphere is to increase the organic content of our farmland *just one-tenth of one percent each year.* Conservation tillage, especially "no-till" farming and the use of mulch and compost, does just that.

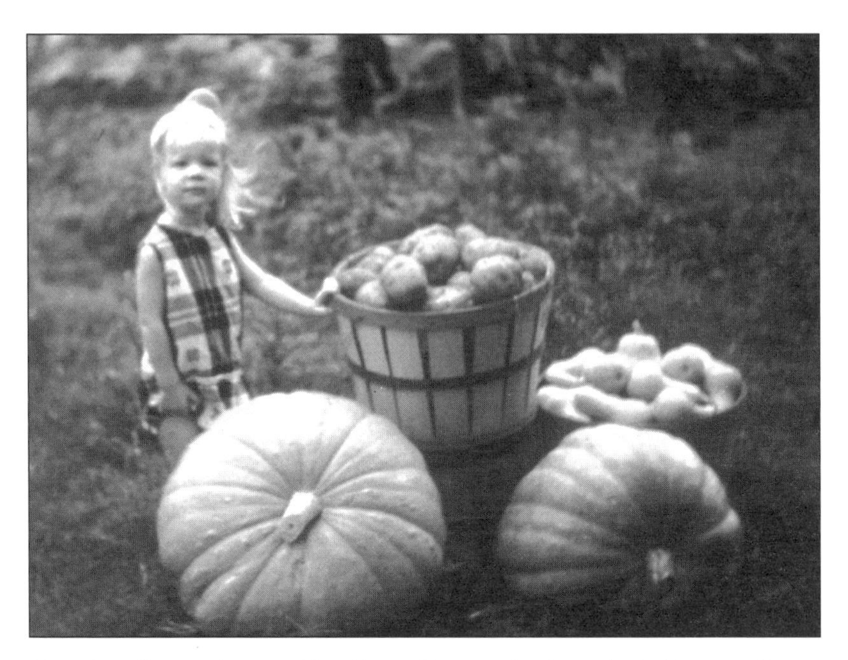

Daughter Kay with vegetables. Everything on the farm, including our five children, is organically grown.

Nitrate toxicity and other toxic products are detected in water wells and aquifers everywhere. In many cases, the nitrate is high enough to cause health problems. This is caused by overusing high-nitrate fertilizers in poor soils. Soil microbes must process fertilizer in order for a plant to use it properly. If the soil is low in organic energy the microbes cannot do the processing. Then the plants become stressed, which usually invites pests and diseases. The sick plants are then treated with yet another toxin. Eventually, the unused nitrates and other toxins seep down to pollute the water table. Low organic content causes this cycle to be repeated over and over.

The quality of our life is connected to the quality of the soil. The quality of the soil determines the quality of the air we breathe, water we drink, and food we eat. If we allow the quality of the our topsoil to degrade to any degree, the life it supports goes with it.

Soil quality is determined by the amount of life, minerals, and energy it contains. Understanding and properly using the energy in carbon and life cycles to maintain quality soil can solve the major problems facing mankind.

The world economy is connected to the soil. In the hands of skilled growers, the wealth produced by fertile soil — such as fruit, nuts, grain, vegetables, flowers, trees, grass, and farm animals — is forever renewable.

Soil eroding due to lack of plant cover and organic matter.

Flooding caused by poor soil's inability to absorb rain fast enough.

Recycling organics, or recycling anything for that matter, is also creating new wealth. New wealth is what sets an economy in motion. Everything else is buying or selling a service.

Are mulching and conservation farming too simple an answer to so many problems? Yes and no. They offer a wonderfully simple answer to many complex problems.

As gardeners, farmers and ranchers that love, understand and work with Nature, we can make a difference. Planet Earth needs our help!

Share the bounty of the earth with the other creatures who live here. A few bug bites on the lettuce won't make it taste any less delicious!

Nature is generous — follow her lead.

Does Nature Always Approve?

My wife and I started operating our farm organically back in 1957. Some call me the grandfather of organics in Texas. I am a grandfather, and old and gray. I don't mind being called either. However there is one thing I do care about and that is *doing things Nature approves of.*

The word "organic" describes a method of production. Years ago it was a good method, but now the word is beginning to get screwed up. The current national organic certification rules are a good method for some farmers and ranchers to market their products in a niche, but I don't think Nature necessarily approves of all the rules. The government spent over ten years and millions of dollars writing stacks of documents telling farmers what they can't do. It is all negative. The founders of the organic movement were positive thinkers. They wrote books on how a farmer needed to build the soil and grow plants so he wouldn't need pesticides. However, the national organic standards are still in a state of evolution and for now they are better than no rules.

Lets look at some examples.

Glyphosate: Sold under 70 or more brand names including Roundup. Farmers who have moved to conservation tillage use glyphosate as a tool. These no-till and low-till methods save many hours in the field, many gallons of diesel fuel, prevent a lot of air pollution, save soil moisture and fertilizer, stabilize soil temperature, stop wind and water erosion. With no-till you don't oxidize the soil and lose all your carbon to the air in the form as CO_2. The soil organic content goes up one tenth of one percent each year instead of continually going down as it does with regular tillage. The benefits are numerous. Not all benefits are mentioned here, but enough to win Nature's approval. On my own farm I tried to kill a large patch of Johnson grass by chiseling it to death. Before I bled the life out of it a rain came and gave it a new and better lease on life. After all the tractor time, wasted fuel, air pollution, and loss of soil carbon, Nature probably called me a fool. In healthy, humus-rich, biologically active soil Nature can quickly, in less than three days, change glyphosate from toxic material to microbe food. However, if used in cold or poor soils it could remain toxic for some time before the microbes become active and find enough energy to completely degrade it.

View of our farm's vegetable crops in 1972. This field was kept clean of Johnson grass by hand hoeing behind the cultivator, labor that is no longer practical for large farms.

I am not suggesting that farmers plant genetically modified Roundup Ready crops so they can soak their land with Roundup. That method doesn't build the soil or create healthy soil life. I am talking about very conservative use of a product when all other methods are unrealistic or counterproductive.

Biosolids: Asian farmers have maintained soil fertility for twenty centuries or longer by using human waste in their fields. We have worn out farm after farm in this country in less than two centuries because of our hang-ups. Our best farmland is used to produce our food. Those farms badly need organic matter; their organic content goes down each year. Soil loss from wind and water erosion is going up each year. Soil loss worldwide it is tremendous, some researchers claim as much as 25,000 acres turn to desert each day of the year. Almost every town and city in this country has a sewer plant. But instead of keeping it clean of toxins and properly processing this organic material so it can go back on the land like Nature demands, we bury it in landfills. To Nature this is a grave injustice

Urea: Is another product forbidden by the organic rules that could be used in beneficial ways if not overused. Microbes accept urea just as they do urine. Urine is organic, but you could pee on a tree too much and kill it.

Above are three examples of things that Nature could approve of if used properly in certain conditions.

Meanwhile we follow rules made by man and pollute and waste Nature's resources without even consulting her for approval.

Note: I am not endorsing glyphosate, only showing that sometimes it is the lesser of two evils.

Health & Logic

When I was a child, our family was considered poor because we didn't have a lot of worldly possessions, but really we were not. I had brothers and sisters to play with and lots of cousins, aunts, and uncles to visit. We all lived on farms and had plenty of fresh farm produce to eat. We were all healthy and happy.

As a young adult, however, I started eating junk foods instead of the fare served at my mother's table, and my good health began to fade. The worst problems were related to my sinuses. My nose got stuffy and the tissues swelled up so that I sometimes couldn't breathe through my nose for a week. My sinuses drained constantly, and I seemed always to have a sore throat. Sinus pressure and headaches were a common occurrence that caused me to miss work often.

When I was 19, I went to work on the railroad, which carried full medical coverage on employees. For two years, I worked with the company doctors to solve my sinus problems. Finally, the third doctor told me there wasn't much medical science could do for sinus problems and suggested I move to Arizona. I began to believe that I was condemned to the miseries of sinus problems for the rest of my life.

When I got married at 21, my sinus problem was getting worse. It not only affected my job, but it was hard to be cheerful around my new bride. I decided to check with one more doctor.

He held my tongue down with a stick, looked down my throat, and said "Ah huh."

When he took the stick out, I said, "Ah huh, what?"

The doctor said, "I think your tonsils need to come out. They may be causing an allergy that gives you sinus problems."

Although I couldn't ever remember having problems with my tonsils, I was desperate. I agreed to check into the doctor's private hospital for the operation.

When it was time for the operation, the doctor gave me some shots in the throat to deaden the area, then had me strip naked and put on a small white apron. To my great embarrassment, the doctor called in a beautiful nurse to assist him.

They strapped me onto an ice-cold stainless-steel chair and started cutting in my deadened throat. Although my throat was numb, the doctor kept pinching my lips with his tools, and it hurt. I tried to tell him, but I couldn't talk. All I could do was spit blood all over him and the pretty nurse. After the operation was over, I felt so bad I was sure I would die.

I didn't die, but I didn't get any better either. After my throat healed, my sinus problem was as bad as ever. I went back to that doctor, and he told me he was still sure the sinus problems were caused by allergies. He wanted me to come back at a later date for allergy tests. I asked what the test consisted of, and he said he would prick me with a bunch of needles. That was enough for me. I left and never went back.

A month or so went by, then one day when I was visiting a co-worker, he asked me to go with him to a natural food store. While he shopped, I sat on a stool at the juice bar, about half-bored, spinning a pamphlet rack to keep myself entertained. All of a sudden, a little gray pamphlet with the title *Sinus* stopped right in front of me. I grabbed it and read. It stated that most sinus troubles are caused by eating refined carbohydrates.

I asked the store owner what a carbohydrate was. Then I asked her what a refined carbohydrate was. She said the worst ones were white flour, white sugar, and alcohol. That described my diet.

After describing my sinus problems to the store owner, I left with a bag of groceries containing whole wheat bread, whole wheat flour, honey, and a bunch of other natural goodies.

It didn't take much explaining to my new wife. She agreed to go with me on the natural diet and change her cooking and baking, using only natural ingredients. It took less than two weeks on this natural diet for my

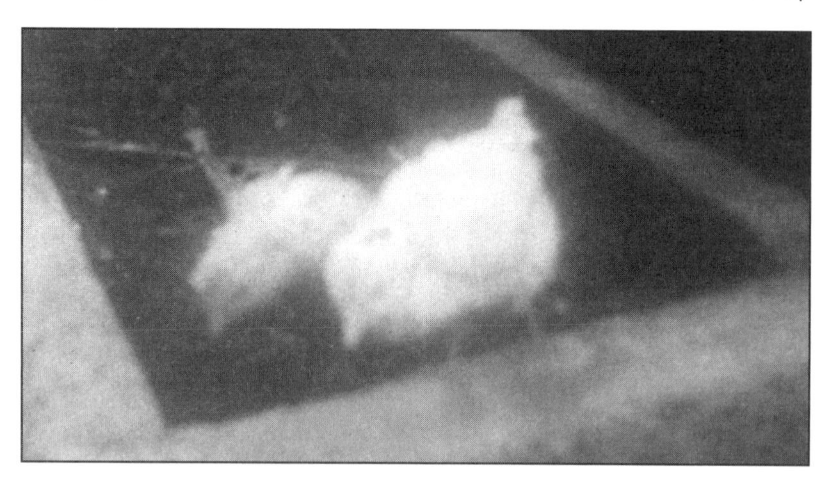

Two chicks the same age, a small chick fed on white bread, and large chick fed on whole wheat bread. This faded old photograph is the only remaining evidence of one of our early experiments with nutrition.

sinus problems to disappear. And it wasn't long before my wife and I both noticed our health and energy improving.

For the first six to eight years, I had to adhere strictly to the natural diet or the sinus problems would quickly come back, but as years went by and my general health kept getting better, I found I could indulge in some alcohol and other refined carbohydrates without too much trouble.

Back on the farm, we always hauled the manure out to the fields and fertilized with the missing minerals when needed. We could readily see the improvements in the crops. I was taught from early on about good and balanced nutrition, especially with the farm animals, because you could easily see their response and contentment when they were put on a good diet. Somehow I didn't make the connection between these lessons and my own health.

Why is it that we have to learn or relearn things the hard way, especially when we are young and in the know-it-all stage? I am sure the Good Lord put this vanity in human nature for a good reason. Could it be that a lesson learned the hard way is one learned forever and easier taught to others?

More on Natural Foods: Some Food Tests

My wife and I became good customers of a local natural food store and friends of the owners. They invited us to become members of Natural Foods Associates, and we agreed to attend a meeting of the group. The speaker that evening gave a very interesting talk.

The speaker told of his life on a dairy farm and about the health problems the milk cows suffered. He told of mastitis, abortions, pink eye, skin and hoof problems, and on and on. Veterinarians were not much help. Finally, the man said, he went to college and studied soils, plant nutrition, and animal nutrition. He finally solved the health problems of his cows by testing the soil where the cattle grazed and adding the missing elements to balance the soil. This fertilizing program provided the elements necessary to maintain health in the cows. If fertilizing didn't take care of the problem, he found hay that had those missing elements and added that to their diet. In addition, he tested any hay or silage he bought for the cows and added feed to balance it and make the nutrition content complete.

This man's dairy became more profitable than most. Soon other dairy operators came to him for advice. After a while he decided to share his accumulated knowledge by teaching a class at a local agriculture college.

During class one day, he told the students that a lot of the food on the grocery store shelves was not fit to eat. The students doubted his statement and challenged him to prove it.

As proof, he suggested they take a big flock of pigeons and divide them up into two equal groups. They put them in separate pens and fed one group on white rice and water and the other on brown rice and water.

The teacher predicted that the pigeons on the white, polished rice would get six degenerative diseases and those on the brown, whole-grain rice would live happily ever after.

Sure enough, the pigeons on the brown rice diet remained healthy and continued mating and reproducing with no problems. The pigeons on the polished rice got all kinds of diseases, stopped reproducing, and started to die. The students were surprised, and the teacher got a surprise too. They all learned something in this experiment. The very first sign of malnutrition in the pigeons eating white rice was not illness. Instead, the pigeons became irritable, discontented, and fought among themselves.

When we heard this story, my wife and I were comforted. We were already eating natural, unprocessed foods as often as possible. We were also inspired. Some of our friends kidded us about the whole wheat bread we ate, so I decided to do a similar test using white and whole wheat bread to feed some of our chickens.

I took six of my wife's three-day-old chicks and put them in a divided coop. The coop was placed outside so that both sides got equal amounts of sunlight, breezes, and weather. Everything else would be the same except for the food. Chicks in one side of the pen got white bread and water; the others got whole wheat bread and water.

The three chicks on the whole wheat grew normally and were healthy. I kept them on the diet for 42 days before turning them out. Two were hens. They went on to lay eggs and prosper. The rooster grew big and beautiful and we had him for Thanksgiving dinner.

The three chicks on the white bread diet were all dead by the 17th day. The first died on the 13th day. They were all sickly and died slow, agonizing deaths. I don't know what kind of diseases they had, but by the sixth day, they had stopped growing normally. They seemed to be getting blubbery fat. Their legs were spread far apart and they had a hard time getting around. About this same time, their droppings started turning green instead of the normal brown and white. When the second chick died (on the 16th day), I cut it open and found a thick layer of almost-clear, Jello-like fluid under its skin.

As in the pigeon experiment, I also noticed that the very first indication that the chicks weren't getting a balanced diet was that they were irritable and discontented. It makes me wonder about some of the problems we have in our society. Could diet have something to do with the broken homes, crime, delinquency, and other problems we see increasing yearly?

Except for whole wheat flour, most of the food we ate was raised on our farm, and it was all organic. We reared five children on good nutrition, and they were always healthy. The doctor bills we had were very few. The worst came when one of the boys caught his toe in the bicycle chain and when our daughter fell off a horse and hurt her arm. Most importantly, our children were always contented and happy. They never whined or complained like many other children we saw. Our children were a joy to be around. They loved school and made good grades, and they were absent only when the creek came up and marooned us.

I consider myself lucky to have had health problems because I was forced to learn lessons in nutrition the hard, but thorough way. I learned that there is a lot of truth in the old saying, "You are what you eat," and I believe that means both physically and mentally.

Marketing Organic Produce

The anticipation of waiting for the crop to come in each new season, along with the hope that it will be better than the year before, is what holds many people on the farm. Others like being their own boss, and they enjoy the gamble and satisfaction of operating a business with Nature as their partner. But if the produce doesn't make it to market and bring a price above the cost of production, the business end of the partnership is soon dissolved.

I always enjoyed the planting and harvesting and all the other labors of farming, but marketing was a different matter altogether. At times, selling the produce was rewarding, and other times it was discouraging.

When we were farming, we tried every marketing method we could dream up. At first, we tried selling to health food stores, but they couldn't handle enough volume. In the '60s and '70s, they were still mostly selling pills and herbal formulas and didn't have coolers and equipment to handle fresh produce.

We tried selling directly from the farm, but that also had its problems. Some city people would see all the abundance of vegetables in the fields and figure, since we had so much anyway, we should be selling it cheaper or giving some of it away. Obviously, it just grew there without any effort, why should we get money for it? Clearly, these price complainers never lived on a farm or even grew a garden!

Then there were the customers who understood the efforts of growing beautiful produce and didn't mind paying a fair price. They caused a special problem. They loved to talk farming, gardening, and growing. At first, Delphine and I loved their visits and we toured these people around our farm, but we soon learned that all the talking and touring was taking up too much time. We weren't getting work done that needed to be done. Not being able to give each of these good customers the time they sometimes wanted and deserved was the hardest thing I did some days.

If our farm had been on a busier road, a roadside stand would have been the best and most profitable marketing technique, but we were just too far off the beaten path. Sometimes we let the two older boys take the pickup full and park at an intersection of two busy roads with four-way stop signs. The boys really enjoyed this. It was educational for them, and we

Organic vegetables ready for market in 1973. The proof of our soil quality was in the flavor of these vegetables.

made good money, but there were complaints from neighboring grocery stores and sometimes the local law. Besides, my wife was always worrying about the boys when they were out on the road.

For a time, we sold a lot of our vegetables to a natural food store in Austin. They paid us a good price and appreciated the organic produce, but the 70-mile distance prevented us from doing a big business there.

Through a friend, we sold produce to a local cafeteria chain, but that too had its limits. When we had a certain vegetable peaking in production, we couldn't force the customers to eat accordingly.

I decided to try a large independent grocery store that was noted for the quality of produce that it sold. The owner of the store grew up on a vegetable farm and knew the heartaches of farming. When I approached him, I told him I was an organic vegetable grower and asked if he would like to carry our produce. He told me he wasn't interested because he understood that organic vegetables cost more and usually were full of bug holes. Since this was in the '60s, organic growing and pot-smoking hippies were thought to be on about the same level.

Because of this man's reputation in the grocery business, Delphine was determined that he see our produce for himself. She loaded some in the truck and went to talk with him. He told her he wasn't interested, but she kept after him to at least look at the vegetables. "Okay, lady, let's go look, but I am very busy," he told her. When he got to the truck and took a look at what she had brought, his attitude changed in a hurry. He thought they were beautiful and was ready to buy them on the spot. Delphine sat down and negotiated with him, and we ended up with a good relationship with him and his store that lasted for some time. Other than what we sold to our regular customers and the cafeteria, this man bought all our produce and sold it from special tables in his store with display signs reading, "Organically Grown by the Beck Family."

On another occasion, my wife's determination was again a marketing success. Our potato crop came in especially good one year. Most of the potatoes were giants, which didn't sell well at the grocery store. They were beginning to pile up, so we decided to try to sell some at other locations.

Del remembered the barbecue place up the road a few miles that always had good potato salad. She decided to see if she could make a sale there. The store owner's initial reaction was negative. He said Texas potatoes don't make good potato salad, but Del persisted. She took a sack off the truck and put them on his dock and said he could at least give them a try at no charge. The next morning, shortly after five o'clock, the phone was ringing. The barbecue place wanted more of those excellent potatoes.

Because of the size of our compost business, our vegetable farming has been reduced to family gardening. I think, though, that if I ever again get back into the organic farming business, I would try Booker T. Whatley's method of clientele membership as explained in his book, *How to Make $100,000 Farming 25 Acres.*

There have been other important developments that have helped organic growers market their produce since I stopped farming commercially. One of the most important is the growth in popularity of farmers' markets. Almost every town in Texas and throughout the country now has a regularly scheduled farmer's market at which growers can bring their produce in season. People flock to these markets to get really fresh, good food, and organic growers are well represented. Many people can only find fresh organic produce at farmer's markets and go there for just that reason. Since more and more people are becoming aware of the benefits of organically grown food, there is more demand — and you can sell at retail prices at these markets.

Most farmer's markets charge a minimal weekly fee for farmers to participate. The only other cost is in the grower's time. You can go to the market every week, or you can go just when you have excess produce you need to sell. Some growers take their sweet corn to farmers' markets and sell every bit of it, then sit out the rest of the year. Some home gardeners who get overly enthusiastic at planting time take their excess and sell it at the markets. These markets are great opportunities to get your name known in your community as a quality grower.

In my own state, the Texas Organic Farmers and Gardeners Association is working to help farmers and small growers become successful using organic methods. (Learn more about the organization and their work by visiting their website at www.texasorganicgrowers.org). Find your own local or state organization and get to know organic farmers in your area.

Marketing directly to the consumer naturally brings the best price. I'm sure that however I chose to market, I would sell only to people who appreciate the gambles, worry, and sweat that go into farming. Having customers who don't appreciate the amount of labor and risk involved takes the satisfaction out of farming, regardless of the price.

Warning

I don't like being an alarmist or talking about other companies and their products, but there are some products that are having a harmful effect on all of us. Modern science has designed herbicides that seem to never go away and end up in fields and gardens everywhere.

These products are called Picloram, Pinene, Borlin, Grazon, and Tordon. They are selective herbicides created by DowElanco to kill broadleaf weeds. While the products do not kill grass, they do contaminate it and as a result much of the hay and manure that farmers and gardeners would normally use as feed, mulch or compost has become not only worthless but positively damaging to the soil. And it looks as if the damage will last for many years to come. Someone who has used the product may not be able to grow broadleaf plants such as legumes, vegetables or trees in years subsequent to the application of the herbicide.

I was giving a talk to a Master Gardener's group in a small country town east of San Antonio when an elderly man asked if something could be toxic in horse manure. He said he had been gardening using horse manure all his life, but about a year ago he used some manure that effectively sterilized his garden spot. I was at a loss for an answer to the problem. Luckily, however, the Agricultural Extension agent was in the audience and explained that these herbicides were probably the cause of the problem.

The Extension agent had experienced the same problem. He used Coastal Bermuda hay as a mulch because it is usually free of noxious weed seeds, but once after putting it on his garden just before a rain, everything in the garden died. Tests at Texas A&M found Picloram-type herbicides that had leached into his soil from the mulch. A&M suggested he dig up the soil and haul it away, because it could be five or more years before he could grow a garden in that soil.

I have since had many calls from gardeners and farmers telling of manure, hay and even compost killing their gardens or fields. One gentleman told of finding herbicide-damaged spots randomly spaced on both sides of a power line that was sprayed many months earlier with a herbicide. Some of the spots were as much as a quarter of a mile from the line on either side. He pondered this mystery for quite a while before he noticed an old mule grazing under the unfenced powerline. They looked again at the

One of our many organic kitchen gardens grown without any man-made chemicals. Using products that have elements arranged into molecules that are strange to Nature will sooner or later harm the natural environment.

damaged spots and found that in each case, the mule had roamed in and left manure.

These persistent herbicides were designed to spray under powerlines and over pipelines because they will stop trees and brush from growing there for many years. The problem is that the product is easily distributed by animals, the wind and water. Many ranchers now use the product in their grass pastures to control mesquite invasion.

The standard reference book, *Agricultural Chemicals, Book II: Herbicides* (13th edition), by W.T. Thompson, says the following regarding these herbicides:

"*Precautions:* Avoid drift. Do not apply under the drip line of desired trees. Do not apply to irrigation ditches. Avoid movement of treated soil. Herbicidally active residues may remain in the soil for a considerable length of time. Very minute quantities will injure many broadleaf crop plants. Do not apply where surface water from the treated area can run off onto cropland. Do not apply to frozen or saturated ground. Do not move livestock from a treated area to any area where some injury cannot be tolerated without first letting them graze on an untreated area for seven days, as it takes this long for the chemical to leave their urine."

I wrote DowElanco by certified mail (and got the return receipt showing that they received the letter) asking them if composting would destroy the harmful effects of Picloram. They failed to answer, which either means that they don't know, or that composting may not detoxify the compound.

So far I have no studies telling if this product shows up in the meat and milk of animals grazing in treated areas or feeding on contaminated hay. Are we eating and drinking it?!

At the moment, the best advice I can give is "gardener beware!" I and all agricultural agents I have spoken with would like to see strict limitations on the use of this product or for it to be taken off the market entirely.

Natural Laws & World Economy

Economists tells us that the only true or virgin wealth a nation has is what is pumped or mined out of the ground and what farmers and ranchers produce with their skill using sunlight, water and soil.

The wealth you pump or mine from the ground will some day be used up, but with recycling and good farm and ranch management, the wealth grown from the soil can be renewable forever and ever.

Recycling organics or recycling anything, for that matter, is creating new wealth. New wealth is what sets an economy in motion. Everything else is buying or selling a service.

In a natural environment, there is no waste. Nature designed a system of life that is never ending. One form of life dies and decays so that another form can be born and grow. The circle continues in perfect harmony, as along as Nature is allowed to control the process. Like all laws of Nature, recycling is a positive law. Still, we continue to seriously violate that law by constantly breaking the cycle. We do not return the depleted life to the soil so that it can nourish the next generation. Sooner or later we will suffer the consequences. As the soil organic content goes down, the quality of the soil declines and the life it supports is pulled down along with it.

The biggest problems facing mankind today are eroding soils and water shortage. Both are caused by the loss of soil organic matter. As the soil organic content decreases, the less water the soil can hold and the less rain can penetrate. The result is more runoff, bigger floods, more soil erosion, and drier soils. That requires pumping more water from falling aquifers.

Because of declining soil organic matter, Earth is gaining up to 10,000,000 acres of desert each year. Mexico, our neighbor to the south, gains over a half-million acres of desert every year. More than 60 percent of Mexico's farmland is severely degraded and another 30 percent is in varying stages of ecological decay.

Here in this country, the state of California gains 10,000 acres of desert every year. According to soil scientists, much of the farmland across this nation is down to 20 percent or less of its original organic values. Because

Materials for composting — sawdust, horse stable bedding, onions and jalapenos, and paunch manure. In Nature, every expired life form is designed to be recycled.

we lose 3 billion tons of topsoil each year, crop quality and production is falling and irrigation, fertilizer and pesticides needs are going up.

Here in Texas we are not immune to soil loss. Back in 1950, the soil organic content of the Rio Grande valley was 3 percent and higher. Now it is down to .5 percent and less. Older farmers tell us it now takes twice the irrigation water to grow the same crops they grew back then.

Planet Earth is about 74 percent water, but only 3 percent is fresh water and Texas wasn't blessed with very much of that. Our modern farming methods are destroying productive farmland at an alarming rate. Poor (chemical) farming practices burn up soil organic matter faster than Nature can replace it. Many conventional farming methods are not sustainable. Recycling and organic farming can reverse this road to desertification and starvation. Organic farming is sustainable.

Organic foods are more nutritious, providing more sustenance per pound, so it would not be necessary to produce as much food to provide for people's needs. For example, the protein content or organic wheat is around 18 percent and higher, while conventional chemically grown wheat tests at only 10-13 percent protein.

As farmers, ranchers and gardeners that understand the laws of Nature, recycling and organic growing, we have an obligation to help every man, woman, child, farmer and rancher in Texas and the rest of the country understand Nature's recycling laws.

The mountains of manure that are piling up around feedlots, dairies, and poultry and pig houses have to find their way back to the farmland that so desperately needs it. With all of our present recycling efforts, there is still way too much organic waste from homes, restaurants and industries that are being buried in landfills. This valuable organic material is useless in a landfill and priceless in the soil of farms and ranches.

Biosolids began as food on the best of our farmlands, yet they are returned not to the land but to the landfill. We have to get over our hang-ups and learn to use biosolids to the benefit of us all. Biosolids, with toxins removed, have been proven to be one of our best soil builders.

Used correctly, animal waste, human included, is a better fertilizer than any chemical mix man can formulate. Nature designed it and has used it since the beginning. It has no fillers. It consists of once-living material.

The most important thing missing from chemical fertilizers is the energy the soil life needs to process the fertilizer, energy that comes from once-living things. Without this energy, an endless cycle of soil exhaustion is begun. Eventually crop quality and production fall off. Then more chemical fertilizers are used, depleting more energy. Pests then move in and more chemicals are used to try to meet those challenges. Soon the energy and life is gone from the soil and we gain more acres of desert and have less stored water.

Chemical fertilizers wouldn't be nearly as destructive if all carbon-rich materials such as yard waste, wood and paper, kitchen wastes and other organic material were returned to the land. That would also help solve the landfill space problem.

Industries that handle waste and generate waste, and especially the bureaucrats and politicians that regulate those industries, need to understand the importance of returning organic waste back from whence it came.

Recycling is positive law. The penalty for violating that law cannot be avoided. Eventually, Nature will come to collect.

Water: Quality, Quantity & Organic Agriculture

No life, not even the simplest, can exist without water. Three-quarters of the Earth is covered with water, but most of it is too salty to drink. Only three percent of all the water on Earth is fresh water. Agriculture uses 80-90 percent of that small amount. And each year, that three percent is getting more and more contaminated with sewage, pesticides, fertilizers, herbicides and other toxins.

Water consumption per capita is continually going up. Texas, California, and Florida are already experiencing water shortages and contamination, at times severe. The population of the Earth is continuing to grow. Our grandchildren will live to see the population double.

The book, *Tapped Out,* by the late Paul Simon, former United States senator and director of the Public Policy Institute at Southern Illinois University, presents a very gloomy forecast. Simon writes, "We must act quickly to avoid a major catastrophe."

The seemingly obvious answer to our freshwater shortage is to utilize seawater. But, as Simon points out, desalination of water is very expensive and energy consuming. It costs more than $2,000 per acre to use desalinized water in agriculture. Although new technology for desalinization is being developed that may make it more cost effective, it is still in the future.

Building dams to create new lakes will not solve the problem either. In many areas, soil conditions make building lakes impossible. Instead of creating collectors of clean water, the new basins become silted, polluted mudholes. In arid areas, lakes lose great amounts of water to extreme evaporation.

Global warming is also believed to contribute to water problems. Given all these contributors, it is easy to see that Simon is not overstating the seriousness of the water crisis. He mentions several ways to help solve the problem, but he misses one of the most important and best solutions — organic-rich soil, the best and easiest answer to quality and quantity of fresh water.

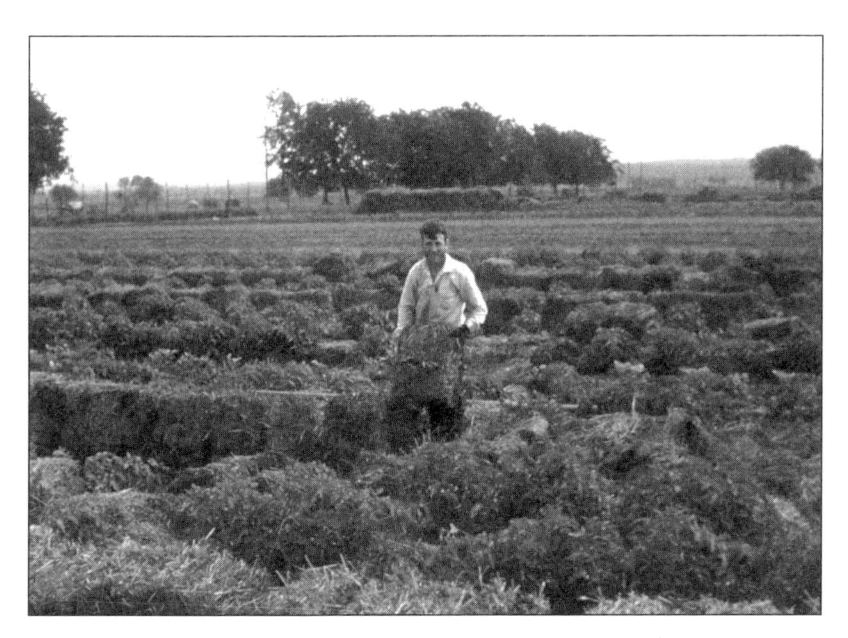

Mulching tomatoes with hay in 1971. Nature has mulched the surface of the Earth, to conserve water and build and protect the soil, since the beginning.

Simon, like most people, does not have a clear understanding of how Nature builds and maintains fertile topsoil and how rich soil collects and saves fresh water. Modern agriculture generally ignore this process.

Farmers, ranchers, landscapers, gardeners, and sports turfkeepers that build organic soil and use mulch see the process and understand it well. Around Texas, we now have numerous sports fields and hundreds of lawns that have a thin layer of compost applied regularly. There are many farmers building the organic content of their soil by recycling animal waste and by using low- or even no-till methods that do not disturb the soil, leaving crop residue on top as a mulch. All are reporting their irrigation needs to be less, in many cases, 30 to 50 percent less. Also, these practitioners notice that they need less fertilizer and pesticides. All of this helps prevent water pollution.

Organic matter is the reservoir for water, nitrogen, phosphorus, sulfur, boron, zinc — in short, it is a general catchpan for all nutrients. Also, with a good supply of organic matter as an energy source, the microbes in the soil are able to degrade and detoxify pesticides and other pollutants in the water as it passes through the soil. This is important to maintaining water purity.

After realizing that 55 inches of water is lost each year from lakes and bare soil in central Texas due to evaporation, and after studying the Edwards Aquifer (San Antonio's only water supply), Dr. Jerry Parsons came to the conclusion that there is only one answer to San Antonio's water problems. Dr. Parsons, local Agricultural Extension agent, believes that answer is mulch on the soil and organic matter in the soil.

According to a United States Department of Agriculture (USDA) study, a block of soil containing 4 to 5 percent organic matter, weighing 100 pounds, occupying a space of 3 feet by 1 foot by 6 inches deep, can hold 165 to 195 pounds of water. This means that a field with such rich soil could absorb a 4 to 6 inch rain in an hour! This saves water, stops erosion, and helps prevent flood damage.

Soils rich in organic matter also produce more abundant crops. Unfortunately, most soils in the U.S. are way below that organic content — generally between .5 to perhaps 2.5 percent. Soil with that organic content can only absorb about 1/2 inch of rain. When the Rio Grande Valley was first opened for agriculture, the soil organic content was between 3 and 5 percent. According to soil test labs, the current organic content is about 0.5 percent.

Lack of organic matter in the soil is the biggest cause of our water problems. California alone is losing 10,000 acres of usable soil to desert each year because of loss of soil organic matter. Worldwide, 26,000 acres daily are turning to desert and being lost to water insoak and food production.

Since agriculture and landscaping use up to 90 percent of our fresh water, conservation must start there. Building soil organic content, growing cover crops, selecting correct plant varieties, proper tillage, and recycling back to the land all organic waste, biosolids included, is our only salvation. These practices solve our water quantity and quality problems, our soil loss problems, and our food production problems. Organic matter is mostly carbon. Increasing soil organic content takes carbon from the air and places it where it is needed, and that helps check global warming.

Scientists have calculated that if, each year, we increase the organic content of the soil by 0.1 percent, we can offset all the excess carbon we put into the air. Is this solution too simple?

It has been demonstrated over and over that organically grown plants require from 10 to 50 percent less irrigation. If 90 percent of our water goes to irrigation, saving just 10 percent of that 90 is a lot of water freed up for more agriculture, industry and human consumption.

Foliar sprays work best if applied in the evening. Bright sunlight will dry and degrade the spray so that it is much less effective. In the evening the insect control or fertilizer will have plenty of time to be absorbed by the plant.

Soil Building

New Year's Resolutions for Gardeners

- Before you perform any activity, use any product or do anything, always ask, "Will Nature approve?"
- Plant a garden. Gardening is the only time you can have your cake and eat it too.
- Don't allow gardening to become a chore. Keep gardening fun. Gardening can and should be therapeutic and relaxing exercise.
- Consider failures in the garden as learning experiences. Failures make successes a lot sweeter.
- Don't curse the weeds; Nature designed them so the earth could always have a protective cover, sometimes green, sometimes brown. The weeds help the gardener get exercise between planting and harvest time.
- Study Nature, there is no end to her mystery and excitement. Study the reproduction activities of insects; they are way more interesting, outlandish, exotic, and bizarre than anything you will ever find in a racy novel.
- Read books on Nature. Life in the soil alone can furnish more mystery and suspense than any good author can dream up.
- Study each pest, each insect, weed and disease before you stomp on it, hoe it, or spray it. It may be trying to show or tell us something that could help us in some way. Nature has designed every living creature to be of use and service to us. If we spent time and money and studied from that point of view, a lot of problems would be solved.
- Don't be selfish. The time, space, shelter, food and water of the earth environment belong to all creatures. Be willing to share a small portion of your plants, harvest and space with the four-legged, the feathered, and the creepy crawlies.

Kitchen garden view in 2001. We can be happy and healthy if we live in harmony with Nature.

- Before you rake the leaves ask the tree why it shed them, the tree may want to keep the leaves as blanket over its roots for the winter and then as mulch and compost through the spring and summer.
- If you catch lawn clippings ask Nature what you should do with them. Nature designed grass to be harvested, but in the wild the harvesting animal always deposited something in return in the form of manure and urine. We too should return something. A mulch of compost would be much appreciated.
- Practice soil and water conservation. Mulching and composting are the most positive and absolute ways to conserve soil and water. Nature has been doing it for eons, since the very beginning.
- Don't complain about the weather; you can't do anything to change it. Just think how boring life would be without the four seasons. Without gloomy weather we couldn't appreciate and enjoy good weather. Besides, how would we ever start a conversation with a stranger?
- Take time to smell the roses.

Observe the Cycle of Life

Walk into the woods and meadows and visit with Nature. You will be in the presence of abundant life. Especially in the spring, you will find many types of plants, grasses, trees, animals, and insects — large and small. There will be life in abundance.

Now take a closer look. There is an equal amount of death, particularly in the winter. There will be dead grass and leaves, fallen limbs and trees, even dead animals and insects.

Every living thing will sooner or later die; no living creature, plant or animal, escapes death. In Nature, every dead thing is deposited in the very place it dies, and there it serves as a mulch protecting the soil until it finally decays and in due time is covered and replaced by still later deposits of expired life.

When a plant or animal dies, even though it may be consumed higher in the food chain, it will eventually be eaten by the decomposing microbes. They will decay or disassemble it and put it back into the soil. If they didn't, our planet would now be miles deep in dead things.

This life-death-decay-life cycle has built the thin layer of fertile soil that covers our arable land. It nourishes and grows our plants which are the bridge of life between the soil and man.

In the beginning, our planet was just a round mass of minerals moving in its planned orbit through space. At some point, the Almighty saw fit to breathe life onto earth, very meager and primitive life, but life with a crucial mission.

As these micro-forms of life lived and reproduced, they fed on and etched away at the rocky mineral earth surface, and as they died, their remains formed humus and mild acids to etch away still more minerals. This process went on and on until very small amounts of our first soil was formed.

Even though extremely small, the life, death, and decay of each preceding life form has been creating better conditions for future life forms than were there before. The decay process builds with added interest to the soil's

Cow pasture and woods.

bank account, and after countless centuries of creating conditions for higher and more complex forms of life, Man, the most complex of all life, was able to exist and be sustained.

Man . . . does he know? And can he trace his life support system far enough back to understand the life cycles? Man has accumulated much knowledge, but in areas of his healthy existence he seems to be slow to learn. Man sees death as a loss, or something to be sorrowful of, and he considers decay as something ugly. He doesn't understand why Nature always returns the dead back to the soil from where it came.

If man understood the laws of recycle and return, he would without delay put back into the farmlands all the animal manure and other organic waste he generates. He wouldn't be daily burying the thousands of tons of these life-generating materials in landfills that seal and lock them away from the natural soil-building processes for centuries to come.

In Nature, there is no waste. All is reused, and usually made into something of still greater value for the sustenance of life.

If man continues to break this law of return, he will not only stop the life-generating processes of the soil. He will actually cause the soil to degenerate — a process that will sooner or later degrade all life . . . including man himself.

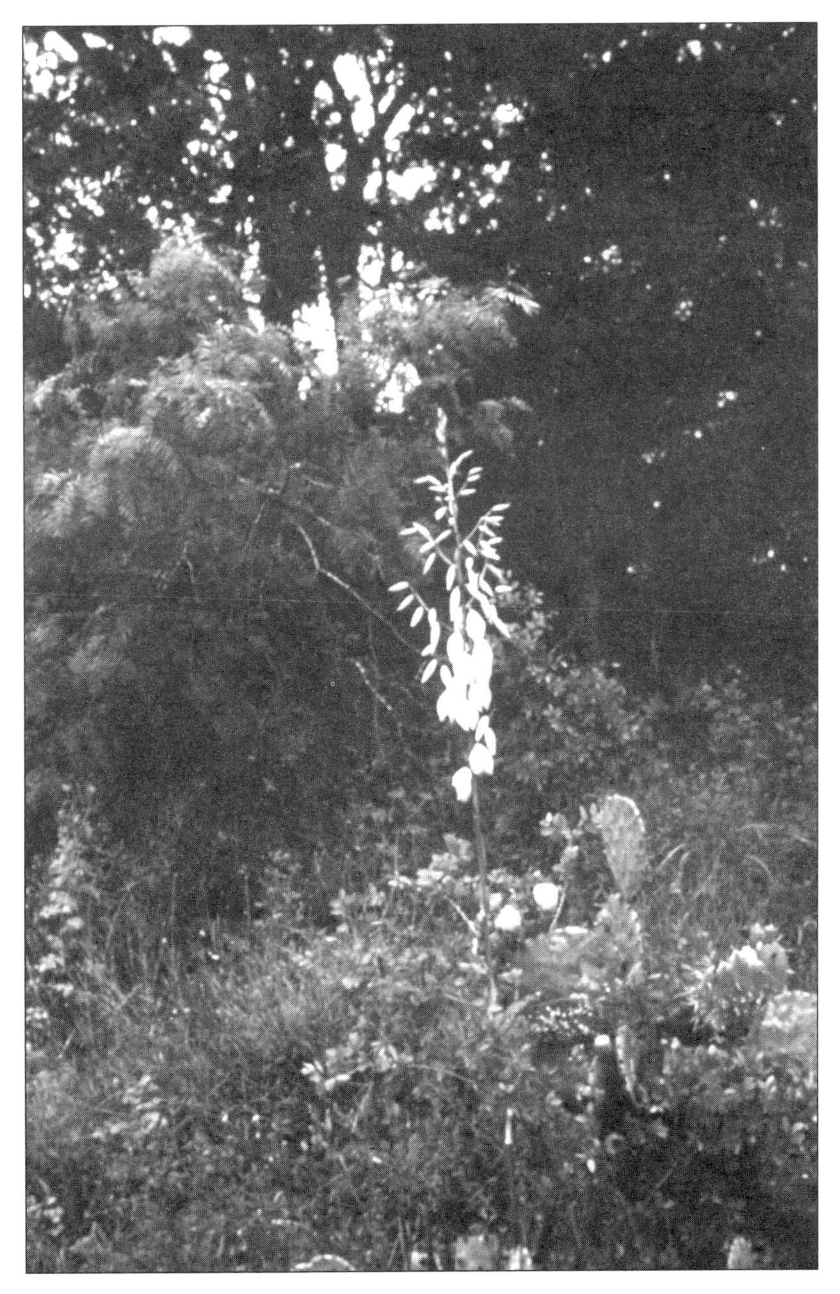

There is no end to the secrets of Nature that are revealed in the prairie and woods.

Why Recycle?

Planet Earth

Ours is the only planet known to support life. All life on Earth is maintained by a thin layer of soil covering a small portion of the Earth's surface. The quality of all life on this planet is determined by the quality of that thin layer of topsoil. If we allow the quality of that thin layer to degrade, all life on earth, man included, will degrade to the same degree. The parent to all soil is mineral rock. The wind, rain, freezing and thawing break the rock into smaller sizes to start the soil-making process. Small rock particles do not become fertile soil until some life form has interacted with them.

The first life forms to attack the rock are microbes. They use elements from the air to grow and reproduce and slowly etch away at the rock surface. They exude, die and decompose, forming humus and mild acids on the rock, which dissolves minerals to further enrich the accumulating soil. This process goes on and on until higher plants and then animal life can be sustained. The death and decay of each life has a generating effect. Each time a living thing dies and decays on the soil, it creates a more fertile condition than was there before.

The energy to keep this cycle revved up comes from the sun. Plants alone have the ability to collect solar energy. This energy then passes through the food chain to all other life forms. Through the excrement and finally death of the many life forms, the sun's energy is passed to the soil to fuel the life systems in the soil and keep the cycle going so that man, the highest form of life, can be sustained. The plants bridge the void between soil and man.

Study the woods and prairie, you will see much life, plant and animal, large and small. Then look down, you will see many expired life forms covering the soil. A mulch of dead things- twigs, leaves, grass, insects , manure and even dead animals. Dig into this mulch and you will find it beginning to decay. The deeper you dig, the more advanced the decay until it fades into rich moist topsoil.

Nature has been building fertile topsoil by mulching and composting the surface of the earth since the beginning of time. With our modern way of living we consume, use, wear out and discard mountains of once-living

Industrial waste — sawdust, wood chips, and paper to blend into compost. To Nature, waste is as valuable as the product it came from.

materials. Most of this we waste by sealing it in landfills where it is locked away from its soil-building destiny for centuries to come. In the landfills, these natural resources are a waste. In the streams and lakes they are pollution. But on farmlands they become fertilizer. We must loop these natural resources back to food-producing soils so the life cycle can be maintained.

In the towns and cities, these organic materials should be collected at feasible sites. Then through the art of composting these once-alive materials can be partly decayed to a condition that is sanitary and easy to transport to the countryside, where Nature can reuse it.

Reports from the governments of all countries, the U.S. included, show widespread humus depletion and topsoil erosion from the food-producing soils. The degraded soils can only grow degraded plants which forces the higher life forms to follow that same path. Only proper recycling of all organic materials, coupled with good farming practices, can stop and reverse this little-noticed decline that creeps through all life.

Water Conservation

Sticky substances are exuded by microbes as they break down the organic materials on and in the soil. This sticky substance glues the powdery soil particles together to form a fine crumb structure. This crumb structure allows carbon dioxide-oxygen exchange necessary for healthy root growth and the proliferation of the beneficial soil life that controls pathogens in the soil.

The crumb structure also allows water to soak into the soil from rain, especially heavy rains. Research has shown that good farmland soil with 4 to 5 percent of organic matter can soak up a 6 inch rain where and when it falls. Most of our soils can now only soak up about one half of their natural capacity. Water that soaks into the soil is held in the humus and clay of the soil for future plant use. Any amount of water the soil can't hold is filtered by the organic matter of the soil as it continues on down to feed the aquifers that supply drinking water and keep the springs flowing at a constant rate instead of periodically going dry.

Water that can't soak in has to run off. Minerals and powdery soil with no crumb structure are carried with the water. This potential soil increases the volume of flooding water, which rushes to the streams and then into the rivers causing damaging floods.

Instead of studying Nature and taking a close look for the cause of floods, human reasoning sees only rain as the problem. The true cause of bad flooding is ignored and large dams are being built to collect the flood water in lakes. Now more energy is being wasted to pump the water back to the farmland where it should have remained. The soil carried by the flooding waters collects at the bottom of the lakes. With each new flood gradually filling the lakes with more soil, they will eventually become big mudholes.

Food Production

Why doesn't man pay more attention to the natural chemistry, physics and biology of the world and see himself as part of that natural world, of its perfect design? Is it greed? Is it vanity? Or could it be that soil fertility has eroded to a level that no longer nourishes the body and the mind? Is man losing his ability to see and think logically?

History books are full of stories about the decline and fall of many great nations. Soil decline was always involved in the beginning of the fall. Poor soils result in failure of the economy and then the defense system. But if history were closely studied and the truth was known, you would find it was really the decline of the mind that made the difference — and the mind begins to decline as soon as the soil begins to produce food that is empty of nutrients.

My friend's experiments with pigeons and my own with young chickens reported earlier in the book showed us how important nutritious food is to all living things.

Look at our society and others all around the world. You can find many examples that show evidence of eating too much white rice and white bread. Or could it be symptoms of soil decline?

Soil Microbes

Sir Albert Howard, the author of *The Soil and Health*, was one of the first scientists who recognized that the health of the soil determines the health of the plants and the health of the animals that eat from them. Albert Howard is known as the father of compost. However, he learned from the Chinese, who have maintained soil fertility for forty centuries. We have worn out farm after farm in two centuries.

When Howard first used compost around failing plants, he noticed an almost miraculous recovery. The plants also became resistant to pests. He then fed animals from the composted, healthy plants and noticed they didn't contract diseases, even when allowed to mix with sick animals that had very contagious diseases. Health did indeed pass from one life to the next through the food chain. Perfectly healthy plants and animals have resistance to diseases.

Albert Howard believed his compost to be rich in nutrients but was disappointed when test returns showed it to be low in NPK (nitrogen, potassium, phosphorous). He thought he had not used enough of it to produce the amazing results, so he was anxious to learn how a little compost could have such a powerful effect. After studying the roots of the composted plants, he found the reasons: the beneficial root colonizing microbes, especially the mycorrhizal fungi, were present in very high populations, and no harmful root pathogens were present. The roots of the nearby uncomposted plants were being attacked by pathogens and very few, if any, of the beneficial microbes were present.

I have a friend who grows cotton up in the high plains of Texas. He was slowly going broke, so he decided to look at other, and possibly better, ways than the conventional farming methods he was using. He cut his acreage from 2,500 to the 240 acres he owned. He then started using organic methods, among them biological sprays which included free nitrogen fixing microbes, which he applied along with feed-grade molasses for an energy source.

After a few years on the natural program he discovered he could quit irrigating even though he was in a low rainfall area. In drier years his production is below that of his irrigating neighbors, but his profit per acre is always greater since he has no irrigation or pesticide expenses. I have seen this man's cotton stand up showing no signs of stress while the neighbor's cotton across a dirt road just 70 feet away under conventional farming methods was severely wilting even though it had been irrigated twice that year. To find out how this was possible I got the soil and the roots tested from both farms and there was a striking difference. The roots from the organic farm had 24 percent mycorrhizal colonization with many spores and vesicles. The cotton roots from the conventional farm had only 2 percent colonization with some roots showing none. I discussed these two farms and the difference of soil microbes with Dr. Don Marks of Mycorr Tech Inc. and Dr. Jerry Parsons, our extension agent, and both agreed that overusing chemical fertilizers and pesticides on soils low in organic matter is detrimental to beneficial soil life.

Mycorrhizal fungi form a symbiotic association with the roots of most plants. The fungi grow into or between the cells of the roots and use 10 percent of the carbohydrates the plant passes from the leaves to the roots. The fungi don't have chlorophyll in the presence of sunlight, so they can't manufacture carbohydrates. In return for the energy taken from the plant, the fungi grow out and search far and wide for nutrients and moisture, and feed the plant so it can continue to manufacture more and more carbohydrate energy. The bigger and faster the plant grows, the farther and faster the fungi grow to feed the plant. A plant colonized with mycorrhizal fungi will have the equivalent of ten times more root. Another benefit of this association is that as long as the fungi are flourishing, they can prevent all root pathogens and damaging nematodes from attacking the root. Decaying organic materials on and in the soil keep both the plant and the fungi flourishing to help each other.

There are many beneficial forms of life in the soil. Scientists tell us there is more tonnage of life and numbers of species in the soil than there is growing above it. All of this life gets its energy from the sun. But only the plants, with their green leaves, have the ability to collect the sun's energy. All other life forms depend on the plant to pass energy to them. The plants above and soil life below depend on each other for their healthy existence and continued survival.

Another beneficial microbe that colonized plant roots was introduced to me by Bill Kowalski of Natural Industries. This microbe knocks out several root rots, includling cotton root rot, a common problem in Texas. (See the article, Taming Root Rot.)

Dr. Crawford originally discovered this microbe. He tells me it is a Saprophytic, rhizosphere-colonizing actinomycete, which means it is a microbe that lives on the roots and eats the skin sloughed off by a healthy, normal growing plant. As long as the plant flourishes and the roots grow and lots of root skin is being shed to feed the actinomycete, it doesn't let disease organisms or root-knot nematodes attack the roots.

The soil life and the plant life support each other. Hence the laws of Nature: Destroy the weak and allow survival of the fittest. Without the colonizers feeding and protecting the plant, it falls victim to the natural laws. Weakened plants are attacked by all kinds of pests below and above ground. Nature wants the weak and sick plants to be destroyed. But man interferes. He uses his arsenal of pesticides to keep the unfit plants alive. Then he eats from the poisoned sick plants — and wonders why he gets sick.

Commonsense Composting

The Art of Composting

You can study science books until the biology, physics and chemistry of composting are well understood, but that doesn't make you a master. Composting is an art, and just like any other art, it can only be perfected by doing it and getting the feel of it. I knew nothing about the sciences that happen in compost but learned to make compost by watching things decay in Nature. Gradually, over time, I began to understand the sciences involved.

When I was a curious child between the ages of two and five, our place had a barn with a solid wooden fence running parallel to the east wall. Between the wall and the fence was an area four feet wide. In that little lane were some big hackberry trees. The leaves blown by the wind collected between the barn and that fence up to 14 inches deep. That was one of my favorite places to play. It always smelled so good! I hoped the leaves would eventually build up so high that I could see over the fence, but I noticed every year before the leaves would start falling again, the pile would be way down and the new falling leaves would only bring the pile up to the original height. I would always dig into this leaf pile and find all kinds of neat bugs and worms to play with. It was always nice and moist, even if it had not rained in a long time. I also noticed how the leaves gradually changed into soil and the tree roots were always growing up out of the ground into the decaying leaves. Childhood reasoning told me the roots were eating and drinking from those decaying leaves. By the very young age of five, I had learned from Nature the secret of her life cycles.

Once I got a little bigger, handling manure and other farm waste was always part of my life. It was a necessary farm chore, and I didn't mind it any more than any other chore. I could easily see the rewards of hauling the waste back to the fields. The crops were always bigger in the area where it was applied, more earthworms were there and the soil was softer and easier to plow.

Many books on composting make it so complicated that you need advanced degrees in science to understand them. Most people who successfully make compost learned by observing Nature. It is much easier to

Turning static pile compost.

understand the science after you have mastered the art of composting than the other way around. Studying the science first seems to dampen the desire to experiment. You try to make something work that doesn't, because you are unaware of some factor that wasn't covered in the books. Then you become frustrated. Much of the material written on composting is by people that studied the book sciences, but I am not sure they conferred with Nature as to when, where and how it should be done.

Economics & Nature

If you study Nature, you soon learn that she is very thrifty. She doesn't make an unnecessary move or start a process for no reason. Nature never wastes energy while she recycles expired life. "The Law of Least Effort" was written by her. We need to study all her laws and learn from her. In Nature, every dead thing is deposited in the very place it dies and there it serves as a mulch protecting the soil until it finally decays and in due time is covered and replaced by still more dead things. As these dead things are disassembled by the microbes, the proteins are changed into ammonium gas. Some of the gasses are used by the microbes, some are turned into nitrates, a small amount is used by growing plants, and any ammonium not used is absorbed into clay and humus in the soil and held for future plant use. Little if any escapes to the air.

Carbon dioxide (CO_2) is also released as the microbes break down organic matter. Carbon dioxide release is most abundant in warm weather when plant growth is greatest. The carbon dioxide drifts up from the soil surface and is captured by the leaf surface of the many plants growing above. Little escapes to the air, and what does goes over to feed plants that are growing in areas that don't have decay processes going on under them. The plants take the carbon out of the CO_2, use it for food and release the oxygen.

Some scientists are saying that an excess amount of carbon dioxide in the atmosphere is causing global warming. But science has also proven an abundance of CO_2 in the air allows plants to more efficiently use water and grow better. I believe global warming is being caused by us humans uncovering and creating too much bare soil by some of our agricultural practices, herbicides and paving over. My own testing has shown bare soil in full sun to be 35 degrees warmer than nearby soil under mulch or plant cover.

Mulch also protects the soil from heavy rain drops that settle soil particles together to form a impervious crust. The broken up water droplets filter through the decaying mulch and collect the nutrients released by the microbes and slowly carry it to the roots of plants that put it back into the life cycle.

The layer of mulch also keeps the moisture from moving up and evaporating back into the air. As water moves upward in the soil, it carries dissolved minerals with it. When the water evaporates it leaves the minerals concentrated at the soil surface as salts in a crust that seeds can't sprout or plants grow in. With the evaporation stopped by mulching, the moisture and minerals stay dispersed in the soil for root collection.

Un-Economics & Man

Nature does not agree with some of our wasteful composting ways. We allow moisture, ammonia and carbon dioxide to dissipate into the air. And we waste energy while doing it. Nature decomposes dead things and manure right where they fall. The organic material decays and nourishes new life in that area. If a small amount of nutrients happens to escape that area, it is because the rains carried some to feed the life in the streams, lakes and the oceans.

Many times because people take the "Not In My Backyard" (NIMBY) approach to composting, raw materials have to be hauled great distances to a remote location before composting is allowed. Nature isn't given any consideration. The pollution from noise, tire wear, clutch wear, brake wear, engine exhaust and crankcase exhaust nullifies much of the good done by composting.

I have visited many compost operations and found some to be very inefficient. They were using up more energy to make compost than it contained when it was finished. By dry weight, compost contains about 5 percent minerals and 95 percent energy. You could burn it and measure the BTUs just as with gas, oil or coal since they too were plant life in past times. You gain nothing and Nature loses if you burn up as much or more energy than the compost contains when you get through making it. The energy is

Home garden compost bins. It is false economics to spend more energy to make compost than it will contain when finished.

the most valuable part of the compost, the soil's greatest need. The rest of the soil needs can temporarily be bought in bags. With continued use of compost the need for bagged fertilizers goes down until eventually little, if any, is needed.

A good example of how inefficient some composters are: Once in the past a compost company moved near San Antonio and set up operation at a big feedlot. Then they discovered I was in the composting business. They were fine ethical people, so they came to me and asked if we could get along. They assured me that they would not cut my prices. We quickly became friends and visited each other's locations and exchanged ideas and experiences. On visiting their operation I saw they were composting in an insulated house. The operator bragged it took them only seven days to make compost. It took me six to seven months. This was hard for me to accept, but it so happened that my visit was on the seventh day. He opened the doors and sure enough he had a fine looking compost.

My immediate thoughts were, I need to check into this. Then another thought struck. That house only held seventy yards. He was limited to making ten yards per day. He also told me their construction time from start to finish on the building was almost six months. And before they could load the house, the material had to be ground to proper size; the c/n (carbon-to-nitrogen) ratio had to be perfect and the moisture just right. Once the doors were closed, a switch was turned on and the computer, operating blowers, took over to keep temperature, oxygen and whatever just right by blowing air up through the floor. This was all great, but all that energy and high technology just to let something rot! If I dumped 200 cubic yards on the ground the day he started construction and turned it four times like I normally do, we would both have our first compost to sell on the same day. If I continued to make 200 yards each day six days a week, I would have 200 yards (minus the shrinkage per day) to sell, and he would still only have his 10 yards per day. I was honest and told him his operation wouldn't fly. It didn't. Three separate operators tried before it was finally shut down for good. Now the building is being used to store hay. A very expensive barn.

The micro- and macro-life forms do the never-ending work of the decaying/composting for us. And like any other living entity they need water to drink, air/oxygen to breath, carbon/carbohydrates for energy and protein/nitrogen to build their bodies. They also need minerals, but the carbon and nitrogen materials being composted contain these minerals since they too were alive at one time. The moisture, air, carbon and nitrogen need to be blended and mixed in a way to create the perfect hotel/factory/cafeteria to keep the decomposers comfortable and happy so they can work, eat and multiply. The compost pile itself is their hotel. They don't need an additional high tech, very expensive building that man designed for them to work in. They will work in these high tech contraptions and work well, but if we don't watch it we may end up with a bunch of spoiled microbes that will become lazy and soon demand welfare.

Returning Fertility to the Farm

Most all farm produce — meat, fiber, vegetables and grain — is sent into the cities where it is processed and consumed and eventually ends up in some form of garbage or sludge. A small amount may be composted and used in gardens or the landscape in urban areas. Little, if any, makes it back to the farm from whence it came, where it is most needed and where it belongs. Somehow, with the invention of modern farm chemicals, our human logic (or was it greed?) told us it was no longer worth the effort to recycle the organic materials back to the land. Most industry and agricultural universities jumped on this chemical bandwagon. But there were a few people that understood natural soil fertility and warned of the dangers of wasting and not recycling.

Instead of consulting Nature to see what she recommended, we used human brilliance and the organic-versus-chemical feud started. The guilty are on both sides. Neither the chemical nor the organic supporters are willing to ask Nature's approval of the other method. Everyone benefits when our food-producing soils are improved. There have been and still are many tax-supported programs to help farmers. Some have been questionable. An incentive for the farmer to increase the organic content of the soil would be the most sensible approach. The farmer could grow cover crops instead of cash crops or he could spread compost if he wanted to keep the fields in production while he built the organic content. Another incentive that would be good for the farmer and benefit everyone is to pay for quality rather than quantity of production. The farmer who is well-compensated for high-quality produce will be more able to maintain high organic matter in his soil.

If compost is so needed on farm acres, why am I selling and promoting compost in the cities? Because that is where most of the voters live. When they see the excellent results of using compost in the landscape and on the vegetable garden and taste the quality of compost-grown produce, they will be convinced. When they realize that compost reduces the need for irrigation and pesticides, the city folks will better understand agriculture. It is

Farm view 1993. Howard Garrett poses with an open pollinated corn crop.

their vote that will encourage lawmakers to enact laws for a sound ecology. Until the consumer understands and demands fertile soils and healthy foods, it will be hard to change our wasteful practices.

Valuing What is Valuable

To Nature, compost is extremely valuable. Returning organic materials back to the soil is a must if quality of life is to continue. We, however, as supposedly intelligent creatures, have continually devalued compost. First by saying, "We need to compost the organics because they are filling up our limited landfill space too fast." More value was put on the hole in the ground than on the food the soil dearly needed. Then after a few cities learned to save the landfill space by composting, they devalued it still further by giving it away or selling it too cheap. Anything free or sold for very little is given just that value — very little. With the very low value put on compost, private composters have little interest, which drops a still greater burden on the cities and their valuable holes.

Cities should use as much of their compost on their own properties as possible; usually they will not have enough. It sets a good example to citizens. The citizens equally share in the value of water, fertilizer and pesticide savings. And tax money is not used to compete with private enterprise. This practice also encourages the private composting and mulching industry — another good thing for the economy of the community.

A view of 66 test plots, each 10 feet by 6 feet with a 4-foot buffer space between them. All irrigated with equal drip. Each had an equal number of summer peas, okra and jalapeno peppers. Compost of different types, fertilizers, compost fertilizer mix, mineral sources, and many commercial soil additives were tested. The soil pH in that field was between 7.5 and 8. Nature will revel her secrets to us, but only when we pay attention to her rules, learn to think and do some research and testing of our own.

An Uphill Battle

Nature is crying for help. Compost could be her rescue. Except for a few, our land grant universities have mostly ignored her. I gave a presentation to a dairy group on the value and long term benefits of spreading manure on agricultural soils. The speaker who followed me was an agriculture Ph.D. His first words from the podium were, "Gentlemen, we have to face it. If you have to haul manure across the road or more than a mile or two, it isn't worth the effort. It only has 20 pounds of Nitrogen per ton."

On another occasion a wealthy man attended a presentation I gave and ordered a 60 cubic yard load of compost. Before we had a chance to deliver, he called and canceled. He said his County Ag. agent told him compost would bring in diseases, insects and all kinds of pests. He also said the nitrates would keep the trees green too long in the fall and then they would freeze. These two college-educated gentlemen should have studied more in Nature instead of in the classroom. They would have a better education.

One of my employees, an ex-pro ball player, has three children who also excel in sports. He approached their school and suggested they spread compost on their ball fields. Not only would they save water and fertilizer but the turf would be thicker and softer, which could also help prevent injuries. He was rejected with, "Oh no, our students would get disease and infections from compost." I fail to see their logic, especially since they apply all types of toxic pesticides and chemicals to the turf for those kids to play in. These are not isolated incidences. We have experienced this ignorance many times and so have other composters and organic growers.

We have since spent a few thousand dollars with a well-respected microbiologist on testing. He found no disease-causing organisms in the compost. To some this research still wasn't convincing. There seems to be a mind-set that anything dead or of animal residue is awful and should be disposed of at a dump that is not near their back yard. The research also revealed that 27 percent of the isolates were insect pathogens, and another 18 percent of the isolates were important in the bioremediation of environmental pollutants. Compost tea is now being used to help control the imported fire ant and also being used as a fungicide.

Bioremediation is nothing more than selective composting. If given enough time the microbes in a well-constructed compost pile can disassemble any toxin man has put together. Compost should be used on athletic fields and on any lawn where children play, especially if toxic pesticides have been used there in the past. Compost will help clean up the damage that has been done in the past through the use of toxic chemicals. Our kids are in much more danger from them than they are from good, clean soil.

Because the testing proved there were no harmful pathogens in the compost, we have finally seen it used on two football fields. The results are so good other athletic directors have requested compost for their playing fields.

We have since ended up with a bonus in our sales pitch. The teams that play on the two football fields we composted both won the state championships of 1995, class 5A.

The Judge

A Master Designer created Mother Nature and authored the natural laws. We had no part in making, designing or enacting a single rule. We are only part of Nature. We cannot change, alter or break any of the laws without causing harm to ourselves.

Everything in Nature (even what we call waste) is designed to be perfect and has a purpose. We are the highest beings on earth, so everything on earth was designed to be of service and aid to us. If we studied from this approach we would learn things, make discoveries and see things otherwise blocked from view.

The future of a livable existence on Earth hinges on our knowing and obeying the natural laws. If we allow the environment to rule and Mother Nature to judge, our existence on Earth could only improve.

We too were designed to be perfect . . . except the Master Designer gave us free will.

Greed, envy and jealousy — all traits of human free will — seem to influence public policy, sway bureaucracy and taint our written laws. They even decide where to place sewer plants, landfills and the compost operations demanded by Nature to recycle the huge amounts of waste we create. Placing these facilities could be the easiest decision to make if geology and environment were studied and Nature was given first consideration and allowed to rule.

True, no one wants these sites in their backyard, but we all create waste and it has to go someplace. Moving these sites too far creates pollution from vehicle wear and exhaust. Noise, dust, traffic and strong odors are also created in proportion to the distance that material has to be transported.

Those who live near sites should somehow be compensated. I think cutting property taxes in proportion to the nuisances tolerated would be fair compensation. All other citizens (who also create waste) but who do not have the nuisance should pick up the difference.

When Nature points to the location to place these entities, politics should not be able to overrule her.

Energy: The Essence of Agriculture

Earth, the only known planet to support and sustain life, is home to many beautiful, fascinating and wonderful forms of life. All of these life forms are sustained and maintained by a thin layer of topsoil. That thin layer is created, kept fertile, healthy and productive through the decay of rock for minerals and decay of organic materials for structure and energy. The quality of that topsoil determines the quality of all life on earth, including the fish in the sea. If we allow the thin top layer to degrade to any degree, the life it supports degrades along with it. The Earth's surface is approximately 74 percent water and 6 percent ice leaving 20 percent dry land. But, only about 8 percent is suitable for food crop production. All life, humans, animals, insects, plants and microbes must have *four* things before they can grow and reproduce.

1. Oxygen — the air contains 21 percent oxygen and is kept in balance by the growth of green plants through photosynthesis.
2. Water — cycles between the clouds and earth; 74 percent of the earth is covered by water.
3. Minerals — comes from rock being dissolved by processes and organic acids from the activity of life.
4. Energy — beamed down daily from the sun and collected by green leaves.

All four ingredients are of equal importance. The quality of our topsoil determines their availability and the quality and quantity we are able to use. In modern agriculture oxygen, water and minerals are given attention. Energy in the soil is mostly ignored.

The energy we use — be it gasoline, diesel, coal, natural gas or wood — and all the food we eat come from plant life. Green plants alone have the power to use the energy from the sun to combine carbon with hydrogen to make carbohydrates, an energy source that can combine with other elements to serve as food and energy for all other life forms. Plants store energy in their roots, limbs, leaves, flowers, fruit and seeds. We now have solar

Elbon rye cover crop farm view 1988. Through photosynthesis this field of rye grass has collected from the sun, and stored, loads of energy to be used by all life forms.

cells, but their efficiency at collecting the sun's energy doesn't come near the efficiency of plants, and solar cells can't make food. The energy collected by plants can be stored as a liquid, solid, or gas to be used immediately or stored for later use.

Science tells us there are more numbers of species and tonnage of life under ground than above. All life in the soil below ground and all animal life above ground must get its energy from living or decaying plant life.

Most of the agricultural soils in the U.S. and around the world are low in energy. Many of our food producing soils are dangerously low in energy rich organic matter.

The agriculture books tell us that the soil microbes must first process fertilizers, organic or chemical, into the proper form before plants can properly use it. This is true. However, the microbes cannot do the processing without a sufficient supply of energy.

Organic fertilizers contain an abundant energy supply, whereas chemical fertilizers are lacking the energy the soil life needs for processing. This forces the soil life to draw from the soil energy reserves, eventually depleting the soil energy to a point where chemical fertilizers can no longer be properly processed. The unprocessed fertilizer salts cause plants to stress. Stressed plants require more irrigation, attract troublesome insects and are susceptible to diseases and are less tolerant of hot or cold temperatures.

Soils lacking organic matter starve the microbes, earthworms, grubs, springtails and other beneficial organisms that create the proper crumb structure for aeration and water percolation. Without good soil percolation rainwater runs off which causes soil erosion and flooding. Springs and creeks dry up, aquifers and water wells dry up. During droughts the soil is hard packed and irrigation becomes less effective, resulting in poor crop production.

Soil organic matter is being depleted faster than Nature can replace it. The two main causes are improper and over-tillage (which oxidizes the soil) and the overuse of energy-deficient fertilizers.

Loss of organic matter from our farm soils increases the need for irrigation, while much of our rainwater is being lost down rivers to the salty sea instead of soaking into the soil. All the while, man's population continues to grow, demanding more food and water. We appear to be on a collision course with our destiny.

Organic matter has the energy to make agricultural soils productive. Science tells us that we cannot create or destroy energy, but energy can change. Energy may be found in many forms such as light, heat, sound etc. Every action in Nature involves a source of energy. There can be no life without energy.

Using the Carbon Cycle in Soil & Water Conservation

My first experience seeing the carbon cycle at work (although I didn't understand what I was seeing at the time) was out on the West Texas desert where they were dumping trainload after trainload of New York belt press sludge directly on top of the dry desert soil. Fist-sized chunks of stinky, wet, biologically active biosolids (processed human waste), were spread several inches apart in the native grass that was very poor and scarce. The annual rainfall in that area is less than ten inches. During that visit one of the tractor operators came close and in a low voice, as if he didn't want anyone else to hear, said, "There is something strange about this stuff, it hasn't rained for month, surely none of the moisture was getting to the roots, but it seemed like within just a few days the grass actually turned greener and seemed to be growing some." My first thought was — wishful thinking! But I too noticed the same thing happening when we put moist biosolids compost on the shoulders of a highway for the Texas Department of Transportation to help stop erosion. It was a dry year but the few existing bunches of established grass greened up anyway. Later I again visited the West Texas site where they spread the first New York biosolids. In areas where there was soil, the native grass was green, healthy and so thick you couldn't see the ground. This is good indication of what the grass in the area was like before it was abused with improper grazing and what it could be like again if properly managed.

After reading some NASA research on global warming I found the missing clue to how plants, especially grass, can green up without rain or irrigation. When there is a concentration of carbon dioxide (CO_2) around a plant leaf, the pores, called stomata, which have the ability to open and close, stay shut much longer and close quicker after opening. When the stomata are open they release moisture to the air, which has a cooling affect. There are several results of this process. A NASA scientist concluded that

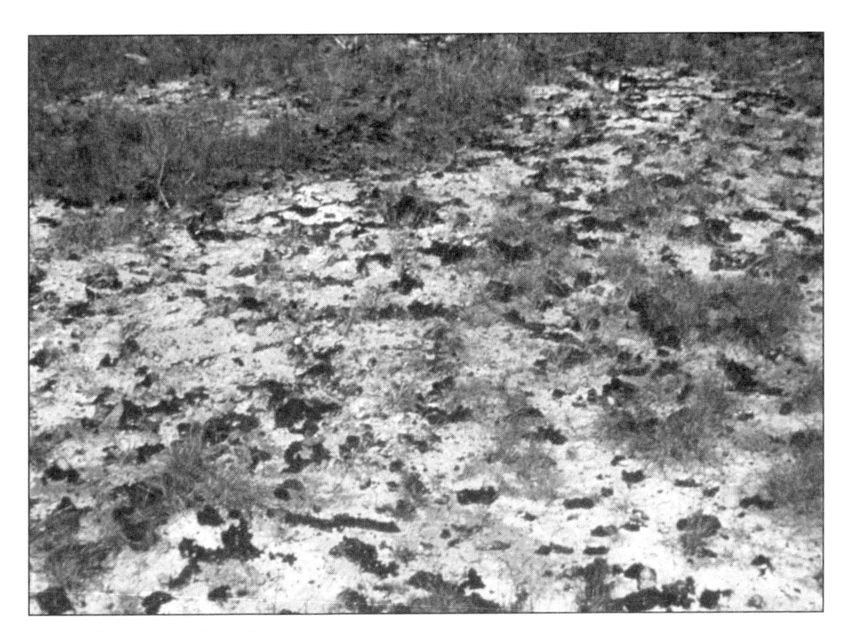

Biosolids spread on desert.

when stomata stayed shut longer there was less cooling effect, a contributor to global warming. But there was also more moisture retained in the soil and in the plant, causing healthier growth.

The NASA scientist didn't mention that a plant transpires into the air 99 percent of the water it pulls from the soil. And when the stomata stay closed longer, especially with large volumes of plant leaves, an immense volume of soil moisture could be saved.

Anytime the insect and micro soil life decomposes something, there is a release of carbon dioxide. Carbon dioxide is slightly heavier than air. When it is released from rotting organic material under and around plants, it tends stay in or near the plant canopy before eventually diffusing into the atmosphere. The stomata on the leaves of plants now have an abundance of carbon dioxide for photosynthesis to create carbohydrates, the energy source for all human and animal life.

Plants do need to transpire some water to the air. The upward movement of water in the plant carries nutrients from the soil to the leaves. Also it takes water from the soil that already is, to some degree, depleted of the nutrients that were dissolved in it. Diffusion now moves more water toward the roots that hopefully will be saturated with more plant nutrients. The depleted moisture is replaced with nutrient-rich moisture that helps the plants grow. However this all needs to be in balance. The soil needs to be rich in soluble nutrients so only a small amount of water needs to be moved up to transpiration. The decay of organic material is greatest when temperature and moisture are also correct for plant growth. The decaying organic

Grass cover of desert 30 months after biosolids were spread.

material on and in the soil releases plant nutrients and holds moisture and at the same time allows the plants to need less moisture. All this puts still more importance on the organic content of the soil.

The plants need the carbon dioxide from the decay of organic matter on and in the soil, but the organic material must be kept on or near the soil surface so the soil doesn't get saturated with CO_2, since the plant roots also give out carbon dioxide.

Of the carbohydrates manufactured by the leaves of plants, 50 to 80 percent is sent down to the roots, which in turn share these nutrients with the large population of soil life that lives in the root zone. Scientists tell us there are around 10,000 species of bacteria and 3,000 species of fungi that use or get some benefit from this carbohydrate energy source. In return, these microbes perform many services for the plants. Science is continually discovering more and more of these benefits, such as protecting the plants from troublesome insects and diseases and gathering nutrients and moisture for the plants.

As long as the plant is able to create carbohydrate/energy, this symbiotic relationship of life forms endures. The more energy that is created, the more each species prospers and helps the others.

Sir Albert Howard, an English soil scientist, way back in the '20s and '30s discovered that when he put compost around plants they thrived with much less insect and disease problems. Howard had his compost tested and discovered the nutrient content just wasn't high enough to give those good results. When Howard checked the plant roots he noticed fungi growing in,

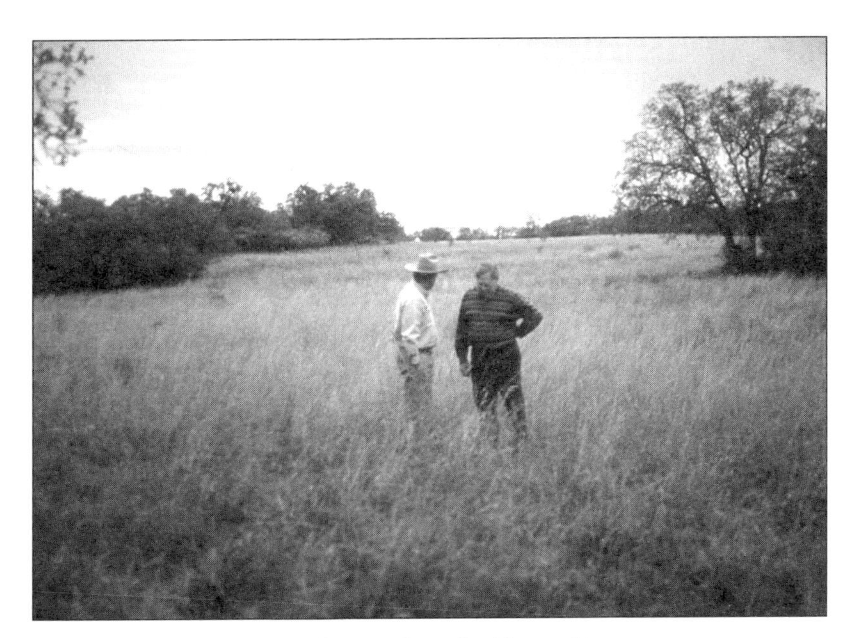

HRM rancher using the carbon cycle to double stocking rates.

around and extending from them. Research proved this to be the mycorrhizae. The mycorrhizal fungi are now known to be extremely important to the health and production of plants. Some recent research by the USDA's Agricultural Research Center (ARS) has shown that mycorrhizae are responsible for a large percent of the humus content formed in rich soils. The plant physiology books tell us a plant will grow and prosper more and more as the concentration of carbon dioxide goes up, even as high as ten times the normal. However, the soil plants are grown in must also be rich and balanced in the major, minor and trace nutrients the plants need. When growers tried to pump carbon dioxide into a greenhouse without balancing the soil it would not work.

The Carbon Cycle & Range Management

The big ranchers who follow Allan Savory's Holistic Resource Management (HRM) teachings have a pretty good handle on using the carbon cycle to full advantage. I have been on some of these ranches, and the ranchers all claimed that they doubled their stocking rates, seldom fed hay, almost did away with vet bills, and are now showing profits even in dry years.

These holistic ranchers have learned to use animals to manage the grass. Even though many don't realize it, they are really managing the carbon cycle. First they divide their spreads into many small pastures or paddocks. They graze these paddocks with heavy stock density. They discovered

Large tomato greenhouse operated 100 percent organically by making use of the carbon cycles with compost and mulch.

when the cows are crowded they seem to graze all the grasses, shrubs and forbs, not just their favorite grasses. Then after the paddock is eaten down to a point, but still leaving plenty of green for photosynthesis, they move the cattle to the next paddock. This high stocking rate of cattle leaves behind a lot of urine and manure. The moist urine and manure with the litter on the ground quickly begins to decay and gives off carbon dioxide. The green grass blades left standing capture it. Then the grass can quickly recover, even in some pretty dry conditions, without straining the roots or using excessive soil moisture. This grazing process also sequesters carbon back into the soil instead of allowing it to disperse into the atmosphere and be called pollution.

Many of these ranchers manage to go through winters without supplemental feeding by saving paddocks of certain species of native grass for winter grazing. Some paddocks will be green with winter growing species. In others it may be dry summer species from winterkill but still standing and full of nutrients or a combination of both. For more information on this natural grazing concept contact the Allan Savory Center for Holistic Management in Albuquerque, New Mexico, phone (505) 842-5252.

Carbon Cycle & Greenhouses

When Delphine and I moved to our new farm over 30 years ago, one of the first things we did was to build a greenhouse to grow bedding plants of

Delphine in her 100 percent organic greenhouse, where pests were never a problem.

tomato, eggplant, cabbage etc. so we could transplant after frost and get a jumpstart on the season.

Whenever some dignitary from Texas A&M came to San Antonio, they sooner or later came to our farm to see what these organic faddists were doing. Four of them were out one day and when they saw my new greenhouse one of them commented, "Beck, there is one thing you won't be able to go organic with." and they all chimed in with agreement.

The greenhouse was put up in 1972 and has been in use ever since, and to this day there has never been a problem with troublesome insects or disease in it. We did nothing to prevent these problems, but looking back I think I now know why. Naturally, we used only organic fertilizers, but the main reason is that instead of gravel or a concrete floor, we maintained a wood-chip mulch that stayed moist from the nutrient-rich drippings from the potted plants above. The decaying mulch gave off an abundance of carbon dioxide for the plants, especially on bright, sunny-but-cold days when the greenhouse had to remain closed.

A friend of mine, Rosco Jordon, had a six thousand square foot greenhouse that he grew tomatoes in each year. Rosco had our same experience of no diseases or insects. And he had very few culls, almost every tomato was perfect. To cut costs he operated his greenhouse similar to ours. For fertilizer he used two pickup truck loads of half rotted, chicken house, woodchip litter-manure mix. For cooling it was natural ventilation by opening the north and south walls. For heating he burned waste crankcase oil in efficient heaters that created no pollution.

At one time I belonged to the Greenhouse Vegetable Growers Association and had the opportunity to tour many greenhouse operations. Rosco Jordon's was by far the cleanest, most productive and profitable I had ever seen. A tornado destroyed the greenhouse after the fourth year ending some valuable research. However, I see no reason the same production could not have continued under these natural methods for many years. Rosco had the carbon cycle working to his advantage.

Carbon Cycle, Vegetables & Row Crops

From many years of growing row crops, vegetables, fruit and pecan trees and grape vines organically, on my own farm and garden, I have learned that building the soil's organic content to highest point possible by using compost and organic mulches and not tilling or disturbing the soil any more than necessary will put the carbon cycle to work to save moisture and increase production and profits. It also lowers insect and disease problems to where little or no control is needed.

When growing vegetables, we sometimes use that fine row cover called Plant Shield or Grow Web over plants as a tent. We would put it up before the seeds emerge or as soon as transplants were put in. The web would trap carbon dioxide, give a few degrees frost protection, and screen insects out, which also stops plants from being infected with viruses. It slows down the wind. It diffuses the sunlight for greater photosensitivity and protects against light hail. Under this web, if there is ample sunlight, the plants will grow three times faster and produce up to three times more. This may get expensive on large acreage, but it can really pay off.

Carbon Cycle & Trees & Vines

If trees and vines are not yet established, concentrate on building the organic content of the soil with cover crops and compost for a few years before planting. If vines and trees are already established, keep an organic mulch around plants at all times. Grow adapted winter cover crop in the winter. In the spring when the trees and vines are actively growing and beginning to need soil moisture, cut the cover crop down to form a mulch. Never disturb the soil between trees or vines more than one inch deep or drive vehicles unnecessarily near plants when the soil is moist enough to make tracks.

Carbon Cycle & Hay Crops

The new cutting, conditioning and windrowing machines for making hay could be used to increase production, build soil, and sequester extra carbon from the air into the soil. This would probably take some research to fine-tune it, but if these mowing machines were set to mow the grasses high enough to allow some green blades to remain, the grass could continue trapping CO_2. The crop could then recover much quicker without straining the roots. The grass could continue to make carbohydrates and feed all the life on and in the root zone that supports the grass. This could result in an extra cutting being obtained as soil quality increases. It would also be beneficial to let the last mowing of the year lie in the field as mulch. If need be, use feed-grade molasses (one gallon per acre) with nitrogen-fixing microbes (Micro-Soil or Agri-Gro) in ample water and spray it on the mulch hay to decay it and make fertilizer faster. Any remaining debris would also be decayed away so it wouldn't interfere with baling the next hay crop.

Understanding Carbon Cycle & Life

In Nature everything cycles. Tides ebb and flow, plants grow and decay, storms come and go. Summer fades into winter then spring revives the Earth once more. It is all part of the natural rhythm of life. Man, because of his numbers and knowledge, now has the ability to alter some of these cycles. Too much CO_2 in the atmosphere from burning fossil fuels has drawn the attention of scientists. Apparently this excess causes global warming, which could change our weather patterns and drastically affect our lives. The scientists look to technology for answers while completely ignoring Nature's balancing processes. Nature has the answer. Why don't we consult her?

Using green plants and sunlight, Nature has been sequestering carbon in the soil since the beginning. The pores on the leaves of plants take in CO_2 and separate the carbon from the oxygen, then release the oxygen into the air. Then the plants combine the carbon with hydrogen to make carbohydrates an energy source for all higher life. Eighty percent of the carbohydrates, are sent to the underground portion of the plant, where it feeds a whole metroplex of beneficial soil life in the root zone. They in turn help the plant collect moisture and minerals to make food for itself and all higher life.

We can assist Nature in the carbon sequestering process. We have a lot of raw materials to work with. The total land area in the continental United States is 1.9 billion acres. Cropland accounts for 455 million acres of that and grassland pasture is 578 million acres. When this country was first settled, all the cropland and rangeland had a soil organic content ranging from 3 to 8 percent. Today the organic content of most of this land is down to less than one-half of what it once was. In some locations the soil organic content is down to less than two tenths of one percent.

According to *Discover* magazine, humans churn out 8 billion tons of carbon dioxide every year worldwide. These 8 billion tons could be captured and put back into the soil if we operated our farms, ranches, ball

The rancher with the tall grass is making full use of the carbon cycle and has doubled his animal-stocking rate by using a good rotation. The rancher on the opposite side of the fence is not taking advantage of the carbon cycle and is losing money. He is grazing too short, which forces the root to give up carbon for new growth. This causes the grass to eventually die out and is replaced by weeds. Grass must have some green leaf surface to take carbon from the air for new growth.

fields, lawns and gardens with practices that increase and maintain the organic material in the soil.

One acre of land 6 inches deep weighs about 2 million pounds. When a soil lab does an organic matter test, they burn off the humus to determine the organic content. (In soil, everything organic will burn; the minerals just sit there. Weight loss from burning is a way to determine how much organic material exists in the soil.) Each one percent of organic matter in the soil represents approximately 5,400 pounds of carbon (C). If oxidized by improper tillage and overuse of chemical, carbon-free fertilizers, that amount of carbon would release to the air about 20,000 pounds (or 10 tons) of carbon dioxide. This oxidation occurs routinely with conventional farm practices.

There are many ways to help control the amount of CO_2 released into the air. Adding organic material to the soil is a very important way because so much of the land's mass is devoted to farming and ranching. If soil is mulched, rarely tilled, and has plants growing, the loss of carbon from the soil in the form of CO_2 is dramatically decreased.

If we increased the organic content of just our cropland in the United States a puny one percent, we would take 4.55 billions tons (over half of what the world generates annually) of CO_2 out of the air and return it to the soil. Green plants using the energy from the sun have the power to do this.

Science tells us that there are more species and more tonnage of life underground than living above it. Tilling the soil upsets this soil life and exposes it to damaging sunrays and oxidation, which releases large amounts of CO_2 into the atmosphere. In a natural environment the soil with its massive amount of carbon-based roots and other soil life is rarely exposed and destroyed. Oxidation, which creates CO_2, does take place in a natural soil environment, but the timing and rate is governed by temperature and moisture to coincide with plant growth so the plants can capture the CO_2 and reprocess it instead of letting it escape to the atmosphere.

The stomata (pores) on a plant leaf are mostly on the underside, and carbon dioxide is slightly heavier than air, so it hovers close to the soil, easily accessible to the plant stomata. As it diffuses and moves up, the plants capture it. The stomata are capable of opening and closing. When there is a concentration of CO_2 near the stomata it quickly gets an ample supply, or you might say a mouth full, it doesn't need to stay open very long. Plants transpire (lose moisture) through the stomata when they are open, so a more concentrated supply of CO_2 near the leaves of plants result in less soil moisture lost.

If proper soil management were taught and practiced worldwide the CO_2 problems, perceived or real would become less and less. Most of the farmlands worldwide are way below the organic content they should and could be. If we would weigh the excess carbon in the air and what is missing from the soil, I'll bet they would be close to equal.

Research in South Texas by the USDA has shown an increase of soil organic content of one tenth of one percent each year in cropland in a no-till program. In this program all crop residue is left on the soil surface to serve as mulch, which regulates soil temperatures, traps rain water, and protects the soil from the hot sun and drying wind. Ranchers operating by Holistic Resources Management methods and organic gardeners and farmers who apply compost and mulch also see the organic soil content go up and experience moisture savings.

Building the organic content of all soils, worldwide, would also help solve the real and imminent problem of water shortages. The higher the soil organic content, the easier the annual rains can penetrate the soil. This prevents flooding, brings up the level of the aquifers and keeps the springs and rivers flowing. In an organic rich soil, water is safe from evaporation. Trapping runoff water in lakes is a poor answer to water shortages. In lakes water evaporates away — the amount depends on local environment. In central Texas the evaporation rate is around 55 inches per year.

Seventy-four percent of the Earth is covered with water, but only 3 percent is fresh and 80 to 90 percent of that fresh water is used for irrigation.

Organic matter in the topsoil helps it hold a greater amount of water which can lessens the need for irrigation. Tests have shown up to 70 percent less in some cases.

Organic matter in the soil reduces the need for fertilizers by holding the nutrients in a non-leachable form, making fertilizers less polluting and more efficient. Plants grow healthier with more production, and less need for pesticides. Recycling all waste could help do this. Biosolids and most of the organic waste that fills up our landfills should be composted to pasteurize and detoxify them. Then they should be recycled back to the land. Building soil organic content is the answer to some of the big problems mankind faces today. Health problems, air pollution, water pollution, food shortages, water shortages and floods are major problems worldwide — but Nature can fix them. No new technology is needed. In a natural environment there is no waste, everything is returned to the soil. Recycling and avoiding over-tillage and its subsequent soil oxidation are simple and viable answers. Environmental problems worldwide can be solved by understanding and working with the carbon cycle on our farms, ranches, gardens and landscapes.

Rejuvenating A Worn-Out Farm

After we had operated our small eight-acre farm organically for 11 years, a friend with the Agricultural Extension Service finally admitted that we were successful. "But," he said, "I don't see how it can be practical on large acreage. We have to feed the world." Here was a sobering thought. Then it turned into a challenge; why couldn't these same principles be practiced on a hundred acres or even a thousand acres? I jokingly mentioned to my wife that we should sell this farm and buy a bigger one. Even though we spent many laborious hours building up this place, including a new house which we spent two years building ourselves, she didn't immediately throw a negative opinion at me. She too loved a new challenge. Besides, we were young and our family needed more room.

Surprisingly, after only a few months of searching we found a place that fulfilled our wishes, but it was really run down. The house was liveable, but all the out-buildings and barn were about to fall down. The fields were so poor that in a rainy year Johnson grass only grew knee-high — talk about a real challenge! With testing, I learned the soil was highly alkaline and void of organic matter. A much different soil than I was accustomed to farming. On the good side, the fields were level and not eroded. It was encouragement from Robert Rodale that really helped. He said that because the soil was alkaline, and given our average rainfall, the minerals were all there but locked up. With a lot of organic matter and time, the soil could again become fertile. So how do I get organic matter? Growing it was the only possible way, and it seemed like the only thing that was adapted to those worn-out fields were weeds. I let them grow to near maturity, then just before they bloomed, mowed them off with a sickle-bar mowing machine, leaving them on top to protect the soil. I did this for two years; the third year I broadcast common sudan grass and disked enough to cover the seed but not bury the weed mulch. I mowed the sudan twice before fall; the soil was now beginning to get a fair mulch cover.

Still, the soil was so sterile that the weeds from the two previous years were not even decayed. Since fall was coming, I decided on a winter legume.

Elbon rye grass cover crop with seed that will not be harvested but left to seed next year's cover crop. The rye followed a nitrogen-fixing, deep-rooted clover crop. The thick, tall rye grass is a good weed suppressor.

I chose hubam clover. I bought scarified seed, inoculated it, then broadcast it with a cyclone seeder and tried to disk it in, but the mulch was so thick and tough, the light harrow couldn't cut through it. It did shake the seeds through so they lay on the soil under the mulch. Luckily a rainy spell came, and every seed must have sprouted. The clover grew and grew. It didn't stop until it was beyond my reach — eight feet tall. It turned into such a beautiful crop I decided not to work it in green, but let it mature and combine the seed.

The harvest was excellent, and we made good money. So good I decided to grow clover again the next year, even though a Botany professor friend told me you cannot make two good clover crops in a row. I really didn't believe him; after all, he wasn't a farmer. Guess what. I didn't make a good second crop even though rainfall was ample. All the weeds, Johnson grass, and native plants gave it too much competition. I learned clover can tolerate, even prefers, a tight, alkaline, low-organic-matter, and low-nitrogen soil. With its strong growth, deep tap root, and nitrogen nodules, it creates a soil condition which is excellent for the other species of plants. They are then able to compete for moisture, sunlight, and root oxygen.

During the fourth year on the new farm, we started growing vegetables. They did okay, but we had our share of insect problems. The soil was still out of balance — too much undecomposed organic matter tying up nitrogen and no humus to fall back on. Even though I had a good railroad job, we couldn't afford any more barren years on the farm. We kept going with vegetables, about 15 acres at a time, and we saw an improvement each year.

We rotated the vegetables with a fall planting of half-and-half elbon rye and vetch seed. Then, six to eight weeks before spring vegetable planting, we worked in a strip of cover crop to prepare a seed bed. We didn't farm a continuous field, but did it in twenty-two or forty-four row strips (our sprinkler system covered twenty-two rows). We left an equal size strip of cover crop which would be planted in vegetables in the fall or following spring. The strip farming method gave us a good beneficial-to-troublesome insect ecology and the cover crops served as wind breaks.

Inside the 22-row strip, we didn't always plant solid either, but did some companion planting, such as legume and non-legume vegetables in two row strips each. Our cover crops were not worked in deep; we shredded them down with a brush hog, then chisel, and then harrowed several times to prepare a seed bed. We learned we couldn't plant a summer legume cover crop because of cotton root rot, so we stayed with the vetch/rye-vegetable rotation through the winter. It worked well. The insect problems got fewer, and the quality of the vegetables continued to increase.

We sold a lot of our produce to natural food stores that made carrot juice. At first they complained that our carrots didn't quite have the quality taste of California organic carrots. But by the fifth year of our production, they said our carrots were just as good. By the seventh year, they preferred our carrots over the California carrots.

For our soil type and location, the cereal (Elbon) rye-vetch is probably the perfect cover crop combination. Both grow well in the winter and in our alkaline, calcareous soil. The rye has a very fibrous root, is a strong grower, never freezes, and is an excellent nematode deterrent. The vetch, a legume, has a tap root; it feeds much deeper than the rye. With the rye taking the nitrogen from the soil, the nodal bacteria on the vetch root must take most of its nitrogen from the air. We also learned to mow the cover crop with the shredder set about eight inches high right after the rye shoots up the seed stem and before it opens. This stimulates it into more growth as it tries to complete its life cycle. That process seems to extend the life of the rye. Also, each mowing gives the vetch sunlight and allows it to grow thicker. In the first years when the soil nitrogen content was low, the vetch could compete, but as the soil got richer each year, the rye outgrew it. The mowing made both plants grow thicker and when you worked them in, you had much greater tonnage of organic matter and much more nitrogen than if you had grown either plant alone.

In areas where we didn't intend to grow vegetables, we let the vetch and rye go to seed, and let it stand through the spring and summer. It helped smother the Johnson grass and other weeds. In addition, we got the many benefits of a mulch on the soil. Come October, we disked shallow, and we had next year's cover crop planted.

When we worked the soil, we never turned it over. We used a shredder to chop up large cover crops, then chiseled as deep as we could, then used the disk harrow. We always kept the organic matter as close to the surface as possible. That is the natural soil profile. When you bury organic matter too deep, the decomposing microbes can't get enough oxygen, and the fermentation makes methane gas. We did haul manure when available and when time permitted, and we usually went straight to the fields with it unless weather or crops didn't permit. In that case, it was piled in giant piles to keep nutrients from leaching away when the pile got wet.

With the cover crop rotation and a limited amount of manure, we could keep the organic content and nitrogen in a good condition, but soil tests still showed the soil was low in phosphate. We tried rock phosphate even though the extension service said it wouldn't work. We had to learn the hard way. Two tons per acre broadcast didn't show much production increase, but we accidentally learned that if we put the phosphate in strips or bands in the bottom of the rows and put the seed or transplant right on it, we could double, even sometimes more than double, production.

By banding the phosphate, the alkaline soil couldn't get to all of it and lock it up. And the roots can grow right in the phosphate and take what they need of it and the other minerals it contains. We also applied a natural humate that was mined in the Alpine, Texas, area. We applied one thousand pounds per acre. We didn't have a control to accurately gauge production increase, but it seem to really enhance quality. Even with a good organic content, the high pH of the soil dropped very little, but the plants could tolerate the alkalinity better.

Besides vegetables, we grew pecan and fruit trees. The pecan were well adapted; they needed water and not much more. The fruit trees were something else we really had to experiment with. Some varieties couldn't tolerate the high pH of 7.7 to 8.5 at all; they just turned yellow unless a heavy mulch over the whole root system was always maintained. From that we learned that any fruit tree we mulched with compost produced much better and didn't have wormy fruit. We used as much as one- to two-cubic yards of compost per tree. This wasn't economical, but we could have high-quality organic fruit from an area where most fruit trees don't readily adapt.

Keeping our farm all organic not only made it more fun, safer, and more challenging, but exciting too. Fertility increased, production increased, and insect problems decreased each year. Potato beetles were a problem on both farms when we first started, and we hand-picked a few to give their natural enemies the upper hand, but each year we saw a decline, and by the seventh or eighth year, they completely vanished. The squash bugs were another problem. In the beginning, we used some sabadilla dust for control. Their numbers also declined each year, but more slowly than the potato beetles.

We had an assortment of other troublesome bugs and they too steadily declined. You could watch the soil fertility definitely play a role in their numbers. The other problems we had were viruses that were brought in with transplants, to which there is no known cure, organic or chemical. The only control is prevention, but even when we got a virus, we could make a crop. Production was directly related to soil fertility.

We no longer farm as large as we did. With the compost business we found an easier way to make money. But one thing we did learn: it was easier to farm organically on a hundred acre operation than it was on the eight acre farm. The larger environment you have control of, the better you can work with Nature. You don't have a close neighbor spraying and possibly fouling up the environment. Our farm was a success, even considered so by my agricultural extension friends, and everything we did to boost production was a natural practice that is feasible on any size farm.

One of the best proofs that our soil was fertile was that the neighbors' farm animals were always looking for a weak spot in the fence to crawl through and graze on our side. Our farm animals never cared to go over to their side. Through the years, the lesson I have learned is that each farm has its own unique environment that must be studied to find the best adapted plants and trees, replace missing nutrients, and discover methods of tillage, planting dates, and all the other things that spell success.

Saving the Big Tree

At one time the old farm had more than a hundred pecan trees growing on it, but abandonment and the drought of the early '50s took their toll. Only about 20 of the large trees were in fair condition; the rest were dead or near death when we bought the place in 1957. On the north side of the house, which was also the front, stood one of the oldest trees. It was probably put there to provide summer shade. The trunk was straight and about thirty inches in diameter; other than its size, it was in very poor condition. From the tips of the limbs down to about five- or six-inch wood, it was already dead. Down near the trunk there was a small number of yellowish, sick-looking leaves, and there was a thick infestation of mealy-bug-type insects feeding under the live bark.

The soil under the tree was packed hard. On one side was the driveway to the garage, and on the opposite side, a school bus was parked everyday between routes, leaving a large oil soak.

That being a most critical spot for a shade tree, and knowing it would take up to fifty years to grow another that size, we sure did not want to lose this tree. We talked to experts. Most said the tree was past the point of no return, but one old nurseryman, Mr. Fanick, said a lot of tender love and care might bring it back. He said it would need feeding, watering, and the leaves should be sprayed with zinc and the trunk sprayed with a product called Boreaway. Then in the fall or winter, it should be cut back to live wood.

Since our finances were extremely low and because the tree might not survive anyway, we decided not to spend any money on it. When winter came I cut it back since we heated with wood and needed it anyway. When I got through, there were only a few large branches left on the trunk. We didn't do any spraying because of cost — besides, the products weren't organic.

I could get manure to feed the tree for free. A neighboring farmer had a wire cage out in the middle of his feedlot into which he put all the animal droppings, wasted hay, corn cobs, etc., so I asked the old farmer if I could have some. He looked at me, thought for a moment, then said, "If you clean it all up you can have it." It amounted to about six cubic yards. We hauled it all and spread it as a mulch under the tree starting about four feet from the trunk to out about six feet beyond the original drip line.

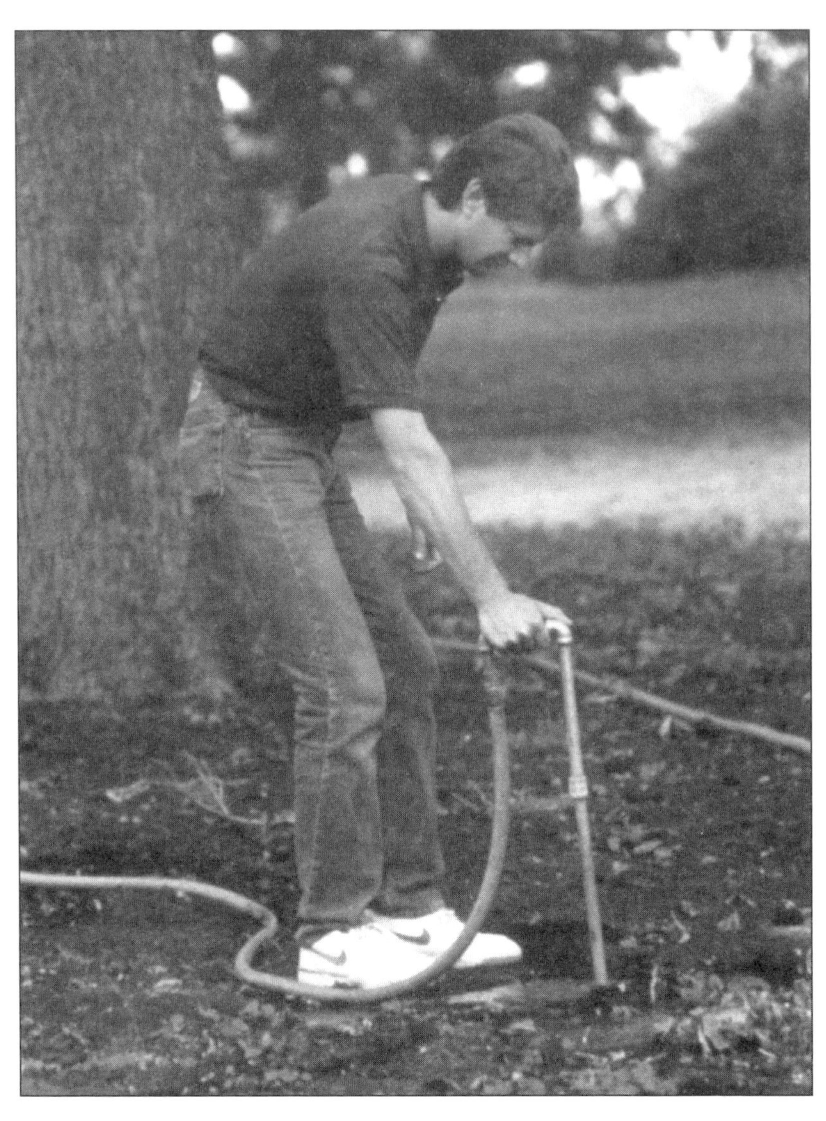

Son Robert using the water drill.

Realizing the hard-packed condition of the soil, I knew the roots couldn't get air, and it would be a long time before the nutrients from the compost could get down into the soil, so I decided to help. I took a half-inch by 5-foot pipe and cut it off one end at an angle; I fitted the other end into a water hose. I turned up the pressure on our water well pump, then took the pipe and started drilling-washing holes in the soil under the tree about four feet apart and eighteen inches deep over the whole mulch area. The holes were made with more of a washing than drilling action which aerated really

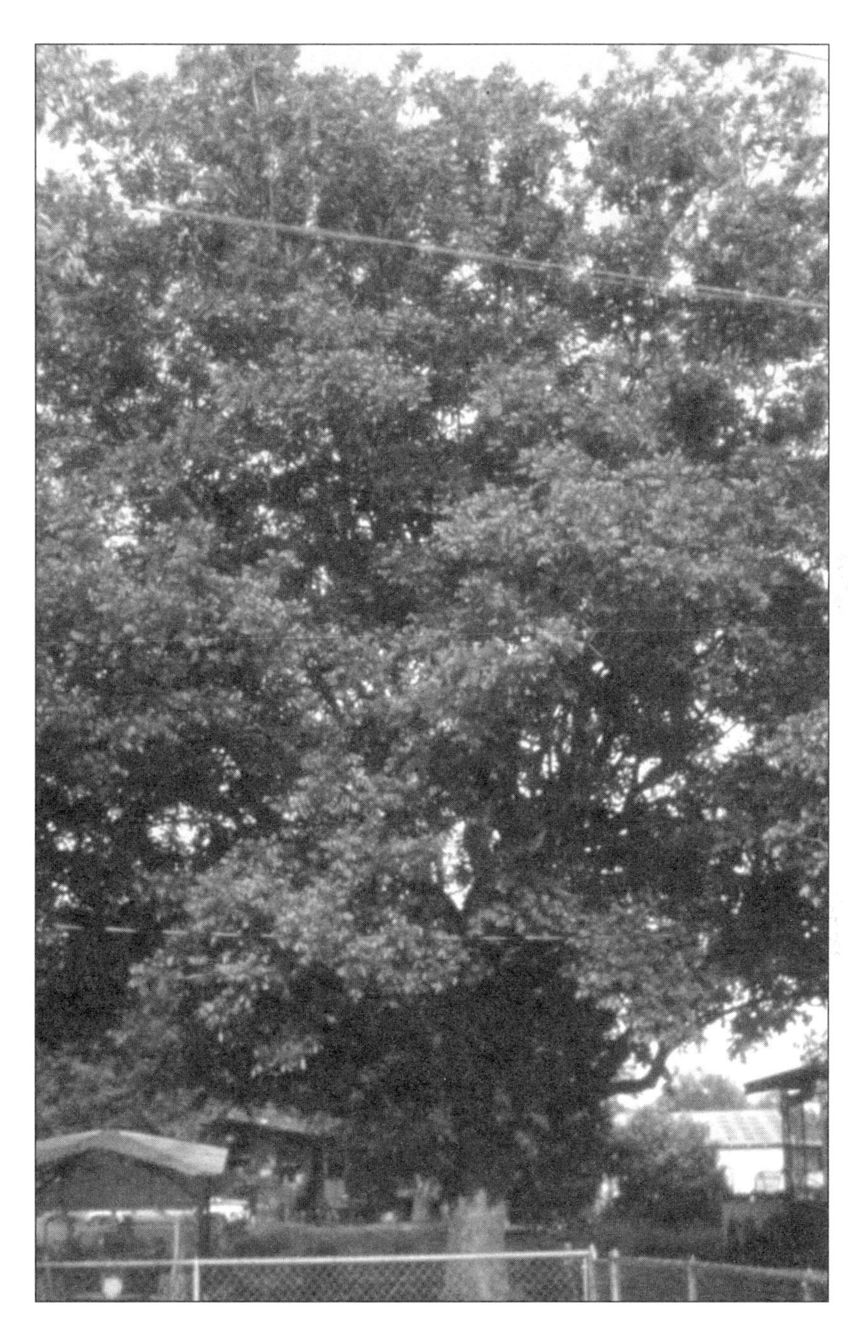

The big pecan tree 40 years later.

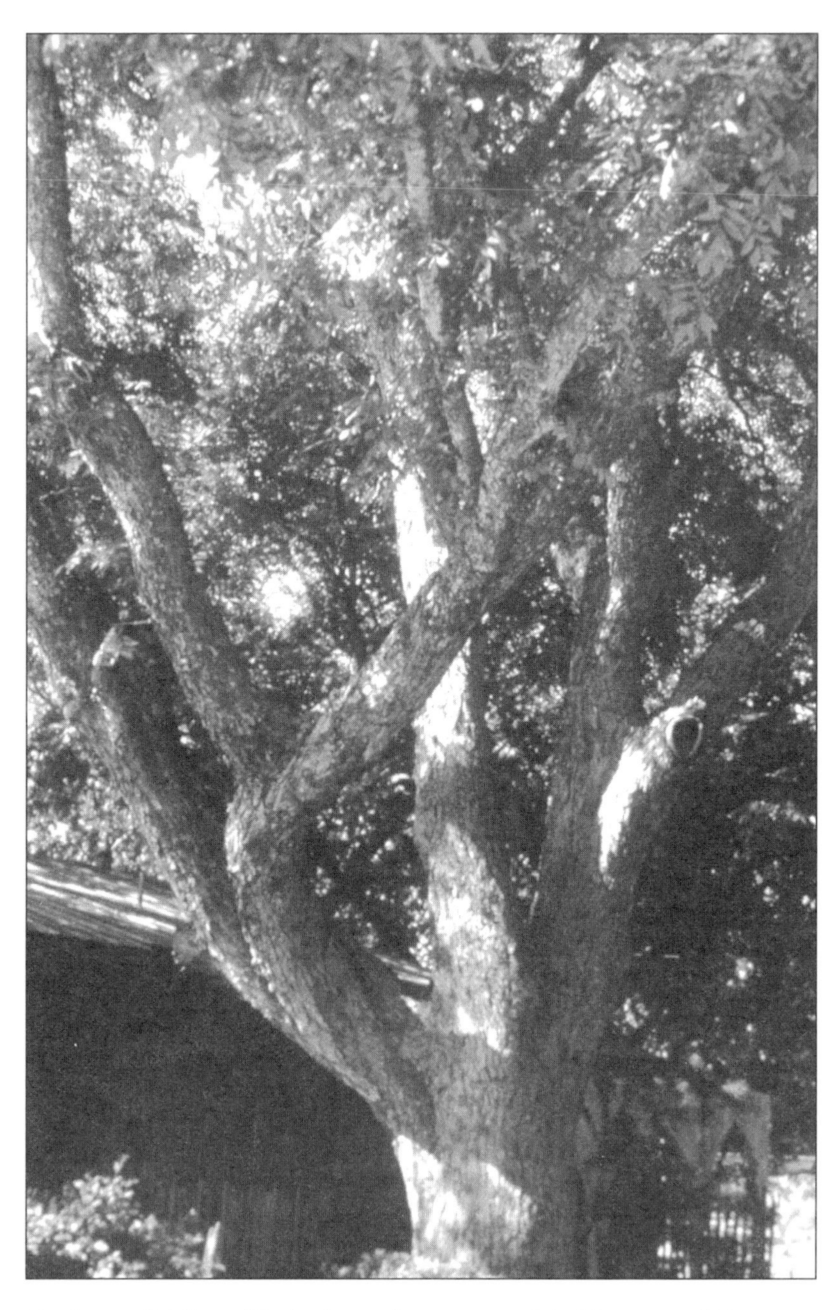

Perfect scaffolding of limbs for perfect canopy of the big tree, and Nature did this on her own, no pruning by man.

Triple meat pecans from the big tree the first few years after compost water-drill treatment.

well without damaging the tree roots. I was washing sub-soil out and the return water was carrying compost tea down into the holes.

Winter passed, spring came, and the tree came out with lots of lush growth. By the third year, it started producing nuts. The neighbors who knew the farm said the nuts were more than twice the original size. But at harvest time, we had the biggest surprise. Instead of nuts with two kernels of meat in each, a big percent were triplets, or three kernels, of meat in each nut. The tree produced good crops of nuts every year, but the number of triplets got fewer and fewer each year.

When the tree came out at first, the new branches were real thick, just a few inches apart; everyone said I would have to prune or thin, but I didn't do anything but let nature take its course. The dominant branches shaded out the weaker limbs and developed a beautiful canopy.

Within two years after the mulching, the bark of the trunk cleared up. No mealy bugs. The health of the tree — its own immunity — somehow prevented the infestation from continuing. The tree has had only that one compost mulch-aeration treatment, and has never even had the recommended zinc spray. To this day — over 45 years later — the tree is beautiful, healthy, and giving lots of cool shade in the summer and delicious nuts in winter.

Leave the Leaves for Healthy Yard Trees

Raking leaves has always been a chore dreaded by homeowners. In the fall the streets are lined by bags that now become a chore for the trash pick-up crews and then the landfill operator. Although a lot of environmental gardeners and homeowners are now composting leaves or saving leaves for someone else to compost. This is good, but let's talk to the trees and see what they have to say. Each year the tree roots go out farther and deeper to gather more minerals for more growth. Each year the branches grow bigger to support a greater numbers of leaves. This larger leaf surface can now collects more sunlight to manufacture more carbohydrate energy. This continues until the cold days of fall. Now the leaves turn beautiful colors or maybe just a dead brown. Then the leaves soon turn loose and fall to the ground. On the ground is where the tree wants the leaves to stay. The leaves contain a lot of the minerals and energy the tree spent much of the year collecting. Remove the leaves and you steal from the tree its reserve food supply for tougher times. Not only did you steal food from the tree you took the blanket it had spread over its roots for winter comfort and to collect spring rain. You enjoyed the beauty and comfort of the cool shade and maybe even some nuts or fruit the tree gave you. So show your appreciation and leave the leaves. And don't steal the tree's comfort and food and take away its ability to collect and store water.

Pecans: The Perfect Food

A good source of vitamins, minerals, proteins and carbohydrates, pecans are a delicious food for humans, animals and insects. However, only those talented enough to break open the perfect package designed to protect the nutritious food are able to enjoy them.

Pecans are a much richer and healthier food than rice or wheat. Both those grains need to be milled and cooked before they become enjoyable. Rice and wheat have a critical harvest period; rain can damage or even destroy the crop, and efficient harvesting requires expensive machinery. But pecans can hang in the tree or lay on the ground through heat, cold, snow, ice or rain for weeks with no damage and sometimes become even more tasty.

Pecans can be eaten raw or roasted or used to flavor cookies, candies, cakes, pies, salads or main courses.

Pecans can be harvested by machines, but most are still picked up by hand. Children love to pick up pecans; it's like an Easter egg hunt. They aren't quickly bored by the process and their little fingers are very efficient at finding the nuts among fallen leaves.

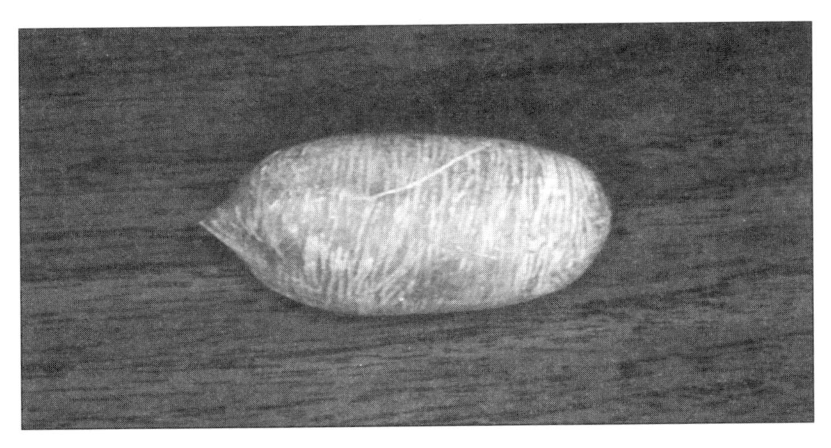

Pecan that was scarified by a squirrel before it was planted so it could quickly draw moisture to sprout.

Pecan tree west of Fort Worth considered to be the biggest and oldest pecan tree in Texas. That's me leaning against it.

To feed the hungry, pecans are king. Whether in a third-world country or right here at home, they are perfect trees to be planted in urban settings where the nuts can be harvested by those who need them. If they are spilled along a roadway, pecans are safe from being quickly eaten by animals or insects and are easily picked up days or even weeks later.

The pecan tree itself is majestic. It provides a home to many animals. Pecan trees provide cool shade during hot summer days, but let the warm sun shine through during the cold winter since the leaves fall to form a protective blanket over the soil, its roots and the earthworms.

Wherever soil is deep with ample moisture, a pecan tree can survive on its own for centuries. In groves or plantations, pecans still require less care than most other food crops. Native to America, the pecan is the state tree of Texas and can be found growing in most areas of the state.

The small native pecans have rich oil and delicious taste, although they require more work to remove the meat from the shell. The hybrid paper-shell pecans are large and easy to shell, but have less flavor.

The pecan is the perfect tree, perfect in the creek bottom and the home yard.

The Life Cycle & Compost

Every living thing will die sooner or later. After its life energy leaves, it soon decays, which is a most necessary process. The decaying process returns the dead plants and animals back to earth, back towards the raw elements from which they were made. These elements in their journey back become the nutrition and vitality to feed the next generation of plants and then animals.

The decaying — or, more accurately, disassembly — process is performed by billions of little creatures we call microorganisms. They will do their job with or without our help. In fact, it is almost impossible to stop them. The microorganisms can turn our organic (once alive) waste back into fertilizer for our farms and gardens, but in big cities where most waste is generated, it is usually dumped in a landfill where these life-sustaining nutrients are locked away from the natural life-death-decay cycle. Few people realize this great loss to our well-being and prosperity.

The microorganisms can be helped and managed in this return cycle. Composting is our term for helping and managing them.

Home Garden Composting

No yard waste should ever be sent to the landfill. If you like the clean, manicured look and think grass clippings must be caught and leaves raked, then do that, but be sure you make use of those clippings and leaves when you are done. Compost them to be used as a soil conditioner/fertilizer in the garden or as a mulch around shrubs and trees to retain moisture, control soil temperatures, and supply dozens of nutritional needs.

The compost pile can be free-standing or in an enclosure of some type. Concrete blocks or lumber are used for enclosures, but I think the most practical is close mesh wire 1/2 to 1/4 inches between strands, 3 to 4 feet wide, and 9 feet or longer, fenced together in a circle. A 9-foot length will make about a three foot circle. I like a larger circle myself because a larger pile can retain the heat and moisture better. The circle can be placed anywhere convenient except where water could run off a roof onto it.

To make compost, the microbes need air, water, carbon material for an energy source, and protein (nitrogen) material to build their bodies from. Even though most materials contain carbon and nitrogen, high carbon

Wire cage compost bin containing the un-decomposed top and outer edge removed from the dark compost next to it that was in the cage for a year and never turned.

materials are sawdust, dried leaves, bark, wood chips, dried grass, or any organic material that you can put on a pile and moisten and nothing happens. It doesn't smell, draw flies or seem to ever rot. High protein or nitrogen materials are manure, kitchen waste, green vegetable matter, animal matter such as blood meal, fish meal, or any organic material that quickly rots, smells, and draws flies when wet.

To build the compost pile, start adding organic materials as they become available. Use all kitchen and yard organic waste except meat unless you have a pile large enough for burying the meat very deep. Grinding the larger twigs and leaves will make them compost faster, or you can just throw them in and later pick or screen them out and put them back to inoculate the next piles until they are completely broken down. I prefer the picking out or screening; it takes less energy and the large twigs help hold the materials apart to aerate better. Adding horse or cow manure up to 25 percent or chicken manure up to 10 percent makes a good rich compost. Too much manure could cause it to get smelly if it is not aerated enough or if it gets too wet. Green grass clippings and kitchen waste have ample nitrogen if manure isn't readily available. To inoculate — or get those microorganisms working — in the beginning, a commercial inoculator can be purchased or a few shovels full of garden soil will do the job. Don't use too much dirt because it adds weight and compresses the pile and makes it harder to turn.

A new, unused wire cage with walking-cane-shaped compost turner hanging on it. When using the turner/aerator you can make more compost in a shorter period.

It is always better to start the compost pile with the carbon materials and add the nitrogen materials a little at a time until the microbes are really working, creating heat without a smell or flies. Then you will know you have the correct carbon to nitrogen (C/N) ratio and can continue building the compost pile successfully. Like any other plant or animal, the microbes need air and water, but they don't like to be drowned. Just keep the pile moist, much like a squeezed-out sponge, and turn or mix it for aeration.

After the first pile is ready, use some of it-such as the larger twigs-to inoculate the next. The compost pile should be aerated. Loose light piles need aeration about once a month. A tight heavier pile will require more aeration, but more than every third day is unnecessary. The pile can be turned with a garden fork or shovel, but the easiest is with a compost turning probe. This is a tool about the size and shape of a walking cane with two wings that fold into a point when pushed into the pile but spread open when pulled up. This doesn't require a lot of strength. On the up stroke, the pile is torn open and some of the bottom is brought toward the top. It is a quick, easy way to aerate a home-garden size pile.

Another easy way to turn the pile is to unpin the wire cage; take it from around the pile; pin it back together next to it, then put the material back in. Each pile should be turned at least once like this to be sure the outside ends up in the middle so it can go through the heating process.

If you have a large garden and enjoy making compost, a number of these wire circle cages can be used. You can keep building them until the first pile is ready, then you empty it and start over. The compost is ready to use when the materials have turned brown and most of them have lost their identity. The material should have an earthy smell.

If your soil is lacking in certain elements, the best way to add them is through the compost pile. Add rock phosphate for phosphorous, granite sand or wood ashes for potash; you can even add minerals like iron sulfate, zinc sulfate, and magnesium sulfate. I know these are chemical, and against organic gardeners' principles, but when the microorganisms get through with them in the compost pile, they will be naturally chelated into an organic form that will remain available to plant-use even in alkaline soils.

I like to wet the pile, if needed, with a fish emulsion solution — 6 to 12 tablespoons per gallon of water. This adds nitrogen but never too much at one time, plus it contains all the nutrients for the microbes and later on for your plants.

Unwanted insects such as pill bugs and ants will get into the compost pile. Turning often and keeping the moisture just right so the pile heats up to 140 to 160 degrees will discourage them. Heat, however, isn't absolutely necessary to make compost. I have never seen a forest floor heat up.

Making compost is as much an art as it is a science. The best way to learn to make good compost is by doing it and not giving up. Most home-garden compost failures are caused by simply keeping the pile too wet. In a rainy season you may cover the top with plastic, but not for too long because you might smother it and cause it to smell. I like to heap up the center of the pile so it sheds water like a thatch roof.

Composting is not only practicing good ecology. You are making plant foods and soil conditioner Nature's own way, with little or no expense to your pocketbook.

Large Scale Composting

Composting is the art of working with the decay or rotting processes in an economical way. Nature takes care of the science, so we must think economics. A measure of compost contains only so much energy, and if we expend more than that amount to make that measure of compost, we gain nothing.

For some mysterious reason, when industrial and municipal authorities approach composting as a method of disposing of their waste, they always look toward sophisticated, highly technical equipment that takes months, even years, to build and costs big bucks — just to perform a process Mother Nature has been doing simply since the beginning.

At Garden-Ville's composting plant near San Antonio, we compost over a 150,000 cubic yards annually with only one piece of equipment, an articulated loader that cost $60,000. A vibrating screen is used for cosmetic

Large static pile of high carbon compost. Notice the wood-decomposing fungi making spore rings, evidence that the circle of life is being completed.

reasons only after the compost is ready but before it is sold. The screen removes plastic, trash, rocks, and bottles, which seem always to find their way into the compostable materials. It also makes the product pretty and uniform.

We make compost in static piles; we sell by volume, so we have to watch for shrinkage. If we have time to wait, we only turn four times. If we need to speed up the process before the spring market demand, then we turn more often, five to six times. Besides manure from many sources, we compost slaughterhouse waste, vegetable waste, and brewery waste. For carbon and bulking materials we use sawdust, rice hulls, peanut hulls, wood shavings, and ground-up tree trimmings.

We build piles from five to ten thousand cubic yards each, depending on how fast the raw materials become available. The material is piled as high as the loader can reach, up to twelve feet. In a real dry season we may have to water the pile, but if we get our average annual rainfall, the material comes in with ample moisture to start the composting process and the rainfall replenishes evaporation.

Composting microorganisms need carbon, nitrogen, oxygen, and moisture, and any one of the four can be jiggled around to prevent smelly conditions. The one you have least control of is water, due to the unpredictability of weather. After a few years of operation, we got a feel for the correct carbon-nitrogen ratio and learned to make huge piles with the least amount of aerating.

We use an area of about nine acres. We start the piles a distance from the screen, and with each turning we move the pile closer. When the compost is ready, it is nearest the screen. This process, start to finish, takes from four to seven months.

With normal rainfall, the large piles absorb the water without too much leaching; however, during a heavy rainy season we have leaching and it is drained off into a grassy field which filters it pretty well. We have close neighbors, and so far none have complained about run-off or smell. We have also been inspected by the health department, EPA, air quality control, and the water district in charge of our aquifer. None of them had any complaints.

We started small and had fly problems, but as we grew the fly problem got less and less until there are almost none. I am not sure what to attribute it to — either better material handling or fly parasites, probably a combination of both.

I have watched two different compost plants go into business in my area. Both used fancy, sophisticated equipment or buildings, much too expensive. They tried to over-manage Nature, and neither survived. They both visited us before starting up and said they were going to make a better product. One bragged he would make compost in seven days when it took me four to six months. I asked him, "How long will it take to build your plant?" "Five months," he said. If I started production the same day he started construction, I could have a product to sell before he even finished his building. So in reality, the open air, slow process is just as fast or faster. A digester or any type of in-vessel facility is also limited in capacity. Open air composting has no limit.

We composted sludge (biosolids from a municipal sewage system) on two different occasions, but learned it had to be composted at a separate location because the home gardeners were always worried we would load them from the wrong pile. Sludge needs to be handled a little differently. We made the piles much smaller; we used the row method: piles ten feet high and about twenty feet wide at the base and the length was determined by convenience. We composted it for twelve months or longer, and we used our largest particle bulking agent, which was tree trimmings. Two parts trimmings and one part sludge was a good blend, and we turned it only after each rain. A sludge compost operation ideally should be built on a slight grade starting at the low end and each turning moves the piles up hill, so the leaching during heavy rains will always run from the oldest, ready-to-sell pile, into a freshly-made pile. It would also be good to catch the leachate in a lagoon and aerate it until a dry season, then spray it back on unfinished piles.

We found the longer sludge was composted, the safer it was and the less sludge odor it had. Also, we could screen through three screen sizes to make three different products: one for lawns, one for bed preparation, and one for mulch. I believe any local horticultural landscaping industry could use up the total supply of sludge from their town or city and not even have enough once they learned its value.

There is no hard-to-master scientific knowledge or expensive building or equipment needed to make compost, only an understanding of eighth-grade biology, time, space, and a desire to work with Nature.

I have consulted with many cities, garbage hauling companies, dairies, and feedlots and their reasons for composting are always to save land-fill space or get rid of a waste product. Few people really understand why Nature decays dead things and where man fits into this cycle. My book, *The Secret Life of Compost,* goes into a lot of detail about all kinds of composting.

Alternative types of compost bins are illustrated in the appendix.

More Secrets of Compost

Compost is nature's finest soil conditioner. Compost is also her finest fertilizer, although not recognized as such by the fertilizer industry because the N, P, and K doesn't add up to a total of at least 21. Compost is the decomposing remains of many once-live entities. Through the decay processes of composting the life forces and necessary elements can be passed from one generation of life to the next. Little, if any extra plant foods need to be added to the soil.

When N, P, K and other minerals are added to the soil the microbes must work on and release them in correct conditions for healthy plant growth. To do this the microbes must have an energy source. Decaying organic matter furnishes the energy and nutrients for microbes to balance out the plant foods in the soil.

The roots take in the nutrients and transport them throughout the plant in solutions through the vascular system. In order for the solutions to move upward the leaves transpire, or lose, moisture out of the pores called stomata.

If the solutions are lacking and not balanced with nutrients the plants must continue to lose moisture out of the leaves until enough nutrients are carried up. If the solutions are loaded with a balance of nutrients, less moisture is needed for transportation resulting in less moisture loss. In rich organic soils, the plant will actually require less water to grow even though rich organic soils can hold more moisture than poor soils. Adding chemical salt fertilizers to soils that are low in organic matter causes plants to require more water while growing.

Compost is the material that performs all of these miracles. Compost is the champion of water conservation. If the composting process occurs under a plant canopy it does even more.

Carbon is an essential part of life. It is the basic building block for all plant life. Carbon is the most abundant element in the compost pile. The decaying organisms combine the carbon in compost with oxygen from the air to make carbon dioxide (CO_2) gas.

Plants must have CO_2 for photosynthesis to make carbohydrates. It has been calculated that one acre field of grain or an acre grove of orange trees

Using compost as a mulch under and around plants or filling furrows (facing page) between plants with compost creates the perfect environment for beneficial microbes, earthworms, water savings, and nutrient release. It also supplies plants with ample carbon dioxide for maximum photosynthesis.

uses over 6 tons of carbon dioxide annually. The air only contains 0.03 percent carbon dioxide.

Still, a bag of modern chemical fertilizer labeled "complete" will not list carbon. Of the ingredients listed, nitrogen will be first. And it is usually the highest number. The same air that has only .03 percent carbon dioxide will

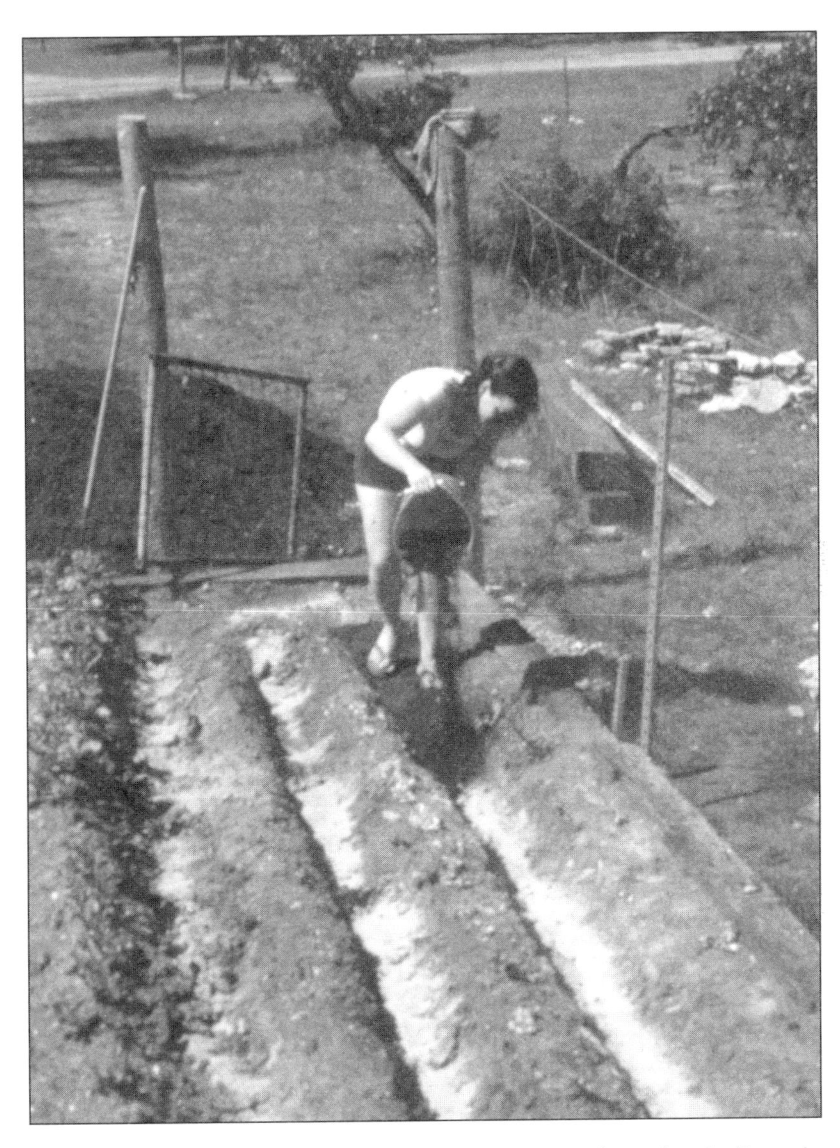

contain 78 percent nitrogen. Plants also use nitrogen from the air. Bacteria are the agents by which 90 percent of needed nitrogen of the air is converted to useful compounds for plants. To do that work the bacteria use the energy that is stored in the carbon-rich materials of compost.

Are we putting the wrong stuff in bags and feeding the wrong thing to the soil for the plants to use?

Science has known for some time that with an abundance or ample carbon dioxide in the air, plants utilized water more efficiently. Plants breathe through the stomata (tiny pores) on the leaf surface. They breathe in carbon dioxide, take out the carbon and release the oxygen. Plants also transpire water through their stomata. In hot, dry weather conditions the plant wants to cut down on water loss so the stomata close as soon as the leaf has absorbed enough carbon dioxide. If carbon dioxide concentrations are low, the stomata must stay open long periods and the plant loses excess water. If there are higher concentrations of CO_2, the stomata quickly absorb enough carbon dioxide for photosynthesis, allowing them to stay closed for longer periods.

A soil covered with decaying mulch, compost or containing an abundance of decaying organic matter will be giving off a lot of CO_2 from the microbe decaying activity. Carbon dioxide is slightly heavier than air, so it hovers near the soil before it diffuses into the atmosphere. All plants, especially lawn grasses, row crops and small plants next to the soil surface can make efficient use of the extra CO_2, resulting in better growth.

With energy and nutrients from compost the microbes can quickly furnish plants with all minerals, including carbon, with much less water being pulled from the soil, lessening the need for rain or irrigation.

At the same time the microbes will be converting the nitrogen from the air to a form the plants can use.

There are many benefits to spreading compost on lawns, flower beds, farms and orchards or wherever plants grow — soil conditioning, aerating, water insoak, water retention and conservation, higher nutrition, soil life stimulation, beneficial microbes that attack insects and diseases, ion exchange, air nitrogen conversion, release of CO_2 in the correct location, air purification, and probably many more benefits not yet discovered. The main reason compost works so well is it is Nature's way. She designed decay and has been composting since her beginning.

Compost Tea

Nature designed life to reproduce. So Nature designed death to make room for the new life. Then Nature designed decay so the dead bodies could be recycled to nourish the new life. Composting is man's way of assisting with the decay/recycling process. Through compost, the life cycle is completed. The compost pile is the factory, living quarters and cafeteria for the decomposing workforce of microbes. The fact that compost was at one time a living entity makes it Nature's finest mulch, soil conditioner and fertilizer.

Over the centuries gardeners and small farmers learned to improve the health and productivity of the soil with the use of compost. But the large farmer and rancher found compost in short supply or considered the labor, equipment and energy needed to spread compost not feasible. However, these large operators didn't always consult with Nature.

In her wisdom, Nature doesn't move compost around. She makes compost on the spot where the living entity (whether it is leaf or animal) lies down to die. As the dead things begin to pile up on the soil they create a mulching effect. The mulch creates a favorable environment for microbes. In this environment the decomposing microbes crowd out the harmful microbes while they eat the dead stuff to keep it from overaccumulating on the soil.

When a plant or animal dies, even though it may be consumed higher in the food chain, the decomposing microbes will eventually eat and disassemble it down to the smallest particle. These particles contain the energy and minerals of the once living. The energy and minerals can now blend with the falling rain and create a tea. As the tea soaks into the ground the nutrients are filtered from the water and held in the root zone. From there the plants collect the life supporting forces of mineral and energy, and place them back into the cycle.

When spraying compost tea you don't get the benefits of the mulch. However, the plants get the health and growth benefits of live, beneficial microbes and nutrients being placed on the leaf surface. The big farmer can create mulch with no-till practices and cover crops. The big rancher can use good grazing techniques, which leaves a cover of living and dead forage that hold the urine and manure deposited to create mulch.

Compost pile from which compost tea leached after a 10-inch heavy rain.

Compost tea machines can be designed that pry microbes loose, without harming them, from the solids they like to cling to. This tea contains a much higher percentage of the good little creatures that help control diseases than tea leached from compost would contain.

As little as five gallons of tea per acre (diluted in enough water to get good coverage, sprayed in the evening, over growing crops) has shown miraculous results in improving production and controlling diseases and insects. It has beneficial effects on the leaf surface as well as on and in the soil. At five gallons per acre the benefits and low cost of using compost tea make it very feasible on any size farm or ranch.

To make good tea always use a well-composted blend of approximately 70 percent carbon (wood waste) material and 30 percent nitrogen-rich (animal) material. These percents don't have to be exact. (Note: the dark stuff, leachate, that drains out of manure piles or unfinished compost is not suitable for spraying on plants.) For a more balanced fungi/bacteria content in the tea, keep it cool (70 to 72 F) while making it. Bacteria seem to dominate when tea is made in warmer temperatures. There is a lot of good compost being made commercially today, but the science of making and using tea for best results is still in its infancy. There is no need to wait for perfection, however. Amateurs everywhere are reporting surprising results.

Making Tea a Simple Way

There are many tea-extracting machines on the market; most are good and some are better. Most are designed with a sack to contain compost or

Grass in pecan grove eight years after the tea ran there from the 10-inch rain.

The rest of the grass in the pecan grove where no compost tea ran.

worm castings that is suspended in water and has air bubbled through it for several hours. Some are designed to agitate the compost bag. Nutrient, usually molasses, is added to the water at the rate of an ounce per gallon to feed the microbes.

I have made tea by using a barrel, with a bottom spigot, full of my best compost. Then adding chlorine-free water to the barrel to fill all the air space. I had the barrel setting up high enough to place a bucket under the spigot. After a few hours I would draw off a couple of buckets full of tea and put it back into the top. After an hour or two I would do it again. This process aerated and agitated it some. I would let it set a few more hours then draw all the liquid out for use. This needs to be used within a day or two. I would dilute it to look like weak iced tea for use in a sprinkle can or pump up sprayer, or I would put it directly through my irrigation system, which would then take care of dilution. I just made sure I got at least five gallons of tea over each acre. I never had to strain this tea. Somehow it filtered itself at the spigot by the time a few buckets were drawn off.

I would use the compost in the barrel at least two times. Draining all the liquid from the barrel caused air to be sucked into the compost, which gave it some oxygen. I would let this set a few hours. Then I would fill the empty spaces with water again that had one ounce of molasses per gallon added to it. Adding worm castings to the compost barrel at this time would be excellent. When reusing the compost you can double the time between the draining off and pouring back and than draining it all for use. After the second round of tea making I would use the compost as a mulch or in potting soil.

Uses of Compost

Compost is Nature's finest soil conditioner and fertilizer. All the elements, nutrients, growth factors, and other components that are in the plant particles being composted are released and recycled back to a form to be used by the next generation of plants. This is Nature's way. Nature has been feeding and growing plants this way since the beginning.

Garden-Ville's compost is a mixture of organic materials (animal manure, wood shavings, hay, seed hulls, stable bedding, etc.), all thoroughly mixed together in huge moist piles and treated with Fertilaid organic activator/fertilizer. The piles are turned several times to promote the aerobic composting action. This natural biological activity causes the piles to heat up to 160 F or more for a period of eight weeks or longer. This heating process renders the compost completely free of any weed seed, nematodes, roots, or harmful pathogenic organisms of any kind. At the same time it increases the beneficial microorganisms that build soil fertility and promote healthy plant growth. Compost is the closest thing we have to a cure-all because it heals Nature's wounds.

Compost as a Soil Conditioner

A 1- to 3-inch layer of compost tilled in 4 to 6 inches deep will aerate, create proper soil texture, and supply nutrients for the roots of vegetables, flowers, and lawn grasses. When planting trees and shrubs, amend the back-fill with a 5 percent mix of compost. Note: When using compost in back-fill around trees, don't use more than 5 percent, and make sure it is well decomposed compost.

Compost as a Mulch

A 1- to 3-inch layer of compost applied as a mulch or top dressing is excellent around any plant — tree, shrub, flower, or vegetable. Apply it after the soil has warmed up in the late spring. When mulching trees, start at the trunk and go out past the dripline. Be sure you don't pile the mulch against the trunk.

All the productive soil on planet Earth originated from the death of living entities.

Compost on Lawns

To maintain healthy lawns or rejuvenate old lawns, apply a one-half inch layer of compost in the fall. It is light and easy to spread, just rake in and water. Tests have proven compost applications to be the best way to maintain a healthy and beautiful lawn. Compost's microorganisms also help break down thatch.

Microorganisms

The earliest life forms were microorganisms. From raw elements they created the soil that supports the plants and higher forms of life. Even to this day there could be no life without the presence of microorganisms. In addition, they play a major role in keeping the many life species in balance. Whenever any one form of life starts to become over-abundant, often a disease caused by microorganisms culls that life form back. Since no living thing exists forever, all plants and animals eventually die, and it is the job of microorganisms to clean up the mess. Without some means of decay or reducing these dead things back to the earth, the whole globe would be thousands of feet deep in dead bodies. The microorganisms not only return dead things back to the earth, but they return it in a state which serves as food for the next generation of life.

Only the microbes have the ability to change these massive piles of waste organic material into compost to feed plants.

Eliot C. Roberts of the Lawn Institute estimates that there are 930 billion microorganisms in each pound of soil under the turf. There are about 70 pounds of them living and working in each 1,000 square feet of root zone. Many of these organisms are very short-lived, so the turnover is rapid. Roberts says that 100 pounds of dead microorganisms will contain close to ten pounds of nitrogen, five pounds of phosphate, two pounds of potassium, one-half pound of calcium oxide, one-half pound of magnesium oxide, and one-third pound of sulfate. With 70 pounds of these little creatures in each 1,000 square feet of root zone soil, the population adds up to enough per acre for excellent crop production. Farmers and gardeners need to promote their well-being through organic gardening and farming practices.

Bacteria and fungi are some of the names we give microorganisms, and the sound of these names makes most people think of dreaded diseases. True, there are some we perceive as bad guys, and they are the ones who make the news. But of the millions of species of microorganisms in existence, these villains number only an extreme few, and they too are part of Nature's scheme. When any form of life falls from perfection and becomes unfit, they attack to destroy. This helps keep each species of life on Earth at its best.

There are volumes written and known about the microorganisms, and there are probably many, many volumes unknown. But we don't need to know it all as long as we realize their importance to our existence and that when they cause problems, it is because sometime, somewhere, a law of Nature was ignored.

Taming Root Rot

Cotton root rot is the limiting factor for a booming apple industry in Texas. I once visited an apple grower in the Hill Country who said he was losing up to a thousand trees a year to cotton root rot. There is nothing modern science can do to stop the loss. Cotton root rot also devastates grapes, peaches, plums, and most other fruit trees. The nursery industry is hit hard as well, because the rot attacks many ornamental plants.

This soil fungus destroys a large percentage of the cotton planted in the southern part of Texas. It got its name because it attacks cotton so virulently. The fungus is only active in soils with a pH above neutral when soil temperature gets above 82 F, so it is often found in the alkaline soils of South Texas.

Millions of dollars in agricultural and horticultural crops are lost each year, and millions more have been spent researching ways to control cotton root rot. Sulphur has been used at the rate of 43,560 pounds per acre and worked a foot deep into the soil trying to lower the pH, but the roots always manage to work themselves below the sulphur and get the rot anyway.

Soil fumigants have been used with some degree of success, but they are very damaging to the beneficial soil life and the control is short-lived. Fumigants are also impractical on large acreage. Aerating the soil helps some, but we don't have equipment powerful enough to aerate as deep as the fungus lives.

Good farmers know that a soil balanced in minerals and containing a lot of decaying organic matter is the best deterrent to insects and diseases, especially soil-borne diseases. The common use of high nitrogen fertilizers, however, speeds up the organic decomposition in the soil and the use of herbicides never allows wild plants to contribute to the organic content. As a result, there is rarely enough organic matter accumulated in the soil to get all the life forces working that could hold cotton root rot in check. So the search continues for a cure, with most of the research money being spent on some manmade product or technique that isn't in tune with Nature and probably won't work.

In studying Nature, you quickly learn that every living creature has a natural enemy to hold it in check. But these checks and balances only work

At a glance you can tell which okra rows were inoculated with the good microbes.

when the whole environment is in balance. I believe cotton root rot can be held in check with the use of beneficial soil microbes.

Microbes capable of stopping the troublesome fungus may have already been discovered. Bill Kowalski of Natural Industries, Inc., of Houston has developed a product that seems to work well. Kowalski came to my office one day and said he had a product I might want to try. It was a natural microbe discovered by Dr. Don L. Crawford of the University of Idaho, which he isolated from the roots of a linseed plant. And this microbe produced potent antifungal metabolites. Tests showed that it inhibited a wide range of fungi — most of which I can't spell or even pronounce!

Cotton root rot, the fungus that causes the biggest problem in this area, wasn't mentioned in the study. After questioning, I found out that the microbe had not been tested for root rot, so I volunteered to do a test.

We always plant a lot of our special okra, so we have plenty of seed to share with our friends and customers. Okra is the perfect test plant for this microbe. It is related to cotton and is very susceptible to cotton root rot. When we moved onto this farm, we found the fields thoroughly contaminated, and in 25 years of trying, we haven't been able to eradicate it. We have been able to suppress it somewhat, however, and the okra lives longer into the summer than it once did.

For this test, we planted okra seeds in mid-April, and by the end of June, I could see a difference between the plants that were treated with the

Roots from the inoculated rows and roots from the control rows. All plants from the inoculated rows were perfect, free of root rot and nematodes. In the control rows 28 percent of the plants were affected with root rot and nematodes.

microbe and those that were not. The treated rows were more uniform in growth and a little taller. By mid-July, the treated rows were averaging a foot taller and looked a little healthier. With the soil temperature rising, I suspected that the cotton root rot was becoming active. It was time for a root inspection.

The first plant I pulled up in the untreated control row was infected with the fungus. I continued pulling up the poorest looking plants and found many of them were infected, some more than others.

I next checked the treated rows by pulling up an equal number of plants, and I tried to find the poorest looking plants, but I found the roots on every plant in these rows were perfectly healthy.

I was so thrilled with the results I was finding, that I pulled up and inspected over fifty plants from each row. The results continued the same, and I also noticed no nematodes on the roots from the treated rows.

After seeing these results I called Dr. Jerry Parsons, a Texas A&M vegetable specialist, to come and verify. Parsons inspected plants from each row himself, he too was surprised at these excellent results and suggested we call Dr. Donald Crawford to see how these microbes worked. Dr. Crawford explained that as a plant grows, the root is also growing, and as it grows it sloughs off root skins and produces exudates of all types that feed good microbes. As long as the root is feeding the good microbes, they will not let any diseases (destructive microbes) attack the root.

After hearing this statement from Dr. Crawford, Dr. Parsons mentioned that he had seen many others test beneficial microbes and get poor results, as he himself had done. They had tried to use microbes as a silver bullet. When the plant got sick, they would inject the microbes to the roots, but it didn't work. Dr. Parsons said he had finally come to understand a true symbiotic association. He explained that we have to do our share to keep the plants healthy and growing so the plants can feed the beneficial microbes — only then can the good microbes survive and protect the plants.

This product, now given the name of Actinovate, is the first thing ever to give me this level of control. Besides the cotton root rot, Dr. Crawford said his test in the lab showed this product also strongly inhibits Phythium, Rhizoctonia, Pythophora, Postia, and Scherotinia. To a lesser degree, it inhibits fungi such as Fusarium, Geotrichum, and Verticillium. (Actinovate is the *Steptomyces lydicus* strain WYCE108, which is a saprophytic, rhizosphere-colonizing actinomycete, for those of you who are scientifically minded.)

I was also given another natural soil microbe that had been tested on cotton root rot. According to a good friend, this microbe when used properly also gives excellent control of the fungus. My friend, whose opinion I greatly respect, says using this microbe in areas where no root rot exist, produces healthier and more productive plants, probably because the microbe has a variety of important, beneficial tasks it performs in the soil of which we are not yet aware.

This last product wasn't discovered by a Ph.D. at a university, but by a farmer named Frank Cavazos, who lives down in the Rio Grande Valley at Mercedes, Texas. Frank now has the product on the market and calls it F-68, because he discovered it in 1968. He is doing well, especialy since large comparative tests in the Rio Grande Valley showed his product to out-perform other well known biological products. It is now used to inoculate some Garden-Ville products.

Beneficial microbes such as these occur naturally and thrive with organic farming practices in organically rich soils. I believe root rot and many other troublesome soil diseases can be controlled by using microbes in a natural way, but these good microbes may need a little help from us. For example, we can place them where they are needed just as we place a few more beneficial insects in areas when they are needed. By maintaining a high organic content in the soil and abandoning the practices such as pesticides and chemical fertilizers that destroy soil life, these beneficial microbes will grow and prosper and make our gardens and farms healthier and more productive.

Phosphate Problems, Soil Testing Problems & Solutions

When I started farming in the mid '50s, southeast of San Antonio, The Texas A&M ag and animal experts both recommended using super phosphate (0-20-0) or bone meal. Tests showed the soil low in phosphorus. Their recommendations proved beneficial to the plants and the grazing animals.

In the late '60s, on my new farm northeast of San Antonio, the use of phosphorus again proved productive. By banding colloidal phosphate in the furrow at planting, I could double production on my fruiting vegetables. The rate applied was two tons per acre. I never at any time noticed micro nutrient deficiency. The soil pH on the vegetable farm was from 7.3 to 8.3, depending on where and when the testing was done.

Then, sometime during the '70s, lawns, shrubs, trees, vegetables and flowers in San Antonio started yellowing from the lack of micronutrients. The problem was found to be iron, zinc and manganese being tied up by phosphate. The extension service put out bulletins telling everyone to stop using phosphate.

I never experienced these problems, but then I had never used the new triple super phosphate that was now on the market. I asked one of the agricultural extension agents if the new 0-46-0 triple super phosphate could be causing all the problems. He thought for a moment then mentioned that the timing correlated perfectly, but he never found anyone to agree.

On my own, I did several tests. I used plants highly susceptible to iron chlorosis. I planted some in pure colloidal phosphate, some in pure rock phosphate and another bunch in soil that I applied the equivalent of 10,800 lbs/acre of the old style 0-20-0 super phosphate. All of the plants were fertilized with bat guano, which has an NPK rating of 10-3-1: All grew normally, showing no deficiencies. I strongly believe the problem was the new triple

The two darker-colored petunia plants are grown in pure colloidal phosphate clay; the two lighter plants are grown in potting soil. Natural forms of phosphate never cause problems, even when used at extremely high rates. Chemically altered phosphate quickly causes problems, even at low rates.

super phosphate. But no one from A&M, USDA or the fertilizer industry would or could give me an answer.

An elderly friend who once worked for large fertilizer companies visited me one day. I asked him for an honest answer to my suggestion that the new 0-46-0 could be causing all the yellowing.

After a long pause he answered, "You are absolutely right, but you are not supposed to know that." He explained that the fertilizer manufacturers made that discovery but kept it a secret. All of them agreed to stop making 0-20-0 phosphate, which also prevented growers from discovering the problem by comparison.

To make 0-20-0, rock phosphate is treated with sulfuric acid to make calcium phosphate (0-20-0) and calcium sulphate (gypsum); these are two natural products that seldom caused any problems.

To make 0-46-0, rock phosphate is treated with phosphoric acid. The much higher phosphate content means much higher NPK fertilizer formulas can be made. Less of it is required, but it sells for a much higher price.

My elderly friend explained that 0-46-0 lies naked in the soil and looks for something to marry up with. It bonds up with zinc, iron and manganese, and the plants can't assimilate them.

Evidently this knowledge is well protected, because to this day agricultural agents tell gardeners and horticulturists to stop using phosphate fertilizers and manure for three to five years. Another problem, some agricultural agents claim, is that the phosphate causes algae blooms in lakes and streams.

I can't understand their reasoning. Manure has been used for centuries without causing soil problems. However, if manure washes into lakes it will grow algae because it is a complete fertilizer.

The fertilizer industry has learned to beef up their high quality phosphate fertilizer products with extra zinc, iron and manganese to help overcome the problems in the landscape. Also, phosphate is not known to leach from the soil, it only moves with the soil. It can't get into lakes unless put there by runoff or soil erosion. Phosphate alone will not grow algae; nitrogen must also be present.

Looking for answers, I did some research. I got virgin soil from a location that has never been plowed or fertilized. I naturally air-dried and well homogenized this soil so I could get identical samples to send to numerous testing labs. I sent seven in all, two to Texas A&M soil test department and five to other labs around the U.S.

The two A&M test results showed excessive soil phosphate with instructions to not add any phosphate fertilizer or manure to the soil for three to four years. The other five labs showed soil phosphate low to medium and gave recommended application rates.

Why are the A&M test results so much different from the other five labs? Something is definitely wrong here.

1. The algae in the lakes should be attacked by stopping erosion and the overuse of highly soluble forms of nitrogen fertilizer.

2. The fertilizer companies should be honest with their customers.

3. Texas A&M's soil testing department should get together with the private testing industry to end mistrust and better serve gardeners and farmers.

4. Fertilizer salesmen should be fully informed, honest and better educated.

5. More and better research needs to be done and shared with the farmers and gardeners.

6. Agricultural agents should keep up with private and public research, and should discriminate between scientifically defensible research and research designed to sell products.

7. All educational institutions need to teach more about Nature and how she operates.

The soil samples were taken from a virgin area that had never has been plowed, fertilized or contaminated in any way. The soil was air dried and thoroughly blended so all seven test samples would be exactly the same.

Test # 1 — A&M

Soil testing dept. Phosphorus, 62 ppm — very high. Soil phosphorus is excessive.

Suggested fertilizer rates. Discontinue the use of commercial fertilizer containing phosphorus or manure for three to four years.

Test # 2 — A&M

Soil testing dept. Phosphorus, 66 ppm — very high. Soil phosphorus is excessive.

Suggested fertilizer rates. Discontinue the use of commercial fertilizer containing phosphorus or manure for 3 to 4 years.

Test #3 — A&M

Feed and Fertilizer testing department (has nothing to do with the soil department). Their test showed 0.18 percent. They considered this low to medium for soil.

Test # 4 — Kinsey Agricultural Services

Phosphorus value of test found was a low of only 146 lbs/acre. Ideal should be 750 lbs/acre recommended adding 640 lbs/acre.

Test # 5 — A&L Lubbock

Their strong Bray test shows medium of 179 lbs/acre. They make no recommendations.

Test #6 — A&L Memphis

Their test shows medium of 48 lbs/acre. They make no recommendations.

Test #7 — Texas Plant and Soil Lab

Their test show low at 12 lbs/acre with a slight residual, their recommendations is: need to build reserves, plants need from 40 to 200 lbs/acre.

The results of the above test were placed on my website <www.malcolmbeck.com> in May 2003. As of January 20, 2004, Texas A&M has admitted, on their website, that they were wrong in their soil testing and have now made the proper corrections.

Fertilizer: Organic (Natural) versus Inorganic (Chemical)

The argument continues. Organic proponents say only organic fertilizer should be used. The chemical proponents have their argument of high analysis and quicker availability.

Why don't we consult Nature and see how she has fed plant life since the very beginning?

Most of the fertilizers called "chemical" actually occur in Nature. In fact, that is where man discovered them. Ammonia, ammonium, ammonium sulphate, nitrites, nitrates, potassium sulphate, calcium phosphate and urea are some of them. But seldom are these chemicals found in the pure state. In Nature, they are almost always bound up in rock or in an organic form with other elements. Or they may be found in a state of transition.

Man-made chemical fertilizers always have a high total NPK, from 20 to 60 percent or more. The total NPK of organic fertilizer blends will always be low. Fourteen percent is about as high as it gets.

The balance of the ingredients in a bag of chemical fertilizer, aside from the NPK, are usually an inert filler or a chemical that isn't needed. The balance of the ingredients in a bag of organic fertilizer beyond the NPK are all necessary soil nutrients. The fact that the material is organic means it came from a once-living entity, which tells us that every ingredient there is important to life. In the best organic fertilizers, everything in the bag is needed and is in correct proportions to feed and sustain the next generation of life.

Many chemical fertilizer formulas that contain major, minor and trace elements are labeled "Complete." That is really a false statement. It takes much more than a few chemicals to maintain the healthy soil and grow healthy plants. For example, there is very little, if any, carbon in a bag of chemical fertilizer. When a plant or animal body is analyzed, one of the most abundant elements in it is carbon, in the form of energy, mainly carbohydrates.

In order for a plant to be properly fed, whether with chemical or natural fertilizer, the microbial life in the soil must first process the fertilizer into

The plant showing no white roots was being grown with an expensive, well-balanced 14-14-14 chemical fertilizer. The plant showing an abundance of white roots and triple the growth was grown with 6-2-2 organic fertilizer. There were about 2,000 plants in each test plot. Results where the same throughout.

a substance and release it in the correct amounts that are perfect for a plant to absorb. In order for the microbes to perform this service, they must have energy. They are not in the presence of sunlight, nor do they have chlorophyll like higher plants, so the microbes must get their energy from decaying plant or animal matter in the soil.

A bag of organic fertilizer has all the carbon/energy to meet the needs of the soil microbes. A bag of chemical fertilizer has no energy. If organic matter is not already present in the soil, the chemicals can quickly become stressful, even toxic, to the plants. This makes plants susceptible to disease and insect problems.

Organic fertilizers are believed to be slower acting than the chemical fertilizers. This is true to a degree. Having a lower NPK analysis and slower-acting, organic fertilizers can be used in higher volume around plants without danger of burning. However, there are some organic fertilizers that are fast-acting, such as bat guano or fish meal, that can show results as quickly as chemical fertilizers. They are still slower to burn the plants than the chemical products and last much longer in the soil.

Unless chemical fertilizers are impregnated or coated with a microbe-inhibitor and some substance to keep them from quickly dissolving, they must be used very cautiously. Especially in sandy soils, they can burn the roots of the plants and quickly leach beyond the reach of the roots. They generally end up polluting a water supply because they are too quickly dissolved and moved out of the soil. In heavy clay soils or any soil with a high organic and humus content, this is less of a problem.

Chemical fertilizers that are blended to fit perfectly with a given soil and then used in the correct season and correct amounts can do nothing more than grow a plant. They do not build or sustain a healthy soil. Organic fertilizers contain the energy and the many other things that continually build soil fertility, crumb structure, increased water holding capacity, food for all beneficial soil life, condition the soil and contribute to the hundreds of other yet-unknown things that cause a plant to grow healthy and perfect.

Only healthy and perfectly grown plants can feed and support healthy animal and human life.

Discovering How to Use Natural Phosphate

Our unconventional way of farming attracted attention from the news media. Both TV and newspapers were out for pictures and stories. Following on their heels were other gardeners and farmers who wrote letters and came for visits. Some were just curiosity seekers, but almost all were encouraging.

Once after a reporter mentioned that I was using bone meal for a source of phosphate, I got a letter from a gentleman in Laredo, Texas, saying that he grew up on a farm and ranch and also believed in organic growing techniques. He also said he had a business of grinding and bagging a natural phosphate rock that came out of bat caves in Mexico. It was being used as a phosphate supplement in animal feed.

His letter said that he often wondered whether his product would work as a fertilizer as well as a feed supplement. He volunteered to give me some if I wanted to try it out. Bone meal was expensive, and although I had heard of rock phosphate, I hadn't found a source until I got that letter. In the past I had asked the agricultural extension service about using rock phosphate on my farm, and they said to forget it. They had experimented with rock phosphate in alkaline soils like mine, and it didn't work. Still, as long as the rock phosphate was free, and since I was naturally hard-headed and had to learn for myself, I figured I had nothing to lose.

We were in the process of transplanting tomato plants when a truck pulling a trailer arrived with a whole ton of the natural phosphate from the gentleman in Laredo, way more than I ever expected for free. To be fair, I felt I really owed this man a good test in return for his generosity. I was in the middle of planting the field with two rows of tomatoes and two rows of legumes alternating.

It was too late to broadcast the phosphate in the tomato field since the furrows were already opened for the transplants. So I sprinkled the phosphate in the bottom of the furrow and set the roots directly on top of it. I did this on one double row in the middle of the tomato patch.

Sprinkle the phosphate in the hole to where the sides and bottom are painted white, set the root or seeds directly on it and backfill the soil. The plants will now have a quick source of calcium and phosphorus for quick root development. When blended in alkaline soils, low in organic matter and microbial activity, the natural phosphorus is tied up and made un-available.

For the first part of the growing season, I couldn't tell much difference, although the phosphate row did seem to have more blooms. When the tomatoes started ripening, I instructed my family and hired help to keep the fruit picked from that row and the rows on either side separate so that I could weigh them and see if there was any difference between the phosphate row and the rows on either side that had no phosphate added.

On the first picking, the phosphate row yielded 20 pounds of tomatoes, the other two rows seven and nine pounds respectively. That ratio continued throughout the whole season. When production really got heavy in the peak of the harvest, we no longer had time to weigh the rows on either side separately. The phosphate row totaled 167 pounds, and the two control rows averaged 75 pounds each.

The rock phosphate had more than doubled production. Then I remembered what the extension service had told me and laughed when I thought, "Those Aggies don't know what they're talking about!"

I ordered enough rock phosphate to cover one quarter of my vegetable farming area at the rate of two tons per acre. The next spring I bought a bottom-drop fertilizer spreader and broadcast and worked the phosphate into the soil. I couldn't wait for harvest time and the big production that would not only make me rich, but the envy of all other farmers! Picking time rolled around. But guess what? There was no increase in production in the phosphate area over the rest of the farm. What was going on here? Why no big increase in production? Maybe those Aggies knew more that I thought!

I told Dr. Sam Cotner, the Agricultural Extension Service Vegetable Specialist, about my two different ways of applying the rock phosphate and the results. He too was puzzled, but he was determined to find the answer. We talked about what I'd done and resolved to apply what he knew to the situation.

Dr. Cotner said that most of the phosphate a vegetable plant needs for its whole life is taken up in the first few weeks of growth. If it can't get enough then, it gets stunted and is stunted forever. He also said that in the early spring when the soil is cool, the plants have a hard time assimilating phosphate. To make matters worse, in alkaline soil, phosphate combines with other elements in such a way that it is inaccessible to the plants. In all their testing of rock phosphate on alkaline soils, they found it to be little help and even super phosphate would soon tie up and become mostly unavailable. He concluded that when I put down thick bands of the rock phosphate in the furrows, it kept the phosphate from combining with the alkaline environment and being bound up. Evidently, the plant roots growing directly in the rock phosphate can get what they need for the life-long health of the plant.

The rock phosphate from Mexico is no longer available, but now a natural colloidal phosphate clay from Florida is being sold, and I am using it with good results. I have grown peas in pure colloidal phosphate without soil or fertilizer. I simply watered and the plants grew healthy, bloomed, and produced seeds. They showed no signs of deficiencies.

There is no point in wasting the phosphate, however. Use it in moderation and let your experimentation determine how much and how often to add to your garden.

The Agricultural Extension service is now advising farmers in alkaline areas to band phosphate in the row. To band phosphate, put down a strip about as wide as the trench and an inch or so below the seeds or directly beheath your transplants. Their latest research shows that phosphate placed one to two inches deep produces better results. When a seed sprouts, it first puts down a tap root for anchorage and moisture, and then it puts out the lateral feeder roots to pick up nutrients. These roots will be an inch or so below the place where the seed is planted. If you are transplanting seedlings, however, the roots are already established, so the phosphate should be directly in contact with them for best results. Paint the soil white with the phosphate in your planting hole or trench in all directions where plants will grow.

In acid soils, rock or colloidal phosphate works well even when broadcast and worked into the soil. But we have found that it works best in any soil pH that has a high organic matter content or is mulched with an organic material. Another benefit of natural phosphate is that it contains many other nutrients necessary to healthy plant growth.

To apply a natural phosphate to existing plants poke half- to 1-inch diameter holes one foot apart 6 inches deep in a circle around the shrub or tree at the outer rim of the canopy and fill about half full of phosphate. You can fill the rest of the hole with dirt if you wish, or let Mother Nature fill it for you. Garden centers often offer bags marked "colloidal clay." Colloidal phosphate clay is colloidal clay with high phosphate content. Not all colloidal clay has the phosphate content.

Understanding Phosphate

Phosphate is the middle letter of NPK, a major element used in abundance by farmers and gardeners. A plant must have phosphate for root development when the seed sprouts or a seedling is transplanted. The availability of phosphate is very low in very acid and very alkaline soils. The availability is also low in cool soils when the microbes are not very active.

An annual plant takes up to 60 percent of its total phosphate needs during the first few weeks of its life. If it does not get enough phosphate then, it will always be behind and never catch up. The result will be a plant that grows poorly, is susceptible to disease, and doesn't produce as well as it should. Soft rock phosphate used directly under the seed or transplant at planting time is the very best method of application, especially in low acid

Our kitchen garden. There is no shortage of phosphate here. The seeds and transplants were started on a light dusting of natural phosphate.

or high alkaline soils. It is not as critical but still useful to use this method in slightly acid to neutral soils.

Plants need a boost of phosphate again for blooming, but in organic-rich soils microbes are active enough and root mass is large enough to supply plenty at that time.

The old style super phosphate 0-20-0 which is made by treating rock phosphate with an equal amount of sulfuric acid was also a good source of phosphate in low acid or high alkaline soils because it became calcium sulfate and calcium phosphate-two natural products found in nature. Little, if any, of this product is now made.

The new triple super phosphate 0-46-0 is added to most chemical fertilizers and should never be used. It is made by treating rock phosphate with phosphoric acid. The end product is considered "naked" and tends to marry up with iron, zinc and manganese and render them unavailable to the plants.

It is almost impossible to overuse soft rock phosphate. You can grow beautiful plants directly in it without any harmful effects. So when you need phosphate in your garden, look for soft rock phosphate or colloidal phosphate. Stay away from triple super phosphates!

Beginner's Luck & the Raised-Bed Garden

A young friend of mine, a co-worker on the railroad, had just moved into a new home, and since he and his wife now had the room, they were planning a garden. Neither of them had ever gardened before, and they were accepting any advice they could get.

Their new home was in the Hill Country north of San Antonio, an area scarce in topsoil, so I suggested using railroad ties to make a raised bed garden. After getting the ties and soil in place, my young friend asked if he should plant on level soil or make hills and valleys like he had seen some farmers do. I suggested shaping beds and furrows and planting on the beds.

A few weeks passed and we were invited to our friend's open house party. Naturally he had to show me the garden. It was then that I realized he really meant it when he said "hills and valleys!" It was more like mountains and valleys. The hills came almost to a point with deep valleys on each side. There were some frost bitten plants trying to grow on the very tops with the soil beginning to erode away from their roots. I felt badly for not explaining to him how to rake the hills down into properly formed seed beds, and without thinking I suggested raking those hills down and replanting. My friend responded, with his feelings slightly hurt, "No way, these are my first little plants and I couldn't destroy them."

Even though the season was early, with plenty of time for replanting, I could see how my friend felt about his garden. I knew that somehow I must help him salvage it.

Knowing the soil in the area to be low in phosphates, nitrogen, and humus, I suggested applying rock phosphate at the rate of one pound per three feet of row in the furrows. Then, I suggested he fill the furrows with compost up to near the top, leaving some soil bare around each plant so the soil could continue to warm up. That way if a late frost came, the warmth from the soil will be available to warm the top part of the plants and they wouldn't freeze. Then, after all danger of frost was past and the soil temperature had warmed up, but before it got hot, he could finish mulching with the compost across the top of the beds at least one inch deep.

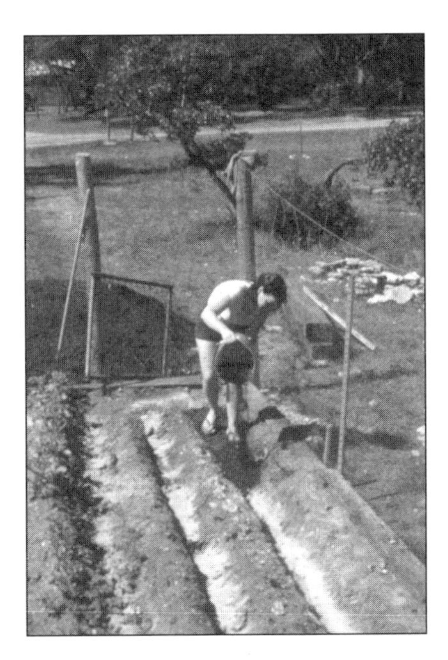

The use of colloidal phosphate covered with compost in the furrows created one of the most productive gardens I have ever witnessed.

Even though we worked different shifts and different jobs on the railroad, I often ran into my gardening friend. He always had fresh vegetables of some kind from his garden in his lunchbox, among them tomatoes, okra, cucumbers, beans, and squash. When it grew late in the season, I knew his crops would soon play out, but my friend always had squash. He brought it in August, September, and October. When he still had it in November, I asked him if he had planted a fall garden. He said, "Oh, no. These are still from my first little plants you saw in the spring and wanted me to rake out!" He thought it was normal to harvest yellow squash continually from the same plants for six months, and he wasn't even aware of the great success he was having.

My friend also brought sweet potatoes in his lunch, and I jokingly added, "I guess you also grew those sweet potatoes." He said, "Yes sir! Let me tell you about them. My wife found one sprouting in the vegetable bin one day so she took it out and buried it in the garden and a bunch of sprouts came up. Not knowing a sweet potato from a weed, I accidentally pulled the potato up. My wife scolded me for it, so I replanted and watered it. It wasn't long before it took over one whole end of the garden. A neighbor told us when and how to dig them, and so far, we've gotten over 50 pounds."

This beginning gardener still doesn't realize his good fortune and probably thinks gardening is a snap. Of course, we experienced gardeners know better, but then maybe it wasn't all beginner's luck. The high beds or hills allowed for more compost in the middle and actually gave more mulch-to-soil contact for a given area. This contact zone between soil and mulch is really the high fertility zone, or the area with the highest microorganism activity, and the value of having a large area of contact becomes obvious when studying the benefits of mulching.

Successes such as this beginner had are what makes us want to garden, but if this beginner keeps on gardening, sooner or later he will experience some failures, and failures are what we learn the most from. Without an occasional failure, the successes wouldn't be nearly as enjoyable.

Raised-Bed Gardens

Why?

Raised gardens ensure greater success with higher yield; the roots have better drainage and get more oxygen, and they have a deeper growing area. Gardens can be grown in areas where the soil is poor or in areas where not enough topsoil exists. The walls around raised gardens enhance landscaping and help keep pets and small children out of the garden.

How?

1. Remove weeds from the area by digging out all rhizome-type grass (Johnson grass, Bermuda grass, carpet grass, or nut grass, etc.)

The best and easiest way to get rid of the troublesome weeds, grass and seeds is by solarizing the soil using the heat of the sun. Dig a small trench around the area you want cleaned up, then thoroughly wet the area to the depth of one foot or more. Then stretch clear or black plastic over the area including the trench and use sand or soil to anchor the plastic in the trench so no heat or moisture escapes. Do this in the hottest time of the year for a week or longer. The moist soil will conduct the heat deep enough into the soil to destroy all pests and unwanted plant life, but the earthworms will quickly escape the area or go deep enough to avoid the heat.

2. Place retaining walls around the area using cedar timbers or logs, tile, rocks, or other suitable materials, and seal cracks to keep out creeping rhizome-type grasses. Begin an inch or two below soil level and up to the desired height of six to eighteen inches.

3. Fill to within an inch or two from the top with a good, well-draining, organic-rich soil that is free of weeds, weed seeds, roots, and nematodes.

4. See diagram for shaping of the soil and for application of top mulching.

Where?

Select a location that gets at least eight hours of direct sunlight per day. Morning sun is most important. Afternoon sun can be so harsh that it shuts down the ability of plants to grow efficiently.

Size?

For ease of working and harvesting, four feet is the ideal width. The length will depend upon the amount of planting area required.

Reworking?

After the garden plants are finished in any area, turn the spent plants into the raised bed soil. This maintains the organic content or richness of the soil for the next vegetable planting. The garden will now be ready to replant the following season, in a winter cover crop, or fall vegetable crop.

Additional Benefits of a Raised Bed Garden:

1. The timbers will tie together stronger when stacked two or more high.
2. No need to stoop, just sit on the wall while gardening.
3. Fungus problems seem to be minimized because of better air circulation.
4. Insect damage also seems to be less because the plants are healthier.
5. The overall appearance of the garden is more attractive due to the raised effect.

Mulching

One year, back when I was a kid on the farm, my dad decided to plant a peach and plum orchard, and my brother and I were given the job of keeping the trees watered. The water had to be pumped by hand and carried in buckets, so you can imagine how much water those trees got! After a long hot summer, only three trees were still alive. One was near the house and got the wash water poured on it; another was next to a concrete slab, and the third one had a bunch of hay piled next to it.

My dad, headstrong man that he was, still wanted an orchard and decided to replant. After some strong encouragement with his leather belt to keep the trees watered this time, our creative minds took over. We had noticed that one of the surviving trees was near a haystack under which we always dug to find fishing worms — worms that thrive in a moist atmosphere. Maybe piling hay around the trees would help keep the ground moist. We talked Dad into helping us (or rather we helped him), and this time — success! Even with little watering, the orchard survived.

Through the ages, trees have been shedding their leaves, and the smaller plants and grasses have been dying and falling to the earth, providing a natural, protective mulch cover.

With a little study, we can understand how this mulch protects the soil from erosion, sunbaking, and crust-formation which prevent water from soaking in. A mulch of leaves and grass on the soil helps prevent heavy rains from rushing off to the creeks and rivers, swelling them into swift, destructive muddy torrents. We can also see how this organic blanket holds the moisture in the soil for plant use and keeps the soil temperature cool in the hot summers and warm in the cold winters.

With the scratch of a finger, we find the earthworm feeding in the moist rich layer of decomposing mulch next to the soil. With the aid of earthworms and many smaller soil organisms, such as bacteria, algae, fungi, etc., the decay of mulch is completing the cycle of life by turning the mulch into humus and feeding a new generation of plants all the life-sustaining nutrients that were in its tissues — tissues which came from the preceding generations of plants.

When we walk on the mulch-covered earth, our feet don't get muddy and the soil doesn't pack. Mulches around trees and plants also enhance the beauty of the landscaping and help in controlling weeds. These are some of the obvious and easily understood benefits of mulch. But mulches provide many more unseen and not so well understood benefits.

Because the surface soil packs to a crust and reaches extreme temperatures, plant roots usually do not use the top inch or two of soil. With a mulch cover, the roots come up even into the mulch itself, and the root zone of the plant increases. The soil surface right under the mulch is the most fertile.

The greatest benefit of an organic mulch on the soil is derived from the activity of the decomposing microorganisms and the products they form. Growth-promoting hormones and certain toxins and antibiotics that don't harm plants are formed, and these help to control diseases, root rot, and damping off fungi.

A decaying mulch of bark, leaves, grass, etc., promotes the growth of a mycorrhiza fungus that envelopes plant roots with a mycelium, absorbing nutrients from the soil and even directly from decaying organic matter and passing them on to the plant roots. This mycorrhizal association is very beneficial to trees. In the tropical forest, trees couldn't grow without it. Another beneficial fungus, one that traps and destroys root-knot nematodes, also grows in the decomposing organic matter. During the decomposition of organic materials, the microorganisms secrete a sticky substance which glues the soil into little crumbs, promoting good soil granulation and thus better soil structure.

In general, mulching improves the health, and can even increase the life-span, of trees and plants. Some even claim that mulches improve the flavor of fruit!

After reading about all the near miracles mulches perform, I'm sure you will want to mulch your plants and trees and wonder which is the best to use. Compost, a mixture of many types of partially decayed organic materials including manures, is the best mulch. A thin layer of compost under native tree trimmings is the ideal mulching combination. You duplicate the forest floor this way and have a rich source of nutrients. Corn cobs are next. Many other organic materials, including leaves, hay, grass clippings, seed hulls, etc., make good mulches. Let availability of material dictate which one you use. However, any that could contain weed seeds, nematodes, or diseases should first be well composted through a heat cycle. When mulching with high carbon-low nitrogen materials such as sawdust and wood chips, extra nitrogen should be added to offset the temporary nitrogen tie-up caused by the decaying organisms.

Three inches of mulch is desirable, but anything from one to six inches is all right. Depth of the mulch depends on the size of the plant and material used. A fluffy straw mulch would naturally be used thicker.

When mulching established trees, start a foot from the trunk and mulch out to a foot or more beyond the drip line of the canopy. Trees in lawns should be mulched with a half-inch layer of compost in the spring and fall. Actually, the whole lawn should be mulched with compost in the

These fruit trees are grown in a high pH (above 8) soil. Iron chelate and iron sulphate were used in an attempt at correcting the iron chlorosis problems, but they did little good until a heavy mulch was maintained around the trees. As long as the mulch was maintained, the trees stayed green and produced good fruit.

fall. Mulching with compost, rather than adding more soil, makes the lawn fluffy. The grass receives less damage when walked on, and the yard doesn't rise above the walkways and house foundation as when dirt is added each year.

Some inorganic materials can also be used for mulching:

1. Dark plastic film can be used to warm the soil extra early in the spring, allowing a jump on the season with vegetables. It also controls weeds well and holds moisture, but it causes the soil to overheat in the summer, and it feeds no organic matter into the soil. The water it sheds can cause erosion in nearby soil during heavy rains.

2. Aluminum foil controls weeds and holds moisture, but is used primarily to reflect light back onto leaves for greater photosynthesis. Overheating and lack of organic matter are the drawbacks to using foil as a mulch.

3. Gravel (or stone), one of the better inorganic mulches, is beneficial for (a) using around trees to give them greater anchorage against strong winds, (b) stopping weed growth, (c) conserving moisture, (d) moderating daily temperature fluctuations, (e) absorbing heat during the day and releasing it at night, which could provide protection for buds and blossoms directly above the stones on frosty nights, (f) discouraging mice and other animals from burrowing, digging, and scratching soil away from the roots and trunks, and (g) providing, as they weather, calcium, magnesium, etc., depending on the rock composition, for the mulched plants.

The drawbacks of mulching are very few:

1. A heavy mulch around certain plants during extreme wet seasons can hold too much moisture.

2. Covering the soil with organic mulch around vegetables too early in the season can hold them back by keeping the soil too cool. However, this same effect could be beneficial to certain deciduous plants and fruit trees that you want to have a longer dormant period.

Although mulching initially seems to be a lot of work, in the long haul it actually saves work by reducing the amount of weed hoeing and vegetable washing required for clean produce.

The benefits of mulching far outweigh the drawbacks. After all, how could we go wrong by following one of Mother Nature's programs that has been proven to work throughout the ages?

Benefits of organic mulch on the soil:

1. Increases root zone
2. Maintains even soil temperature
3. Conserves moisture
4. Prevents crusting, increasing in-soak and aeration
5. Stops erosion
6. Controls weeds, eliminates cultivating
7. Keeps heavy rain drops from splashing soil on lower leaves
8. Provides walkways-your feet don't get muddy
9. Increases the number and activity of the beneficial soil life (earthworms and microorganisms)
10. All the benefits of tilling organic matter into the soil
11. Provides extra carbon dioxide for greater photosynthesis

Benefits of organic matter in the top four inches of soil:

1. Growth-promoting hormones
2. Toxins and antibiotics
3. Mycorrhizal fungi
4. Nematode-destroying fungi
5. Sticky substances
6. Unlocks minerals
7. Nitrogen-fixing microorganisms
8. Increases moisture-holding capacity
9. Increases air space for drainage and aeration
10. Acts as a buffer against chemicals and high/low soil pH
11. Maintains the soil base exchange capacity
12. Releases nutrients over a long period of time
13. Gives soil good tilth — easy to work and till, wet or dry
14. Recycles waste products and prevents erosion

The Many Benefits of Mulching

Study and mimic the forest floor and plants in their native habitat. In areas such as rain forests, plants have a thick layer of mulch around them. As much as six inches of plant debris is piled around these lush plants. In desert areas, on the other hand, there is very little mulch. Most plants require mulch between these two extremes. Four inches of loose fibrous materials works well around trees and shrubs. The finer and smaller the particle size, the thinner the layer needs to be. Thick layers of very fine material block air to the roots of plants. In their search for air the roots will grow up into the mulch, which can be harmful to the plants if the layer of mulch is not constantly maintained.

The shredded branches from tree trimmings and large two-inch bark would be considered a fibrous or loose mulch. Leaves or leaves mixed with some grass clippings and one-inch size bark would be a medium mulch. When using medium mulch, the layer should be about two inches thick. One-half-inch and smaller materials, such as fine-screened and double-ground barks should be applied thinly, only up to one inch. These tiny particles quickly settle together and prevent air and water from penetrating properly. This finer, smaller material should be used around small flowers and vegetables. Note: Small, fine-ground, fresh pine bark releases phonols, trepans and tannins that can be toxic to certain plants and can slow their growth considerably.

The mulch on the forest floor is never a pure product. Instead, it is a mixture of grass, leaves, a few sticks or twigs, and a very small percent of manure and dead animal life. The homeowner and gardener will have an accumulation of material in similar ratios. If an abundance of green grass clippings, kitchen scraps, manure or other high-protein products accumulate, it is best to compost them before using them. The compost can be put down under a fibrous, dry-brown, high-carbon mulch. This duplicates the profile of the forest floor.

When applying mulch around plants, cover as much of the root area as possible. Do not pile the mulch up against tree trunks. It isn't needed against the trunk and may do harm.

Mulch is helpful in flower and vegetable gardens as a weed deterrent. Weed seeds that blow onto bare earth quickly sprout and become a problem. Weeds that blow onto mulched areas are less likely to sprout, and weeds that come up through a layer of mulch are much easier to remove.

Although mostly ignored, research and common sense have shown that a high organic content in the soil is needed for soil microbes to detoxify pesticide residue and also to furnish the energy the microbes need to make high-analysis fertilizers available to plants without the fertilizer itself becoming toxic. Again, we discover another great benefit and the importance of using organic mulches. The toxic materials in pesticides and fertilizers kill the microbial life of the soil. Mulch and the organisms that live in it can help reduce that toxicity.

Mulching the Lawn

The Don't Bag It program and the new mulching lawn mowers are the best and most natural things to do for the lawn. Why did it take so many years to figure that out? Most lawns, however, would still benefit from additional mulching. Naturally, you wouldn't use the same mulch you put around flowers, shrubs, and trees on your lawn. One-half inch of fine-screened compost applied in the fall or early winter after the grass has stopped growing is a good mulch. Water in thoroughly and you'll find the thatch improves dramatically. It never fails. Even a fine horticulturist like Dr. Parsons found that mulching with compost improved his lawn.

The improvements to lawns from mulching with compost are very quickly evident. The contrast between the mulched and un-mulched areas is so visible that many people have brought me pictures of mulched and un-mulched areas. They are amazed.

People tell me: "My lawn stays greener in the fall and comes out earlier in the spring." "I have no freeze damage." "The lawn is thicker, no weeds, no diseases." "I can fertilize less or not at all." "I have fewer grub worms, no chinch bugs." The one thing they all say is, "I water less." Most tell me they water about half as much as they did before mulching.

Lawns are our biggest water consumers, making them the most important place to practice water conservation.

An experience related by a friend of mine illustrates the immediate water saving of compost mulch on a lawn. When Jim moved to San Antonio, he spread Dillo Dirt (sludge that has been composted with yard waste by the city of Austin) over the lawn of his new home. At the same time, Jim's neighbor was out spreading topsoil and fertilizer. When the neighbor learned Jim had spread sludge, he wasn't too happy. Time went by; the hot, dry season came, and Jim's lawn still looked great. The neighbor's lawn and

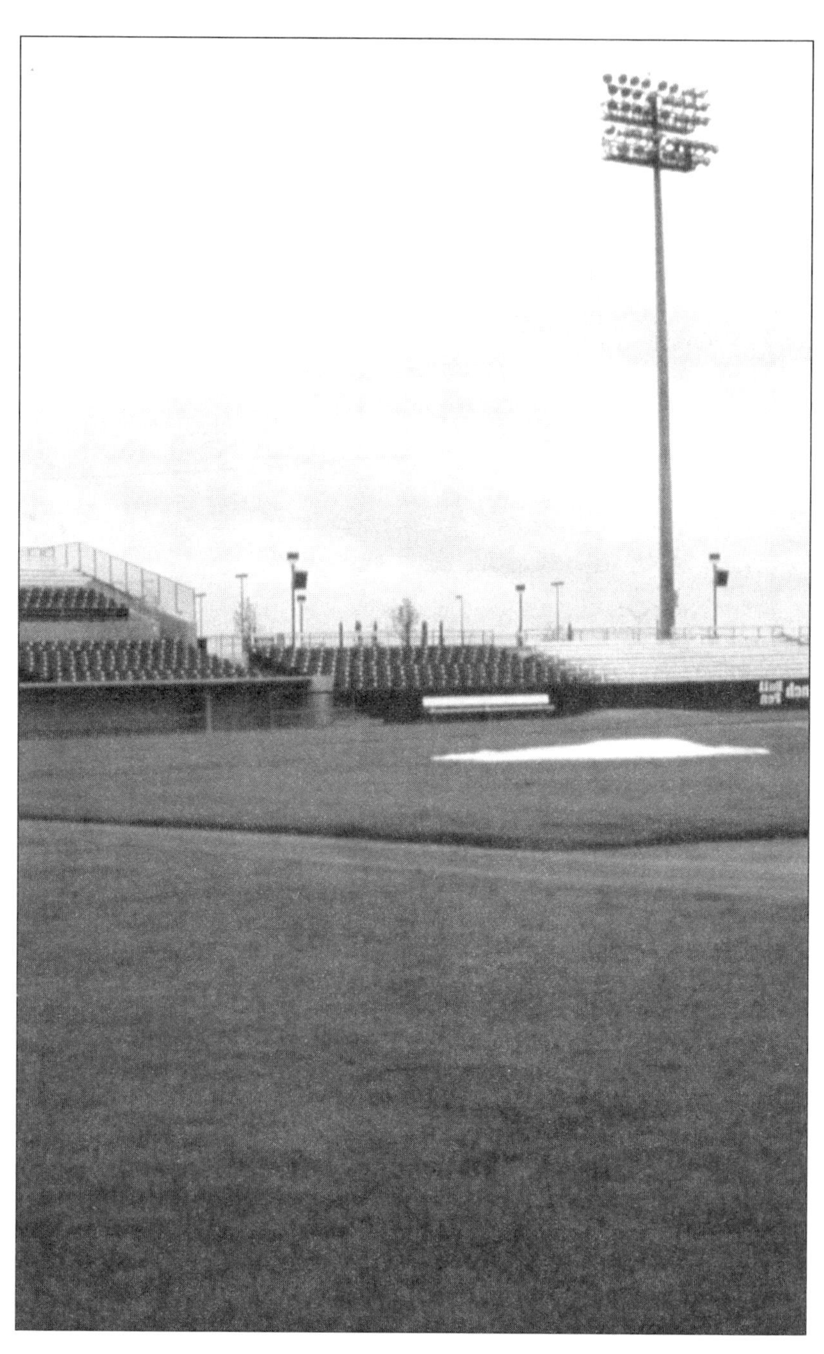

A baseball field mulched with a half-inch of fine-screened compost in the fall of the year helped keep the lawn green and reduced irrigation 30 percent.

all the other surrounding lawns began to show late summer stress. Jim happened to meet the neighbor outside one day and mentioned that his lawn looked better. The neighbor replied, "Your lawn looks great, and my water bill is killing me just to keep my lawn alive!" The neighbor told Jim that his water bill had been in excess of $200 per month for the past two months. Jim was slightly embarrassed to tell him that his own water bill was $38 and $42 for the same two dry months.

The two yards were the same size. Jim has a wife and two young daughters. Four people were using water in their home; only the neighbor and his wife were using water at their house. Jim watered every ten days, while the neighbor watered daily. Both lawns have the same species of lawn grass.

The neighbor's yard probably had no crumb structure, no humus, no beneficial soil life, or root colonizing microbes. The grass probably had fewer roots which grew shallower, and it was more susceptible to insects and diseases.

Jim's yard probably has all the benefits and good things provided by mulching and decaying organic matter I have mentioned earlier. But there is more. Science now tells us that the carbon in humus-decayed organic matter in the soil can attract moisture from the air on humid days, and the mycorrhizal fungi can collect it and supply the roots of the plants. Also, as the microbes break down organic matter, they release carbon dioxide, which is slightly heavier than air. The CO_2 tends to stay low near the grass before it finally defuses into the air. The green leaves of all plants feed from CO_2. They take out the carbon and release the oxygen, which we need. When there is an abundance of CO_2 for the leaves to feed from, they utilize water a lot more efficiently.

Conserving moisture, slowing flood waters, slowing global warming, lessening the need for pesticides, healthier plants, smothering weeds, saving money, recycling materials considered waste — and on and on. And we still have not yet discovered all the benefits of mulching.

In order for mulch to perform all these miracles, it must continually be decaying at the surface of the earth, so we must continually be adding new layers on the top.

If we just practice what we now know about mulching, we could cut the pumpage from our aquifers and reservoirs by one half or more. Our lawns would always be green and our springs would always flow.

Mycorrhizae: Beneficial Fungi in Fertile Soil

Mycorrhizal fungi form a symbiotic association with the roots of most plants. The fungi grow into or between the cells of the roots and use 10 percent of the carbohydrates the plant passes from the leaves to the roots. The fungi do not have chlorophyll in the presence of sunlight, so they can't manufacture carbohydrates. In return for the energy taken from the plants, the fungi grow out and search far and wide for nutrients and moisture. They feed the plant so it can continue to manufacture more and more carbohydrate energy. A plant well colonized with mycorrhizal fungi will have the equivalent of ten times more roots than one without the fungi.

Another benefit of this association is that, as long as the fungus is flourishing, it can prevent all root pathogens and damaging nematodes from attacking the plant root.

Decaying organic mulch on the soil keeps both the plant and the many beneficial soil species, such as the mycorrhizal fungi, flourishing so they can help each other.

The appearance of mycorrhizal fungi was reported in 1885 by a German botanist, A.B. Frank, who believed that water and soil nutrients might be entering trees through these fungi. This fungus acts as a link between the soil and rootlets of the plant. It flourishes in humus. When the association is present, plants are strikingly vigorous, achieve good growth, and gain resistance against attacks by insects and diseases.

Among forest trees and other plants, including food crops, the mycorrhizal association is widespread, habitual, and at times essential. It is stimulated when there is ample light, adequate pH of the soil, good aeration, humus, and moderate soil fertility. It is inhibited by the presence of many chemical fertilizers.

It has been found that these fungi can play an important role in plants grown in infertile soils where phosphorus, zinc, and copper are especially scarce. Mycorrhizae assist tree growth in such soils. As the plants prosper, so do the fungi, since they depend on food from the plants for their own

Organic cotton.

energy. They use about 10 percent of the carbohydrates transported from plant leaves to the roots.

According to Dr. Don Marx, USDA, efficient systems work as follows: As plant roots grow, they encounter zygomycetes, a family of soil fungi. These fungi enter the roots through root hair or root epidermal cells, and grow in the soil. They form hyphae, a network of tiny, thread-like tubes. The hyphae seek out nutrients that are poorly available in the soil areas unexplored by the roots. Hence, the root system is extended by the fungi, since the hyphae enable the plant to explore more areas and to obtain more essential nutrients in useable solution forms than could be possible otherwise.

Within the root, the fungus forms two different structures: vesicles and arbuscles. The former are round, balloon-like structures that store carbohydrates from the roots. The latter are highly branched structures that accumulate nutrients, absorbed by the hyphae, that can be released to the plant.

In studies at Ohio's Agricultural Research and Development Center, it has been learned that the more fertile the soil, the less need there is for mycorrhizae. Also, it has been found that certain fungi perform nutrient-uptake function better than others. By inoculating apple seedlings with an effective mycorrhizal fungi before planting, growth is stimulated.

The practical beneficial effects of mycorrhizae have been demonstrated convincingly in different parts of the world. Attempts to re-forest areas, which failed because of a lack of mycorrhizal fungi, became successful after the soil was inoculated with pure cultures of mycorrhizae-producing fungi

Conventionally grown cotton. These two fields are on opposite sides of a dirt lane in the Lubbock, Texas, area. Neither field was irrigated. Plants in both fields were tested for mycorrhizae on the roots, and the organically grown field was so well colonized with the beneficial fungi, it had the equivalent of 10 times more roots than the conventionally grown, wilted field.

or with soils taken from an old forest stand. In Russia, for example, certain steppes have been reforested with oak, after it was found that seedlings inoculated with mycorrhizal fungi were able to resist the extreme climatic conditions. Similarly, high mountain regions of Austria were successfully reforested with spruce by means of mycorrhizae.

In the United States, experiments with prairie soil inoculation produced beneficial effects on poplar cuttings, with better growth and higher survival rate. White pine seedlings cultivated in inoculated prairie soil contained 86 percent more nitrogen, 230 percent more phosphorus, and 75 percent more potassium than plants in untreated soil. It has been demonstrated that mycorrhizal associations unlock food elements from the soil. In experiments, pine seedlings with the fungus had four times as much phosphorus as pine seedlings without it.

Mycorrhizal association is of prime importance in tree nurseries and plantation practices. But it is also important to a variety of other plants, including many cultivated food crops such as cereal grasses, legumes, fruit trees, and berries.

Mycorrhizal fungi growing on a small pine tree (photo courtesy of the USDA).

Native Mulch Test Results

Many people understand the value of mulching, but some think the only acceptable material is pine bark. Even when the supply is hundreds of miles away and the price is exorbitant, people think it is their only choice. In San Antonio, citizens have been getting pine bark from more than 200 miles away. At the same time, they were dumping, burning, and burying a mulch material that was equally as good and in some ways better. At one dump site alone, over a million cubic yards has already accumulated. This mulch material is native tree trimmings that have been run through a shredder/chipper. Some people don't like it because it is a local product and others say it doesn't look good.

At Garden-Ville, we decided to see if this native material could be made acceptable. A specially designed grinder was purchased to re-grind it. The new machine turned out a uniform, nice looking material, but were the mulching qualities as good as bark? To find out, a cubic yard of each was placed in an open field about 15 feet apart and spread to a layer four inches thick. A water sprinkler was placed between them and both were watered well. The test began on June 3, 1989. On June 13, it rained one half inch, then we entered a drought period, and that was the last moisture the two mulches got until a rain 108 days later. Every week I poked a moisture meter through each mulched area at least one inch into the soil. For the first 60 days, the meter needle moved as far as it could to the wet side of the dial. Not until the 65th day did the needle start moving back from wet to moist. The last reading was taken on the 105th day, and the needle still read in the moist area, although on the low side. The same instrument was used to check both mulched areas, and readings were always taken near the center. The readings were always exactly the same in both the pine bark and native mulch. The bare soil between the two mulches read completely dry on the meter at the same depth by the 15th day after the June 13 rain.

One day in August the temperature got up to 104 F. Curious about the temperature under the mulch, I used a thermometer with a probe and checked both mulched areas. The soil under the pine bark was 85 F; under the native mulch it was one-half degree cooler, probably because of the slightly lighter color of the mulch. Then I checked the bare soil between the two piles and at the same depth, the soil temperature was 120 F — 35

The lighter colored mulch is the native, the darker is pine bark. The native proved to be the better mulch in every test except smell — some folks like the smell of pine. A small cover of pine mulch over the native solved this problem.

degrees difference between mulched and un-mulched soil. On an average summer day, the temperature under the two mulches was always between 80 F and 83 F during the hottest part of the evening.

The pine, a flake or nugget type of mulch, was more easily blown or washed out of place. The native mulch seemed to bind together and stay in place better.

After using this native mulch around my home and orchard for a while, I noted that the plants seemed to be growing much better than those I had mulched with pine bark. I thought perhaps this was just my imagination or wishful thinking, but I found out that I wasn't alone. Landscapers began buying native mulch instead of pine bark. They said they were noticing that the native mulch acted as a fertilizer and made the plants grow instead of holding them back like bark did.

I discussed the fertilizing effect of the native mulch with a retired county extension agent who works for me as a consultant. He told me about a study Texas A&M did on the feed value of small twigs and branches for animals. The study showed that these small parts of the tree are rich in protein and that is why goats and mules and other farm animals browse on them.

The tree trimmers who produce native mulch are cutting mostly from the small branches that stick up into phone and electric lines. These branches have the live cambium bark, live buds, and green leaves that are full of protein. When these materials are used as mulch, the decomposing microbes working at the soil level are breaking up the proteins and releasing nitrogen which the plant can readily use. When bark is used as a mulch, the microbes working at the soil level don't find enough nitrogen in the high-carbon dead bark even for their own use, so they rob it out of the soil and take it away from the mulched plants.

With all the emphasis on water conservation, rising fuel prices, and the pollution trucks contribute to the environment — not to mention the lower price — native mulch looks better all the time!

Cedar Flakes for Mulching & Growing

Back in the early seventies, a gardening friend suggested he and I form a company to promote and sell cedar flakes as a horticultural product. He knew of a mill in the Hill Country that was grinding old cedar stumps and steam cooking the small chips or flakes to get the cedar oil. The oil was being used in all types of aromatics and sold at a high price. The flakes were considered a by-product and could be purchased cheaply. My friend was a real gardening enthusiast, always trying something new, and growing some beautiful hanging baskets in all different ratios of cedar, some almost 100 percent. Other gardeners were using a more expensive medium, such as imported peat, and weren't doing any better. I, too, like to experiment with different growing media, but we decided that if we were going to become successful in business, we needed to know as much as possible about our product, and we also needed other people's experiences. We gave a lot of the cedar flakes to other gardeners and even took two big loads to Texas A&M University.

All our research showed that cedar flakes were a good bet as mulching material and a growing medium, so my partner and I started our business. As time went on, our venture grew. More and more nurserymen were learning to use cedar flakes in their potting mixes to replace peat and bark which were much more costly. We were up to four delivery trucks and thinking of purchasing another when business started sliding. At first we thought the drop in business would only be temporary, but it passed that point. We got worried and started asking our lost customers what the problem was. We learned that a report had come out of Texas A&M saying that cedar had a growth retardant effect. We followed the lead back and learned a graduate student had used our two donated loads of cedar as a research project toward his doctorate. He wrote a 70-page dissertation on the cedar.

In his publication, he wrote that his "experience indicated the possible existence of plant inhibitors in cedar mulch." The student didn't say it definitely did, only that it was possible that cedar contained growth inhibitors. This hint of bad news traveled fast through the industry, and any grower

These sweet potatoes were grown in this bed of pure cedar chips, 12 inches deep.

having problems now had a scapegoat to blame failures on. Luckily, we didn't lose all our customers. The older, more experienced nurserymen went on using cedar with no problems. They said there was nothing wrong with it, and that people who had problems didn't understand carbon/nitrogen ratios and nutrient tie-up. They also said that they didn't always get the same results with a given amount of fertilizer.

My partner and I decided to have testing done on the cedar flakes. After many tests and great expense, there were still no growth inhibitors or toxins of any kind found in the cedar. In my amateur research, I also got mixed results. There was possibly something strange about cedar that we hadn't yet discovered. I kept studying the lab test results, and more than a year went by before I found the culprit. It was too obvious.

The dry weight of cedar flakes is around 190 pounds per cubic yard. Saturated 100 percent, it weighs up to 1,600 pounds per cubic yard. I did more testing. If I took dry cedar flakes and soaked them in a fertilizer solution until near saturation, I had an excellent product and all plants grew well. Even if I let the cedar flakes dry out before using them in a growing medium, the results were still excellent. But if the first moisture the cedar got was rain or tap water, the plants didn't grow as well. It had a hard time getting enough nutrients to the plants.

Cedar flakes have a high carbon-to-nitrogen ratio and decomposing microorganisms use the carbon as an energy source. If the cedar was soaked with plain water, there were few other nutrients in the cedar. As a result, the

Five rows of one-gallon pots, each containing a different growing medium with the same number of radish plants. Cedar media produced the largest, most plentiful plants. Note: Although the ash juniper cedar that grows north and west of San Antonio is not toxic in any form, the Virginian juniper that grows to the east is toxic to plants.

microorganisms had to rob the nitrogen from the plant roots. If the cedar was soaked with a nutrient solution, there was plenty of nitrogen in the cedar for the microorganisms, so they didn't need to rob the plants.

Reading back through the graduate student's summary, I noticed that he said the leachates (what is washed away with thorough watering) contained the growth inhibitor. I remembered that we had given A&M two loads of cedar. The first was dry and dusty; the second load I took was soaking wet with rain water. This difference could have affected his results. When he used the wet cedar in his growing tests, the fertilizer solutions he applied would have mostly leached on through without benefiting the plants. When he used dry cedar, the fertilizer would have been absorbed so that there were plenty of nutrients for both the plant and the microorganisms.

The student also may not have understood that the cedar flakes were thoroughly leached with steam to get the cedar oil. This process removed all other leachates as well. In his leaching tests, he just removed the very fine wood particles. Taking out the small particles slowed down the nutrient tie-up in the remaining material since the microorganisms decompose fine particles first. The finer particles are a better energy source. The microorganisms can consume them faster, which also means they will need more nitrogen and other nutrients faster. If there isn't enough nitrogen for both plants and microorganisms, the plants will suffer.

Once this carbon-to-nitrogen ratio decay principle was understood, I could use cedar anywhere with good and predictable results. I have grown tomatoes, potatoes, cabbage, and many other plants in pure cedar flakes, getting excellent growth and production. I have also found cedar to be the best product to use when heeling-in balled and burlapped and bare-root trees. Cedar is acid, it inhibits root rot, it is very slow to decay, and roots seem to love it.

The most spectacular thing grown in pure cedar flakes were sweet potatoes. I planted eight slips (sweet potato plants) in a raised bed that was 12 inches deep, 8 feet long, and 4 feet wide. This bed contained about one cubic yard of cedar to which I added one gallon of colloidal phosphate clay for mineral and six quarts of bat guano for nitrogen. After the fertilizers were well mixed into the flakes, I put in the plants and watered with a nutrient solution of two tablespoons fish emulsion, one tablespoon liquid seaweed, one tablespoon of feed-grade molasses, and one teaspoon of a biological product called Agri-Gro mixed into three gallons of water. After the plants were well established and growing, I used this mixture in two gallons of water every time I watered. I watered in the morning and drenched the whole plant every time.

The plants were beautiful and, except for a few grasshoppers, not a single pest, disease, or insect bothered them. I let the plants grow until frost was expected, then let the flakes dry in preparation for harvest. Sweet potatoes store much better if they are harvested dry.

The dry cedar was so loose I just pulled the potatoes out by hand without using a spade. The bed was almost solid potato. Some were three feet long; others were shorter but nearly six inches in diameter. There were more than 137 pounds of sweet potatoes dug from that single raised bed. That is the equivalent of 109 tons per acre — the kind of production farmers dream of.

A gardening friend to whom I gave some cedar planted potatoes in the pure flakes. One day when I was visiting, he pulled up a potato plant and picked some fist-size, pretty, and clean potatoes off the roots. He then put the plant back in the spot he'd pulled it from, pressed the moist cedar tight, and the plant continued to grow without ever wilting. This would be almost impossible in normal garden soil. If the plant didn't die, it would surely wilt and be sick for a long time. The cedar from which the plant was pulled was loose; no roots were torn, and each root-hair was clinging to a small cedar particle.

I used to buy a few bare-root pecan trees each year to plant on the farm. When they arrived from the shipper, I placed the roots in moist cedar flakes, and they kept well. One year I gave two trees to a neighbor, and he kept putting off transplanting them until the middle of June. When he came to get them, they were already sprouted out about four inches. I suggested he leave them until they went dormant again in the winter because seldom does a pecan survive bare-root transplanting in the middle of summer. He didn't want to wait, and when we pulled the trees out of the cedar we found a tremendous amount of new white root growth with a lot of small cedar particles clinging to them. I helped the neighbor plant the trees. Not only did they survive, like the potato plants, they didn't even wilt.

The cedar tree (actually it is a juniper, *Juniperus ashei)* has a bad name as an invader and can become so thick it will completely smother good pastureland. Like any other tree, however, cedar tree seeds don't sprout where there is a good sod cover, but only where it is thinned by heavy grazing. A lot of people will tell you that nothing grows under a cedar tree. They don't realize that the thick shade and heavy mulch of cedar needles usually prevent other plants from getting started. That's why ranchers chop off the branches, not bothering to remove the stump. The stump won't re-sprout, and with the shading branches gone, the grass grows well in that spot because the decaying needles enrich and acidify the soil. These soil-building and acidifying qualities of the cedar actually make it a valuable plant in Nature. Because it can thrive in rocky limestone and drought conditions, you can really call it a pioneer plant.

This story of the juniper (misnamed cedar) again proves that everything — be it mineral, microbe, plant, or animal — is beneficial and even necessary. We could understand the important contributions such plants make if we would first patiently study them and not jump to conclusions and be so quick to condemn.

Using the Cedar Eater

The Cedar Eater is a giant articulated loader with the bucket removed and replaced with a rotating drum with knives or hammers similar to a mill used in big tub grinders.

It can roll up to any size tree and in a few minutes grind stump, limbs and all right down to ground level leaving a good mulch spread out over the area. It can be ground fine or left coarse depending on desire or need. A coarse grind is a good environment for native grasses to get re-established.

The blue berry cedar (ashi juniper) does not resprout, making the cedar eater very effective as a control on these trees.

The mulch shades and cools the soil, keeping temperatures even. It breaks up falling raindrops and keeps a crust from forming. It holds water in place, preventing erosion. Mulch slows evaporation, keeping soil moist

One of the big mean machines, nicknamed Cedar Eater because of its main use.

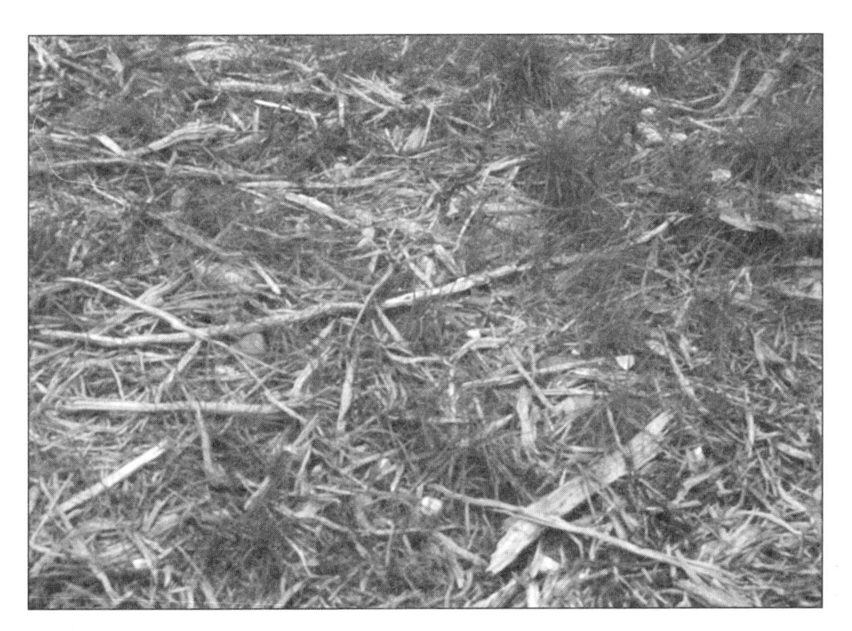

A cedar thicket mulched down to the ground.

for long periods. The mulch encourages earthworm and microbial activity, enriches the soil and allows oxygen and rain penetration. All of this activity builds fertile soil where only barren caliche was before.

Cedar thicket can be turned into productive grazing land that traps water to fill the aquifers. The Cedar Eater does not disturb the topsoil as bulldozing does. However, in some locations bulldozing may be preferred or more economical.

The Cedar Eater mulch will last for many years before completely decomposing. Mulching is Nature's way of building and protecting topsoil and conserving water.

Molasses — Sweet & Super

Molasses was one sweet treat we were never without when I was growing up. We put it on bread with butter for a snack. It was great on hot cornbread and really flavored up beans if stirred in the pot when they were very hot. My grandpa would eat molasses over cottage cheese every morning for breakfast, and he stayed healthy to his death at a very old age.

Back then I would never have guessed that molasses would have any value in growing plants or use in insect control. My friend who grows organic cotton up in the high plains uses molasses and a nitrogen-fixing microbe as his only fertilizer. (Nitrogen fixing means the nitrogen is made available to plants as nutrients.) I asked him what the molasses did, and he said it made the microbes work better.

I had to find out for myself, so I ran a test. I used two containers of equal size with equal amounts of potting soil and the same number of rye grass seeds. One container was given only tap water; the other was given equal water with two tablespoons of molasses per gallon stirred in. After eight weeks, the molasses watered plants were almost twice the size of the plants in the other container.

I was amazed, but I didn't understand how molasses could make that much difference. We had the compost in the potting soil tested and found that it contained some of the same free-nitrogen-fixing microbes that the cotton grower used. (He used an Agri-Gro product containing the microbes.) One of these nitrogen-fixing microbes is Azotobacter, a microbe that can fix nitrogen straight from the air without living on the root of a legume as long as it has a source of energy such as sugar or molasses. Both are rich in carbohydrates, a good source of energy. In lab tests, Dr. Louis M. Thompson discovered that if given sugar weekly, the Azotobacter could fix from the air the equivalent of a thousand pounds of nitrogen per acre in ten weeks.

We recommend that molasses, one to three tablespoons, be added to each gallon of liquid fertilizer mix. It definitely makes a difference. It is also used as a binder in all of our dry fertilizer formulas.

Every gardener has his or her own favorite fertilizer recipe. Both Howard Garrett and John Dromgoole have popular recipes that contain

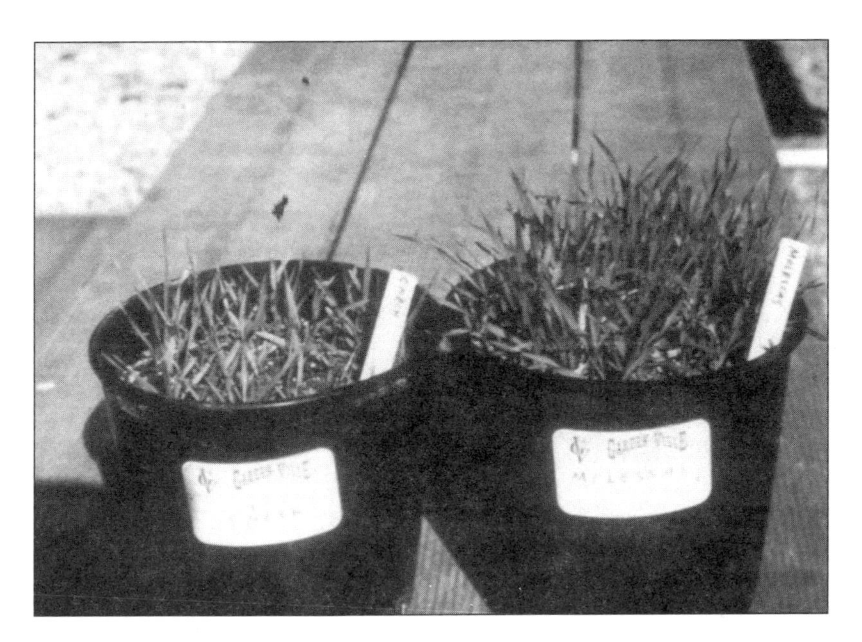

Two equal containers of potting soil with equal number of rye seeds. Both got equal water and no fertilizer; the larger plants had enough molasses added to the water to make it resemble weak tea.

molasses and other organic materials. You can experiment with your favorites and come up with your own best recipe.

I always foliar feed my fruit trees early each spring with fish emulsion and seaweed. Now I add molasses to the mix. The strangest thing I noticed when using molasses with the mix was that fire ants would move out from under the trees. I also got reports from Houston that fire ants would move away from the lawns after an application of dry fertilizer that contained molasses.

I got an opportunity to see if molasses really moved fire ants. In my vineyard I had a 500-foot row of root stock vines cut back to a stump that needed grafting. The fire ants had made themselves at home along that row because of the drip pipe that kept the soil soft and gave them a good supply of water. The mounds averaged three feet apart. There was no way a person could work there without being eaten alive!

I dissolved four tablespoons of molasses in each gallon of water and sprayed along the drip pipe. By the next day, the fire ants had moved out four feet in each direction. We were able to graft the vines without a single ant bothering us. With this success at moving the ants, I decided to spray the whole orchard and get rid of those pests. I learned, however, if the ants have no convenient place to move, they just stay where they are. I began wondering if the energy-rich molasses stimulates a soil microbe that the ants don't like. Thus began development of Garden-Ville Fire Ant Control.

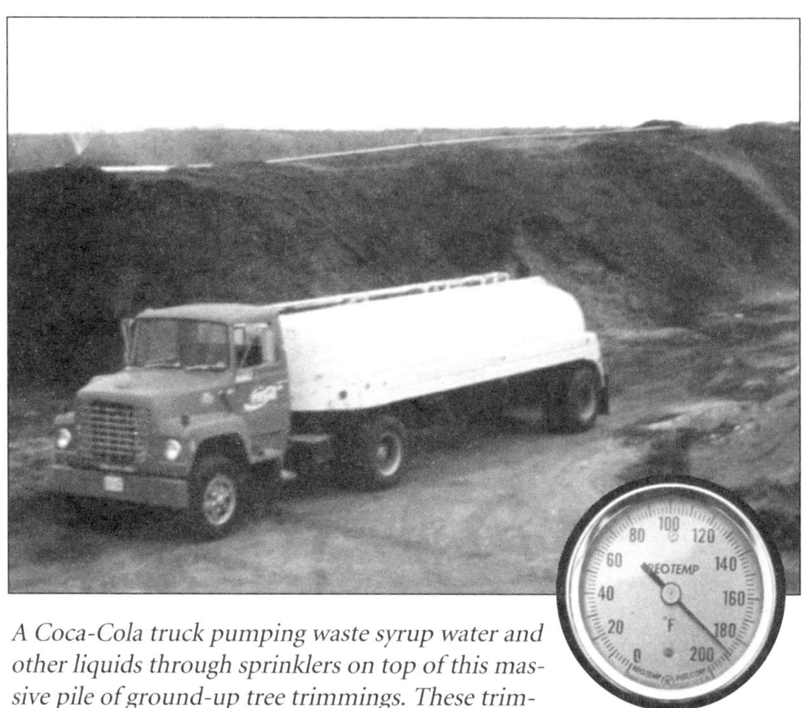

A Coca-Cola truck pumping waste syrup water and other liquids through sprinklers on top of this massive pile of ground-up tree trimmings. These trimmings started composting, and the temperature kept rising until it reached 188 F. Other large piles of tree trimmings that were wetted with plain water showed no temperature rise.

A friend of mine up in dairy country uses a hydro cyclone to separate the liquids from the solids in cow manure. He noticed when spraying the liquids on hay fields that the fire ants tended to disappear. Tests of our compost have shown it to contain insect pathogens. The manure liquids and the compost tea both had some results as ant killers. The two together worked a little better. We knew that dormant oil sprays killed some insects, and that citrus peel extracts were used to kill insects, so we decided to mix orange oil with molasses and liquid cow manure. After months of research, we finally found the correct blend that not only killed ants but any insects. It even smelled okay and would not burn the leaves of plants. It quickly degraded into a good energy-rich soil conditioner.

Needless to say, we offered our product to the market as Garden-Ville Fire Ant Control. We have many happy customers. You can even make your own if you don't want to buy ours. More information is included in the article on fire ant control.

To control powdery midlew, use the ultra-fine sun spray oil according to directions, but add a heaping tablespoon of baking soda or potassium bicarbonate per gallon of water.

A New Discovery

Back in the mid-1970s Dr. Jerry Parsons introduced a fellow to me who had some white rocks that he called "zeolite." He wanted me to see if they were of any value in growing plants. I never got around to testing the rocks and eventually lost them. Five or six years later another guy brought me a bag of white sand he called zeolite and wanted me to test it, and again I didn't get around to doing the test. In 1994 still another guy brought me some zeolite. Given all of this interest, I finally decided to give it a test.

I used two large nursery containers with potting soil and some organic fertilizer blended in each. To one container I added three volume ounces of the zeolite, then planted an equal number of turnip seeds in each. The plants came up and grew to a height of about six inches, then the plants without the zeolite stalled. The plants with the zeolite continued to grow, eventually doubling the control plants. Maybe this stuff does help plants grow. Some time later while visiting with a friend I learned he had a grant to research zeolite, and after two years of testing he concluded it had no value in horticulture.

I knew of this friend's operation, and he was considered a good grower. My test was probably a fluke so I decided to do the test over. Again, the zeolite-grown plants more then doubled in size. Now I knew it made plants grow better, but could I use more and make plants grow better still, or could I have used less and achieved the same results? In a new test I used six pots, two for control and four with each a different amount per pot. Again the zeolite-grown plants outgrew the controls, but the extra amount didn't make the plants grow better.

What Is Zeolite?

It is a natural mineral that originated from volcanic ash, found in large quantities in the United States. It has a very high CEC (cation exchange capacity) with the ability to select one or more components from a gaseous or liquid mixture to the exclusion of the others. This is known as "molecular sieving".

Other than making an excellent cat litter and household deodorizer, zeolite has many uses such as filtering radioactive-waste, sewage-effluent treatment, agricultural-wastewater treatment, stack-gas cleanup, oil-spill

The two plants in the center received no zeolite.

cleanup, oxygen production, coal gasification, natural gas purifier, and solar energy cooling. It has also been used in petroleum production. Zeolite is used in pesticide carriers, heavy metal traps, and in animal nutrition for better food digestion and absorption, resulting in better feed-conversion and drier, less odorous manure and droppings. Zeolite is especially beneficial in large poultry houses to absorb ammonium from the droppings, creating a much healthier environment for birds. Aquaculture is also a big user of zeolite to filter ammonium from the water.

New uses are constantly being discovered for zeolite, such as an exploration aid in mining. It's being used in metallurgy and in paper products and construction. It has even been fed to humans to absorb ingested toxic metals; the zeolite captured them, rendered them harmless, and expelled them.

I never saw any adverse effects when using larger amounts to grow plants, and it worked the same growing any species of plant. In fact the pure product can be impregnated with plant nutrients and used to grow plants. NASA is doing just that for space-age growing and even has it patented.

After studying and learning of all the many uses zeolite has and with my own testing we decided to bag and sell zeolite, but it needed a more respectful name so we named it "Efficient-Z."

Directions for Use

When potting plants use one ounce (volume) per gallon of soil. In the garden use 15 pounds per hundred square feet. On the farm use two tons per acre. Always mix well into the soil. On established lawns top dress with 50 pounds per 1,000 square feet. Applications need not be made every year.

How it Works

Nitrogen is the dominant functional element in the proteins of manure, urine, food waste in fact all organic materials and organic fertilizers. The beneficial soil microbes need nitrogen to build their tissue, they breakdown the proteins in the organics releasing nitrogen in the form of ammonia gas, the ammonia which is neutral, quickly takes on an extra hydrogen ion and becomes ammonium, a cation that is attracted to the zeolite, which has a negative charge.

The microbes that break down organic matter usually release more ammonia than they need, nature designed it this way so the plant could receive nitrogen also, but if the plants are small or not present at the time of ammonia release, the excess does not get used up, especially if too much organic fertilizer was applied, the excess ammonium dissolves in water, leaches beyond the root zone, is wasted and goes on to pollute the ground water and streams. The excess ammonium can even wastefully dissipate into the air. Efficient-Z with its high CEC (cation exchange capacity) up to three times higher than clay, absorbs any excess ammonium and holds it preventing leaching but readily gives it up when the plants and soil microbes need more.

Efficient-Z also holds potassium, and other cation plant foods then later releasing it when needed. This holding and later releasing of plant nutrients in effect makes organic fertilizers, considered the most efficient still more efficient. These economic and environmental benefits makes Efficient-Z an important natural product for agriculture and horticulture in our economy and society today.

Miracle Plant from the Sea

Seaweed (kelp) is a tonic for man, plant and animal. Through the natural processes and cycles of nature, seaweed manages to concentrate nutrients in a most accessible and beneficial form. As rain and snow fall, minerals and other nutrients are washed from the soil of all the continents on the Earth into creeks, streams and rivers. All the continents drain into the rivers, and the rivers carry the dissolved nutrients and minerals into the oceans. The sea plants select the correct mineral nutrients in correct amounts to best sustain plant life. When we bring those sea plants back onto dry land, we have access to their bounty. Human and animals benefit from the nutrients in these plants if they eat them. Applying seaweed meal to the soil or liquid seaweed as a foliar spray completes the cycle, bringing the lost nutrient minerals back to the land.

Traditional Use

Plant growers have known the value of using seaweed for centuries. Seaweed is being used world-wide to grow healthy plants and animals and is used as a mineral supplement for humans.

Directions for Use

Seaweed Meal — Apply 1 to 2 pints per 100 square feet or 100 feet of row. Till the meal into the top 4 inches of the soil. For trees and shrubs, use one pint per inch of trunk diameter. Lightly work in over the root zone or place under mulch. To enrich compost piles, add one to two pints per cubic yard.

Liquid Seaweed — One to two tablespoons of liquid seaweed mixed into a gallon of water makes one gallon of (RTU) ready-to-use solution.

Root Feeding — Water the root zone with RTU solution 2 to 4 times per growing season.

Folliar Feeding All Plants — A quick and efficient way to get micronutrients into plants. Use the RTU solution to thoroughly mist foliage. Early morning or late evening applications are best.

The Antique Rose Emporium near San Antonio uses liquid seaweed at two tablespoons and molasses at one tablespoon per gallon of water in their foliar and soil treatment program.

Flowers and Vegetables — Start applications as soon as newly emerging plants have 3 to 4 leaves and continue applications every 7 to 10 days.

Trees and Shrubs — Start applications when the new leaves come out in spring and continue applications every 7 to 10 days.

Seeds and Bulbs/Cuttings and Rootings — Soak overnight in RTU solution. After planting, water with the same solution.

Transplanting — Mist foliage, roots and all, before planting with RTU solution and then use every 7 to 10 days.

Lawns — Spray one gallon of RTU solution per 1000 square feet four to six times per season.

Humans and Animals — Seaweed tablets are sold wherever minerals and vitamins are sold. Seaweed meal is used in all high-quality animal feeds or can be fed free choice.

A thorough misting with two tablespoons seaweed plus one tablespoon molasses per gallon of water has been found to effectively control insects, especially red spider mites, on many plants.

Experimenting with Magic Energy from Nature: Paramagnetism

"Nature's Secret Force of Growth," known and used by the ancients, paramagnetism has been rediscovered and made known by a true natural scientist, Dr. Philip S. Callahan. I first heard Dr. Callahan talk about these magical rocks and their secret powers at an Acres U.S.A. Conference, and soon after, I began collecting and studying volcanic rocks that contain this mysterious force.

Paramagnetism is a low-level-energy physical force that has shown to have beneficial effects on all forms of life.

Because of our organic farm and compost business, we make and sell all kinds of natural farming, gardening and horticultural supplies. I am constantly searching for, trying, and testing new products. In the past forty years, I have tested many widgets, gadgets, foofoo dusts and snake oils. Some were worthless, most worked sometimes under some conditions, but few worked consistently.

Paramagnetic rocks and sand have shown more consistent results under more conditions than anything I have ever used, other than compost. Paramagnetic rocks and compost complement each other. They will both work alone, but I have found that each works much better when they are used together.

We blend a product using paramagnetic rock and sand, including zeolite collected from four volcanic deposits, plus the addition of a high iron greensand to balance the minerals. We have labeled this blend "Volcanite." It reads 2000+ on the PC meter. Below are some tests comparing Volcanite with controls.

TEST #1 — Six cactus plants grown in potting soil; six cactus plants grown in straight Volcanite and six cactus plants in 60 percent Volcanite and 40 percent potting soil. By three months, the six plants in the 60/40 mix averaged 50 percent bigger and healthier than the other 12 plants. The potting soil was 40 percent compost.

TEST #2 — Two plastic trays 20 x 26 x 6 inches deep were filled with soil contaminated with a hormone herbicide. One tray contained contaminated potting soil; the other contained contaminated potting soil plus Volcanite. Beans were planted in each tray. The plants in both trays soon showed evidence of the herbicide. The plants in both struggled along with distorted leaves that were yellowish and they grew very little. They continued in this shape for five weeks. Then the tray that had the Volcanite in the mix started to green up, grow, and was soon blooming and producing beans even though you could still see some herbicide distortion. The tray without the Volcanite never did green up; the plants grew very little and never bloomed.

TEST #3 — Four tomato plants were planted in a raised bed containing Volcanite in the soil. Fourteen more tomato plants of the same age and variety were planted nearby in the garden soil containing no Volcanite. All the plants were blooming and setting fruit when a late cold norther hit with a high wind, dropping temperatures well below freezing. All the leafed-out trees, shrubs and other plants were severely damaged. All of the tomato plants were killed, except the four in the soil containing Volcanite. This test is too good to be true. However, I can find no other factor contributing to their survival. Those four plants were completely untouched, as if a freeze had never occurred. You can bet I will be trying to duplicate this experiment! Just think what this could do for the citrus industry if we can learn to give trees three to four more degrees of cold tolerance and at the same time have a natural supply of minerals constantly becoming available that could last for years from just one application of volcanic rock.

TEST #4 — Seven one-gallon nursery containers were used. All were filled with potting soil. Two were used as controls. The other five had different rates of Volcanite added. Radishes were planted in each and thinned to six plants per pot. The five pots with the different ratios of Volcanite all grew about the same. The two controls were only about 5 percent smaller. When all the fruit was about nickle-size, the growth of the two controls stopped. On close inspection, I noticed the underside of the leaves were covered with aphids. All seven pots were in a row with the leaves touching. The two controls were in the middle. None of the five Volcanite plants had aphids or got aphids until weeks later when the plants were old and going down hill.

TEST #5 — Four of the plastic trays were filled with potting soil. Volcanite was mixed in trays 1 and 4. All four trays were planted with an equal amount of rye seed. Trays 1 and 2 were watered with electric treated

Two containers with equal soil, fertilizer, water and plants. The container with the larger plants has paramagnetic rocks added on one end and diamagnetic rocks on the other end. The other tray had no rocks added.

water. (Electric water is supposed to make plants grow better and keep calcium from building up in the soil.) Tray 3 was used as the control. Tray 4 with Volcanite and regular water did the best by doubling the amount of grass growing in the control tray. Tray 1 was second best, but grew only about 30 percent bigger than the control. The electric water seemed to cancel some of the Volcanite's benefits. Tray 2 was only about 5 percent better than the control.

I have since done many other tests. Never was there a negative result. All tests, in pots or in the garden, always showed better growth, less insect damage, and better color in the leaves and the blooms when Volcanite was used. The plants seemed to withstand stress of all types better.

Other people were given some of the Volcanite to try. Among them were a rose grower, retired county ag agent, a Ph.D., and a commercial native plant grower. All did tests against controls and all reported amazing results.

Naturally, I had to have one of the first PC meters (a machine that measures paramagnatism) that Bob Pike and Dr. Callahan designed. It is my favorite toy, and I am always testing rocks. On a trip to Enchanted Rock area north of San Antonio, I collected chips flaking off the giant granite rocks, some of the decaying granite in the creek beds, and some fresh chips from the very center of giant granite boulders being cut with a diamond saw. The center of the granite boulders measured 325 on the PC meter; the flaking chips from the outer edge measured 144; and the old decaying granite measures 124. This indicates that paramagnetic rocks could lose the magnetism with exposure, but I would assume this loss would be an extremely slow process.

Some lava sands register only 180 on the PC meter, but sand that looks identical from different locations registered five to ten times higher. I wonder if there could be a million or so years' difference in their ages? Also, why does zeolite, a volcanic ash, read low on the meter? I have tested zeolite from three different locations. The highest tested only 47, with the lowest testing 02 on the PC meter. Fred Walters, the publisher of *Acres U.S.A.*, sent me some volcanic ash he picked up on the roadside after Mount St. Helen erupted. It is similar to some of the zeolites I tested, but the fresh Mount St. Helen ash tested over 2,000. My meter reads to 2,000 and it hit at least that level. It would be interesting to expose this ash to air and annual test to see if it loses power. If it does, how fast?

If a rock can lose its paramagnetism, can it regain it? Out of curiosity I was testing some pieces of brick and broken commode one day and found them both paramagnetic. I didn't know if the clay they were baked from was already paramagnetic. We grind new but broken red clay pipe to make an aggregate that makes a decorative ground cover. The company that makes the pipe is south of San Antonio and in an area where red clay is abundant. The red clay tests 0 to 4 on the PC meter. The pipe baked from the clay reads 75 to 100.

At one of our compost locations, we collect old and broken wood pallets to be ground into a mulch. Over 20,000 had accumulated in one pile. Before we had a chance to grind them, they caught on fire during a time when we had 40-50 mph dry north wind. Needless to say, they all burned up real fast, making an extremely hot fire. The black clay soil down-wind of the fire was burnt to a rock, in fact, it looked like rusty lava rock. This burnt soil tested 329 on the PC meter, while the unburned soil nearby only tested 21. High temperatures must cause paramagnetism. My rich garden soil, however, that has been getting lots of manure, cover crops, and compost reads 138 on the PC meter, while the field nearby that receives less organic material reads only 90. Neither field has ever had paramagnetic rock or sand applied to it. The compost we make reads -2 on the PC meter. In his book, Callahan mentioned that oxygen is paramagnetic. On the internet, some researcher reported that earthworms and even microbes can make soil paramagnetic. More reasons for the organic way of growing!

At our mill we make two types of organic fertilizer. The first type contains two formulas made from food and feed-grade proteins that we run through a $^1/_8$-inch pelleting die to granulate it. The other type contains two formulas blended from VIVO (sludge) that was made into hard, small beads or pellets using extremely high temperatures. The pelleted fertilizer reads 7 on the PC meter. The fertilizer made from the VIVO with high

Two trays of mixed vegetables. The tray on top had paramagnetic sands added to the soil mix.

temperatures reads 40 on the PC meter. At present I am experimenting with upping the PC and mineral value of both formulas with volcanic materials.

I have used all ratios of Volcanite mixed into the soil and/or spread on top of the soil. It works either way, but mixed into the root zone it gives plants extra minerals more quickly. Tests have shown volcanic rock from different locations to contain different minerals. Our Volcanite blend is working well, however, I am constantly seeking to improve it. It may be that different blends may be needed for different parts of the country. Blending could be a whole new science.

As far as the best amount to use, I am still not sure. I have learned that more is not always better. Each situation seems to be a little different. In the root zone of the tomatoes in test #3, I used about 4 pounds per plant. When growing in containers, I used 1-3 tablespoons per gallon of soil mix. Maybe more would have done better, or perhaps less would have done just as well. I learned a lot from all of my testing and experimenting. Mostly I learned how much I still don't know. What an exciting future! One thing I am sure of, however, is that volcanic rock and paramagnetism deserve a prominent place in agriculture.

Volcanite: A New & Enchanting Product

Nature has been re-mineralizing the soils of the earth through volcanic eruptions since the very beginning. One result of this process is the creation of paramagnetic rocks.

Volcanite contains five different, highly paramagnetic crushed volcanic rocks, including zeolite, plus glauconite — a sedimentary mineral — rich sandstone commonly called greensand.

Volcanite reads 1900 to 2000 paramagnetism on the Phil Callahan PC meter. Most agricultural soil in the San Antonio area will read 12 to 25. The soil near volcanoes will read 600 to 700. Lava rock reads up to 850. Some rock formations in the core of volcanoes can read 3800 and up.

Directions for Use

Use 40 to 80 pounds per 1,000 square feet, tilled into the garden or as a top dressing on lawns.

In potting mixes, use up to 50 percent of the mix if desired. Or may be used 100 percent as a cactus mix. However, one tablespoon added to each gallon of soil mix has shown good results.

In commercial container mixes, 25 pounds per cubic yard has been found to be ideal and economical.

Lab testing has shown there are no concentrations of heavy metals in any of the rocks or sand blended in Volcanite.

On the farm or ranch, apply 1,000 to 2,000 pounds per acre. When applied at heavy rates, the benefits last indefinitely.

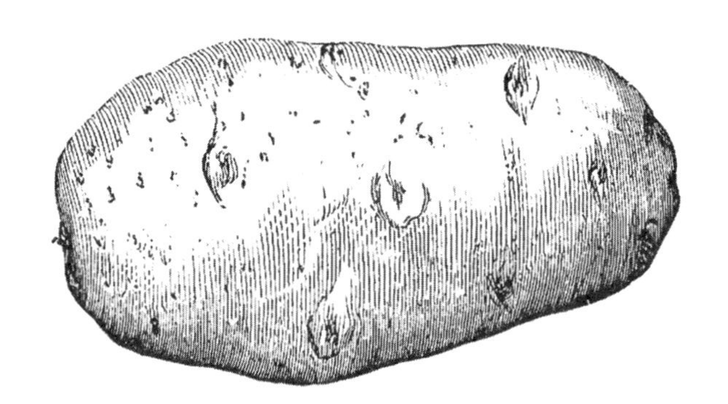

Never dig root crops such as sweet potatoes when the soil is too moist. If dug when the soil is on the dry side, the root crops store much better and longer.

Building Soil on the Farm

Think simple, economical and natural. Remember the forest floor. Nature doesn't compost materials in a pile before she uses them. You don't need to do so either, unless you want to get rid of noxious weed seeds, pathogens, or avoid hauling heavy material. Composting for a short time with few turnings will accomplish these goals. It is best to let as much of the composting activity as possible be completed in the soil.

Orchards, vineyards, and other perennials are crops that would benefit from composting materials for a while before applying, but you do not need the finished quality compost that would be sold in the city.

If you need to hold manure for several months for some reason, pile it up in a location where it can't soak up a lot of water. Some of the best vegetables I ever grew were with cow manure mixed with a little cane hay that was stored in a big pile. The manure was from the stock yards; it had been accumulating for more than a year. A couple of yards were added daily and it was pushed up high with a crawler tractor. It did smell like cow manure; however, cow manure is not an offensive odor unless it comes from feedlots. Range-fed animal manure does not smell bad.

Manure from feedlots is a lot higher in protein, making it higher in nitrogen. The high protein also causes it to smell worse. You may want to compost it to get rid of the odor, but don't burn up a lot of time and energy to get rid of something the soil life doesn't mind having.

Concentrate on getting all manure, spoiled feed, hay, feathers, cobs, hulls, gin waste, ashes and any other organic materials generated on the farm back to the land in the most economical and easiest way possible. Spread it thin and disk in shallow. It is important to mix moist manure into the soil as soon as possible, because as it loses moisture to the air it is also losing ammonia nitrogen. You want the ammonia absorbed onto the clay and humus of the soil where it will be stored for future microbe and plant use.

It is best to apply manure and other organic waste on the stubble as soon as the crops are harvested. But don't drive in the fields when they are wet because it will cause the soil to be compacted. Annual light applications of one to five tons per acre is much better than one heavy application.

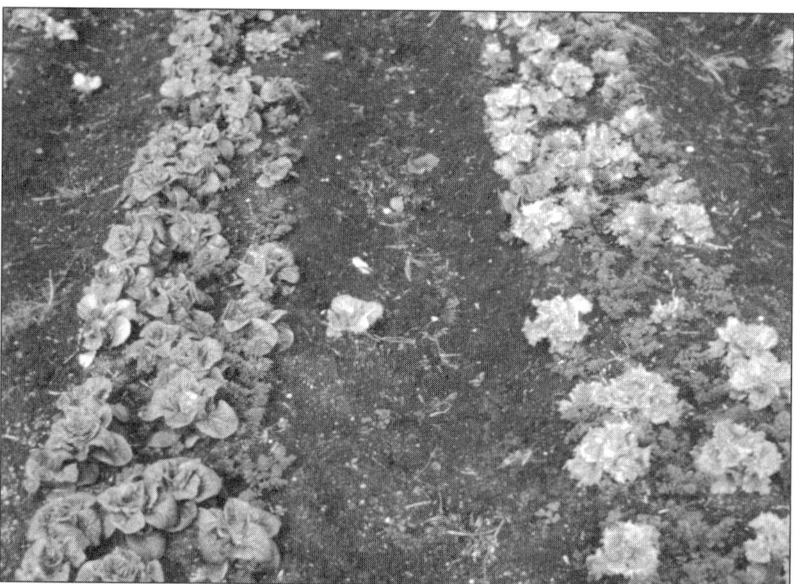

The small, sick vegetable plants on top are 10 days older than the big, healthy plants on bottom. These two photos were taken within the same minute. The only difference between them is that dry, rotted cow manure was added to the soil before planting the second set of beds.

Heavy applications can upset the biology and chemistry of the soil for the next crop, unless it is a cover crop that will be turned back for soil building. In that case it won't matter. Heavy applications, however, could possibly cause ground water and surface water pollution if heavy rains come before the soil life has a chance to digest the material.

When using feed lot, dairy, turkey and chicken manure, get a periodic soil test to make sure you are not over-loading with either potassium or phosphate. Some of the minerals are really pushed to animals in confinement. Manure from range-fed animals is rarely a problem

If you are a weekend or hobby farmer, it will not be as important how or when you handle organic materials as long as you handle them properly and don't pollute. But if you farm for a living, it is most important that you consider the economics and don't waste time, work, fuel or nutrients when getting organic material back to the land. The best advice I can give in addition to all of the above is: always observe Nature. She can teach you things that the books, the Ph.D.s and I don't know. For complete information on large-scale composting, see my book *The Secret Life of Compost.*

Cover Cropping

When compost isn't available, the soil can still be improved organically. I had to do this on my second farm. When I purchased it in 1968, the soil was so poor that in a good year Johnson grass would only get knee-high. The previous owner had planted oats and when they finally headed out, they were all of ankle-tall. We put in a garden, and the plants came up and refused to grow. The soil was yellowish red in color and real sticky. During rains most of the water ran off and the soil would soon be dry. In some areas we set up the irrigation system and sprinkled slowly to try to get moisture deep into the soil. When we went out to move the pipe and sprinklers, we bogged down to our knees. We couldn't wear rubber boots because the suction would hold them in the ground.

We had the honor of a visit from Robert Rodale of *Organic Gardening* shortly after we moved to that farm. After showing Bob around, I asked him what would be the best way to raise soil fertility short of hauling in a lot of compost. (We didn't have enough compost or money to do that!) Bob thought for a moment then said, "The land is level. You don't have bad erosion; the soil is clay. It is probably holding nutrients but the alkalinity has them locked up. What you need is to get organic matter into the soil."

I tell about our experience with cover cropping in "Rejuvenating a Worn-Out Farm." Even after we began making quite a bit of compost, we still used cover crops to build the soil on the farm. We used compost in one small area and cover crops on the rest of the farm. We found through soil testing that we had a shortage of phosphorous in our soil, even though the fertility was steadily improving. After proper colloidal rock phosphate applications, we found that vegetable production was almost the same in the cover-cropped areas as in the composted area. We used no other fertilizer.

Comparing the composted area to the cover crop area, we learned that both methods will work. If you are impatient, compost gets fertility up the quickest, but it will usually be more expensive. Cover cropping takes longer. Compost brings in minerals. Cover crops can only make available the existing soil minerals.

Good Fertility Management

Good fertility management would make use of both cover crops and compost and keep the soil healthy and productive forever. Once soil is built up to a certain fertility, if it is not abused, it has a generating ability to maintain itself and even keep getting better. The root systems go deeper and deeper, bringing up more and more nutrients. The above-ground growth gets bigger and healthier, adding more organic material and mulch. As the annual roots and tops decay, they form organic acids that release more minerals from rock formations. After many years of high production, the minerals could be cropped out in certain areas, but applying compost or rock powders could easily maintain the highest fertility.

The fertile soil of our once-poor farm has proved the ease of maintaining fertility once you get there. Our soil is now much darker, almost black, and after heavy rains there is no puddling. When I walk on the wet soil, the crumb structure is so good I barely leave a track. Pests are rarely a problem, and there is much less need for irrigation in dry seasons.

Even though the crops may look the best and production may be high, the soil may not yet be perfect. Even though a fruit, vegetable or plant or food crop may look perfect, it could still be lacking. It takes time for all the life in the soil to get organized and begin working in harmony. It takes the soil life to really put things in balance and feed the plants correctly. Taste and flavor are the ultimate test.

The results of top fertility are many: no pollution, healthier living, flowing springs, cleaner environment, fewer headaches, fewer weed problems, no need for pesticides, little need for bagged fertilizers, higher production, peace of mind, and money in the bank. Returning organic material to the farm brings all of these great benefits.

Delphine harvests carrots, one of our main crops. It took six years to equal the organically grown produce from California, but by the seventh year our carrots were preferred over the California organic carrots.

Paunch Manure for Healthy Carnivores

In our compost operation we accepted all kinds of clean organic waste. We got paunch manure from a slaughterhouse. Paunch manure is what dumps from the stomach and intestines, the food that the animal had eaten that day and not yet passed out as manure. This stuff makes excellent compost. It is full all types of beneficial microbes and enzymes.

Son Russell and daughter Kay holding their dogs. The big dog, "Bubby," was sick with miserable, bloody skin problems and an awful odor until he began to eat meat scraps from the paunch manure we obtained from a slaughterhouse. Within a few weeks he was restored to good health.

Our dogs and all the dogs from neighbors quickly learned to come and eat from it. Soon the coyotes found it and they also came and had a feast.

We had three big dogs. The oldest always had bad skin problems, with a bad odor; the vet said to feed the dogs some fat such as lard or tallow. It helped some, but the fleas and ticks and bad odor on the old dog remained. Our family never had money to spend on dog doctors. However all of a sudden our old dog started smelling better, soon his coat was healthy and shiny, then we noticed neither he nor any of the other dogs had fleas or ticks. Then neighbors were telling us their dogs that ran loose no longer had fleas. We all thought it must be the weather or the season.

I was giving a talk at a college on soil and health when an M.D. told me a story about how a zoo cured their sick carnivores by feeding them paunch from rumen animals on a tip from an old hunter that noticed that in the wild when a carnivore killed an herbivore they always ate the gut first. I have also listened to ranchers tell about eagles killing baby sheep in the late winter and only eating the gut. They believed the eagles were after some vitamin or other nutrient that was in the digestive tract of these herbivores

I got to thinking back and realized that the ticks and fleas and other canine problems disappeared when we started using the paunch in the compost. We got our proof when we opened a new compost yard miles away and took paunch for composting and the dogs in that neighborhood cleaned up slick and shiny and all fleas and ticks disappeared. Coyotes and other wild meat eaters also visited the fresh-dumped paunch each night. We didn't catch and inspect any of the wild critters but they looked awfully healthy and happy.

Why & How to Use Biosolids

When done properly, composting is the art of allowing dead things to rot in a non-polluting and nuisance-free way. I have been composting and using compost on the farm and in the garden for over 45 years. During that time I have composted waste of almost every kind, including used crank case oil, dead animals and biosolids.

Of all the waste studied and composted, I found composted biosolids to be the richest, most complete and longest lasting plant food and soil builder of all. This product is too valuable to waste. Our soil needs it.

Composted biosolids are pasteurized and free of human and plant pathogens, as well as free of weed seeds. Also, federal and state rules require stringent testing to demonstrate safety with respect to pollutants.

The organic content of the farmlands in the United States is at a critical low point. Soil tests show much of it down to 20 percent or less of what it once was. These organic-poor soils can't accept or hold the annual rains. The rain runs off in a flood, carrying topsoil with it, causing soil erosion. Then during the dry spells we have water shortages.

Every community in the United States has some means of collecting and processing its human waste. This waste contains the humus, nutrients, minerals and energy derived from our farmlands.

Most wastewater treatment plants around the country are capable of processing human waste into a mass of living and dead decomposing microbes commonly known as biosolids. These can go back to agriculture lands. However, the material must be handled properly, so as not to create a nuisance. Many operators and even regulatory agents do not understand the phenomena of "distant noxious odors." Many times a person can be next to a volume of foul-smelling material on the downwind side, and not detect bad odors. But someone farther downwind may detect offensive and noxious odors, the distance may vary up to miles. The cause is not fully understood. Some scientist suggests it is smell receptor overload and the receptors shut off, but with distance, the molecules are spread apart, allowing the smell receptors to be more sensitive. Another explanation is that exposure to sunlight and oxygen may make odor molecules more noxious.

Anytime there are complaints, especially numerous complaints, there's good reason to suspect that the biosolids may not be safe, may not be handled correctly or are being applied in the wrong location. Perceived or real, these problems greatly hinder the ability to get this valuable product back into the land that badly needs it.

The most acceptable way to handle biosolids is to compost it. In 1994, Dr. Rex Moyer at Trinity University did a six-month study of four different compost products made by Garden-Ville. All were found to be free of harmful pathogens that could affect animals or plants. To our surprise, Dr. Moyer found the compost also contained numerous microbes (18 percent of the isolates) that are capable of rendering poisons into a non-toxic state. And many microbes (28 percent of the isolates) that help to control pest insects and disease. Lawns applied with compost are usually free of insects, such as grubs and chinch bugs and disease, such as brown patch.

Garden-Ville makes compost from San Antonio biosolids and yard trimmings. It is used all over the city on lawns, around trees and in gardens to grow flowers and vegetables. Except for not making enough to meet customer demand, there have been no complaints. After many years of study and record keeping, spreading compost on lawns and farmlands has shown to cut water needs from 30 to 60 percent.

Composted biosolids became our fastest selling compost. Horticulturists, lawn care companies, gardeners and small farmers loved it, but they found it a nuisance to spread on large areas. When moist it would not go through a spreader. When dry it was dusty. Many of these customers suggested that if I could somehow pelletize the fine screened material they would make me rich. At that time I owned an old feed mill that had pelleting equipment. I took some of the fine-screened biosolid compost and ran it through the pelleting machine.

I got a hard, black pellet that even smelled good. I saw dollar signs — I would surely get rich with this product because of the low cost of raw material. I immediately got in touch with the state chemist to make sure the bags were properly labeled, and then started getting bids from bag manufacturing companies.

The trial pelleted material was stored in some old feed bags. After two weeks the pellets began to give off a foul odor. By the fourth week the pellets stunk so bad you couldn't get anywhere near them, the most awful smell I have ever experienced. My dollar signs disappeared in the odor. I contacted chemists, biochemists, college professors and a highly respected research institution, but none of them could give me an explanation. Before it was pelletized it had the pleasant smell of the forest floor in the spring.

A month later, I visisted the owner/operator of a company that pelletized turkey manure. This gentleman never experienced a change in the smell after pelleting. Luckily, the consulting microbiologist was also visiting this pelleting plant. I ran my scenario by this scientist and mentioned that no one has been able to explain my foul odors.

"That's easy," he replied, and then explained, "Biosolids are mostly protein molecules shed from the human body. The higher in the food chain

Biosolids from New York spread on the desert in west Texas. Wherever there was soil, the native grasses came back thick in a little over two years. Deer, antelope and other wildlife moved into the area.

you go the more complex the protein molecule. Humans are at the top of the food chain. The human protein molecule is a long chain molecule, almost like plastic, and very immune to destruction. It takes the decomposing microbes 43 days or longer to break into it and feed on it. When they finally do, they have a food supply supreme." He said the human molecule is a suflinated protein and the only way we can hydrolyze it — make it break up in water — is with heat and pressure at the same time. The pelleting die requires extreme pressure, which generates heat. I had torn the molecule open, it had moisture in it, and it was also hydroscopic, with the sulfur causing most of the odor. He repeated that compost derived from human waste is the elite of plant foods. There are none better. The Asians have maintained soil fertility for 40 centuries by using human waste. In this country, we have worn out the land on our farms in less than two centuries because of our stupid hang-ups. If we were smart, we too would learn to use human waste. We can't continue to ignore this natural resource.

Nature demands that all organic materials be recycled. The carbon cycle must be completed. Composting is Nature's way of recycling. Biosolids are the most abundant and richest soil building plant nutrient we have on this Earth. Composting biosolids can rebuild and maintain our eroded farmland and solve the looming water problems.

Required Reading

Over the years I have read and learned from many good books. A lot of them are now out of print and hard to find; however, there are still many good current publications.

My first inspiration came from Rodale Press's little *Organic Gardening and Farming* magazine. My favorite periodical is *Acres U.S.A.* (P.O. Box 91299, Austin TX 78709), which covers mainline eco-agriculture, featuring the newest and latest that all the sciences have to offer for keeping our soils healthy and productive without the use of toxic chemicals.

There are also two good little periodicals being published in Texas. *Homegrown* by Judy Barrett (P.O. Box 524, Taylor, TX 76574) and *The Home Gardener* by Tom Staples (P.O. Box 404 Springtown, TX 76082). Both of these little publications are excellent and will keep the reader up to date on everything organic for the garden and small farm.

Charles Walters has authored and co-authored numerous helpful books. The Acres U.S.A. bookstore offers the best information about eco-farming available. On the must-read list for every serious gardener and farmer is *Eco-Farm* by Charles Walters. This book explains the true science of natural growing in easy-to-understand language.

The latest additions to my must-read list are publications by J. Howard Garrett. Howard is a graduate landscape architect who has worked as a landscaper, golf course maintenance supervisor, and nursery operator. He is also an avid gardener. Howard was educated the conventional chemical way, but in the 1980s, he began to think that there must be a way to work with Nature without all these poisons. He has since turned organic with a burning desire for knowledge of ways to do things the natural way.

Howard and I have combined our efforts on *The Texas Organic Vegetable Garden* and the *Texas Bug Book*. Both of these books are especially designed for Texas gardeners and provide lots of useful information. Look for them at all garden shops and bookstores.

Books contain the discoveries, experiences and mistakes of those before us. Books and publications are a path to wisdom.

Planting & Growing

Roots

The underground portion of a plant will have an equal or greater spread than the growth above. The total root surface area can be more than 100 times greater than the surface area of the trunk, stems, shoots and leaves combined. The roots' function is to anchor the plant and to gather water and minerals for the leaf surface so energy and food can be manufactured for growth and reproduction.

If given a choice, roots would rather not work alone. They solicit the help of many life forms, especially microbes. To lure these life forms to their surface (rhizosphere), roots give off many products. According to *Soil Microbiology* by Martin Alexander, the roots excrete all of the naturally occurring amino acids plus 49 other important exudates which include: 12 organic acids, 13 carbohydrates, four nucleic acid derivatives, four enzymes, eight growth factors and eight other beneficial compounds.

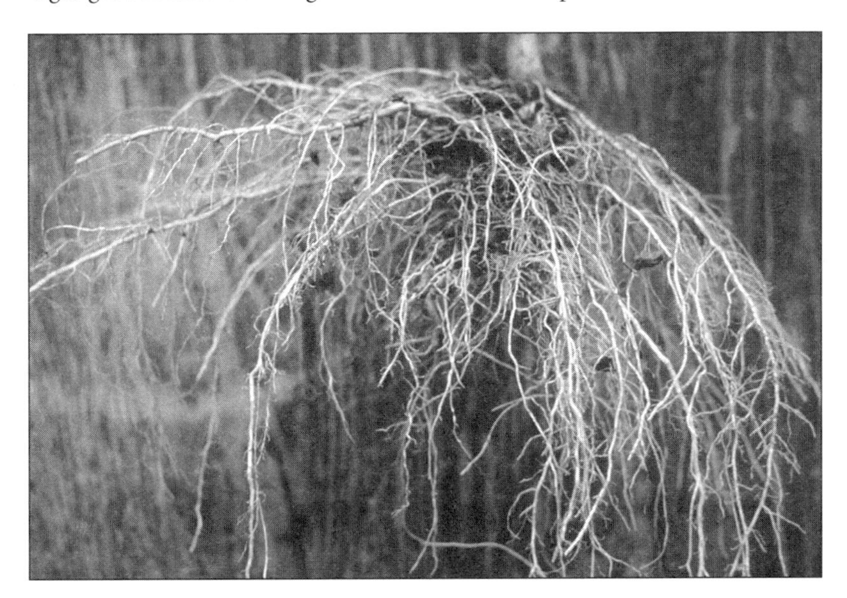

When we pull up a plant, a high percent of the roots stay in the soil — it is almost impossible to measure all the tiny hair roots.

Soil life such as bacteria, fungi, algae, protozoans, earthworms and beneficial nematodes feed on these exudates. To show their appreciation for all these goodies, the soil's life forms help the plants by correcting soil pH, by gathering and processing minerals, and by purging water from the surrounding soil for the plants to use. They also protect the roots from pathogens and harmful nematodes.

There is a whole metroplex of life forms living, dining, reproducing, working, building, moving, policing, fighting, and dying to help the plants that feed them. However, we must do our share to help the plants create these root excrements by placing them in their preferred soil, location, and environment with adequate moisture and nutrients. Then this metroplex of root helpers will build an immune system within the plants to act against diseases and insect pests.

The roots' exudate and the metroplex of beneficial soil creatures are always greatest in organic-rich soils under an organic mulch or sod cover. In organic-poor and exposed soils, the troublesome insects and diseases are always abundant.

This is more proof that nothing can live to itself and survive. By helping each other as Nature teaches, we not only survive, we prosper.

Plants, Carbon Dioxide & Soil Life

Using the sun's energy, plants take carbon out of the carbon dioxide and release the oxygen back to the atmosphere. The carbon is combined with hydrogen and other elements to make carbohydrates (sugars), then, depending on plant species, 60 to 80 percent of this energy goes underground to attract and feed a large biodiversity of microbes including 10,000 species of bacteria and 3,000 species of fungi and other soil life that it takes to keep soil and plants healthy.

The roots of healthy, well-grown plants excrete an amazing amount of things. All of these are used as food and energy by the beneficial soil life that assist plants and animals to grow and be healthy. Here are some of the natural excretions of healthy, organically grown plants:

12 — Organic acids
13 — Carbohydrates
4 — Nucleic Acid Derivatives
4 — Enzymes
8 — Growth Factors
8 — Other beneficial compounds and naturally occurring amino acids.

Bacteria, fungi, algae, protozoans, earthworms and beneficial nematodes rely on these elements to keep the soil alive and healthy.

Pesticides were never needed in either Delphine's greenhouse or the large commercial tomato greenhouse. Both houses were operated organically, creating an abundance of carbon dioxide for the plants. They also had a lower freezing point and more immunity from pests, insects and diseases.

Plant Selection

There are seven rules to follow when growing plants for health and top production:

1. Always use the very best-adapted plants in each environment.
2. Plant in the proper season.
3. Balance the mineral content of the soil.
4. Increase and maintain the organic content of the soil.
5. Do nothing to harm the beneficial soil life.
6. Consider troublesome insects and diseases as symptoms that one of the above five rules has been violated.
7. Have patience. Nature gives birth, but Time controls the cycles.

Of the above seven rules, plant variety is the most important. Mother Nature's plants have adapted to almost every square foot of this planet and can thrive without any care from man. These plants became perfectly adapted through many years of natural selection and survival of the fittest.

Plant breeders usually go for high-breeding. High breds, or hybrids, don't always produce seeds that are true to the parent plant, so other means of propagation must be used for reproduction. I have used hybrids on my organic farm with good success, but it took trial and error before I found the best ones for my location.

Most commercial seed companies sell hybrids and open-pollinated varieties, which are also broadly adapted. Every location, however, has its own set of environmental factors: soil structure, pH, drainage, rainfall, humidity, temperature range, altitude, and so forth. The trick is finding the perfect seed or plant for your particular farm or garden.

I was in a nursery once getting some seeds for the spring garden. I asked the elderly owner, "Which varieties will be best for our location?" He told me that all the seeds in the rack were good, but if I wanted the very best I would have to grow my own on my farm. Then he explained to me the process of natural selection. He said to start with a good open pollinated variety, and each year I should select the best of the first fruit from the very best plants in the garden and use that for next year's seed. If I continued that process year after year and continued to select the best of the best, my

An assortment of plants growing in a small depression on top of Enchanted Rock, which is solid granite.

quality and adaptability would continue to get better each year. This old gentleman practiced what he preached and knew what he was talking about. I found out later that many varieties of trees and other plants had his name on them. Of course, like most gardeners and farmers, I have never found the time to do a lot of this natural selection, although my wife and I have been saving seeds and upgrading a special okra for several years now — and, in fact, it has gotten better and better. Now we have our own corn, tatume squash and peppers.

Planting Dates

The second most important rule for successful gardening is to plant in the proper season. For northern gardeners, this rule may seem odd since there is only one planting season, but here in San Antonio (and much of the south and southwest), there are two planting seasons. We can plant in the spring and the fall, and certain vegetable varieties are adapted best for one or the other season. Plants of the mustard and cabbage families, for example, definitely do best in the fall garden. If they mature as the days get shorter and cooler, they will taste better and be more nutritious. If they are planted in the spring a little late or if the weather warms up very quickly, the plants will bolt, become bitter, and go to seed sooner than they should. You're also almost guaranteed a good crop of harlequin bugs to come eat them up for you under those circumstances.

There are many vegetables adapted for planting both spring and fall in this area — these are varieties that mature in 30-70 days. One such crop is spinach, which can be planted spring or fall as long as the soil temperatures are below 76 F. The seed won't sprout in hot soils, but if you wait until late Fall to plant so that you will harvest on cool days, you will find that the spinach tastes much better than when it is harvested during long, warm days. Summer squash is another plant that matures fast, but it prefers warm soils for germination, so you plant it much earlier in the fall and later in the spring than spinach. All seeds have a preferred soil temperature for sprouting, but the range is usually about 10 degrees in either direction, which gives us some leeway in planting dates. Usually, it is the late spring or early fall freezes that cause problems.

The long-maturing (90-120 days) varieties are planted in the spring only, and usually early as possible. There are other varieties that prefer very warm soil and growing conditions, for example, okra, eggplant, and peppers. If you plant them too early and do get their seed to sprout in the cool spring soil, the plants will probably just sit there and wait until the soil and weather warms up. During that waiting period, the plants are stressed and more susceptible to insects and diseases.

There is a preferred time for every activity on the farm, especially planting.

The varieties of vegetables that mature in 30-70 days are best for fall planting. The long-maturing crops, that need 90-120 days, do best if planted as early in the spring as possible.

The Agricultural Extension Service in our area usually publishes a gardening bulletin that names the best-adapted varieties for spring and fall planting. They also list the best planting dates for each crop. Many seed packages contain planting instructions. Usually they say to plant a certain number of days before or after the last freeze of the spring. The problem is that nobody knows when the last freeze will be. On my farm, there have been years when there were no freezes after January 1, and other years when it freezes as late as April 13.

Selecting a planting date is just one more of the gambles that farmers and gardeners make. A few days can mean the difference between success or failure, and having to re-plant is a big expense on large acreage.

For the gardener, trying to out-guess Nature may be a little frustrating, especially when you guess wrong, but the challenge and gamble just make gardening more fun when you guess right.

Because of the unpredictable weather, some gardeners and even large farmers are fairly successful by letting the moon phases dictate when to plant. If soil conditions permit, we always plant potatoes in the period between the third and seventh day after the full moon in February. Through the years, that's when our best crops were planted.

Even though some scientists still reject the notion of moon-sign planting, moon gardening makes the hobby more fun. There is a good lunar gardening guide on the market, Llewellyn's *Moon Sign Book,* published annually. This book is useful in deciding planting dates, but it doesn't tell you about variety, seasons, soil types, and the many other things you need to know about vegetable growing. Another book helps there. Dr. Sam Cotner of Texas A&M has spent a lifetime studying vegetable growing. His 421 page book, *The Vegetable Book: A Texan's Guide to Gardening,* covers about 47 different crops. Although his recommendations about pest control are usually not organic, the other information in the book is invaluable. If you live in Texas, the book will be very helpful as you decide what to plant and when to plant it.

I once asked Dr. Cotner if he believed in planting by the moon. He said he didn't know of any scientific research proving one way or the other, but that some of the best farmers he knew planted by the moon, and he wasn't going to argue with success.

Maybe, just maybe, moon sign planting can stack the odds in our favor in the when-to-plant gamble!

The Miracle & Patience of Seeds

The old adage "from little acorns mighty oaks grow" is such an astounding statement. The miracle or blueprint of life is in the germ of each seed. That memory bank rivals our most powerful computer chips. The germ is a very small part of the seed. More than 99 percent of a seed is food to get the new plant started while it is developing roots. Seeds also make up a good portion of the food humans and animals eats.

The patience of some seeds makes them still more fascinating. In multiple seed clusters there seems to be a destined time for each separate seed to sprout forth. Some sprout as soon as the moisture and temperature are correct, but some wait until one, two or many seasons later. With some it may be as much as twenty or even a hundred years later that they find conditions perfect for their miraculous emergence.

Several times I have witnessed seeds patiently wait for the perfect combinations of conditions before they would make their transition into the plant world. My first experience was when I planted hubam clover seed in an environment it loves, which was a very poor, alkaline, calcareous clay soil. Its powerful taproot can penetrate deep for moisture and minerals, and the rhizobium bacteria on its roots give it needed nitrogen the soil lacks. Together this would allow it to out-compete all other plants. This clover came up to a perfect stand and grew and grew until it was eight feet tall. A botany professor from a local University brought students to inspect and document this massive clover crop. Then this professor mentioned that I could not grow clover this big and beautiful again for many years. I ask him why. He said he didn't know for sure but that is what the old time farmers always witnessed.

I planted most of my 100-acre farm in this clover. I left it to seed and dry in the field and hired a neighbor to harvest it with his combine. The neighbor did mention that it was the most seed he had ever seen harvested from a clover crop. Clover seed always brings a top price and I made a lot of money, in fact the most I have ever made on this little farm. Needless to say,

There are numerous native plants, small and large, in this photo. They are growing in a very thin layer of soil over limestone rock. They grew and survived because the seeds had the patience to wait for the proper season with ample rainfall before they sprouted.

I returned with scarified clover seed the following fall (scarification allows all the seed to sprout the same season).

My clover seed all came up, but so did millions of other grasses and weeds of every type — some that hadn't been seen in that area for many years. My clover grew, but it had one heck of a struggle with all the competition from the other plants whose seeds had been patiently waiting for the perfect condition the previous clover crop created. The powerful clover tap root and lateral feeder roots loaded with nodules lay there decaying, which stimulated a high microbial count and created many organic acids that finally ate through the protective seed coating to let the germ in all those other plants know that conditions were good and it was time for them to start growing!

Seed-Planting Tips

As a kid on the farm, I learned to compress the soil over the seeds after planting. We did this to make sure there was a good seed-to-soil contact so the seed could absorb moisture from the soil. Moisture moves better through soil that is slightly compressed than it does through a real loose soil.

I remember that the old corn planters we rode back when I was a boy had split wheels with the two halves pressing inward, a one- to two-inch opening in the center directly over where the seed fell. These split pack wheels worked really well if the soil wasn't too moist. If the soil was wet or sticky, the wheel would gum up.

Later, someone devised a flexing rubber pack wheel that mud wouldn't stick to, but it, too, had its drawbacks because sometimes it caused a hard crust directly over the seed. This kind of crust makes it difficult for the seed to push through.

On my first farm, the soil was a sandy loam that easily crusted over. Neither the split-pack wheel nor the flex rubber-covered wheel worked very well. I found a simple way to plant the garden so all the seeds could come up.

For large seeds like beans, corn, and squash, first I'd till up the seed bed, then smooth it out well. Next I'd lay out the seeds exactly where I wanted them, then push them in with my index finger. To make sure they were all at the correct depth, I held my thumb against my index finger at the exact spot I wanted. When my thumb touched the soil, I knew to stop pushing.

When you press a seed into the soil like that, you compress a small column of soil underneath the seed. The soil on top and surrounding the seed is looser than the column right below the seed. The tight soil under the seed is similar to a lamp wick in bringing up moisture to the seed that has a firm soil contact on its underneath side. Although many garden magazine instructions say to firm the soil on top of the seed, this may cause a crust on top. The crust makes it hard for the seeds to get through and also forms a compressed area of soil on top that wicks away the moisture into the air instead of toward the seed.

I got the idea of pushing seeds into the ground from seeing plants sprout in cow tracks during dry seasons. When you press a seed into the ground, a column of soil is pressed together underneath, which makes it into a "wick" to conduct moisture upwards. A layer of loose soil, which is a poor water conductor, remains over the seed and acts as a barrier to stop moisture evaporating.

After pushing a seed into the soil and withdrawing your finger, usually enough soil falls into the hole to cover the seed. If not, you can easily drag in some loose soil over the seed with your little finger in a quick motion before raising your hand to go to the next seed. A seed compressed tight to the soil doesn't need much cover. I learned this while roaming the pastures as a kid. I noticed that seeds always came up best in the cow tracks.

Little seeds, such as carrots or lettuce, can easily be planted too deep. Instead of pushing them into the soil, it's best to prepare the seed bed with a smooth surface, then place the seeds where you want them. Gently press them to the soil with your hand or a board and sprinkle a light covering of soil over them. Instead of soil, I sometimes use vermiculite, clean sand, granite sand, lava sand, or fine screened compost. They all work, but I like compost the best.

When watering any seeds, especially smaller seeds, it is best to use a very fine mist. Large water droplets will settle and pack the very top of the soil into a tight crust, stopping all but the large strong seeds from emerging. Instead of a fine mist, you can also use a drip irrigation system or a leaky (sweat) pipe for watering. This kind of watering works very well and uses less water because of lower evaporation. On our vegetable farm where the area was too large to use misters or leaky pipe, we used aluminum pipe with overhead sprinklers. We planted shallow and then watered a little almost every day to keep the crust soft.

In some fields with heavy clay soils, we planted on the beds and flooded the furrows. This allowed the water to soak the beds without forming a crust on top, but it takes a lot of water and on the high end of the field, the nutrients tend to leach out. Regardless of how you irrigate, a hard rain with big drops can cause the soil to form a crust that small seeds can't push through. I knew one farmer that took advantage of crusting that was caused by sprinklers or rain. He planted his carrots extra thick, and when the soil dried it would crack and the carrots emerged through the cracks with almost perfect spacing.

The Gambler

If you gardeners feel you have problems getting seed to emerge, just think of the big farmers that sometimes have to re-plant large acreage. Sometimes even hundreds of acres have to be replanted with seeds that cost hundreds of dollars per pound. Then even if the seed does come up, the farmers' gambles still aren't over. Insects or disease may attack; pollination may be bad; it may not rain enough or rain excessively during harvest. And finally, who knows what the price will be even if the crop is harvested? You know, the farmer is the only businessman who buys retail and sells wholesale, and someone else usually dictates both prices. Farming is probably the biggest gamble of any business.

Many people consider the urge to gamble a vice, but I sometimes wonder. If the Good Lord hadn't put this vice in human nature, we might still be carrying clubs and living in caves.

Saving Seeds vs. Genetically Engineered Seeds, or, Grandpa Knew Best!

When we bought our first farm, my new bride insisted on having a vegetable garden. For advice I visited with the oldest nurseryman in San Antonio. This old gentleman only had a fourth-grade education, but his knowledge of horticulture was vast. Many plants carried his name. The Texas A&M professors called him when they ran into problems. While looking over his seed rack, I asked the old gentleman if all these varieties were adapted to our area. His answer was "somewhat," then he gave me a sermon: "Son," he said, "if you want something really good for your farm, you have to develop it yourself. You start out with these broadly adapted varieties and save your own seed from the best of the first fruit each year, then eventually you will have plants that are perfectly happy on your farm." Being young with a little know-it-all attitude, I didn't heed his advice. It seemed like too much trouble. Years later I got to see excellent proof of what the old man was talking about.

My family and I finally found the time to visit the farm where Delphine's mother was raised. Two old uncles were still working the place. These old fellows weren't very friendly or talkative; they didn't care for city people, but when they learned we also lived on a farm, they were willing to show me the whole place. These old fellows had a fine collection of antiques. Everything on the farm was old but still in working condition and still being used. The newest piece of farm equipment was an early model Allis Chalmers tractor to replace the draft animals. One old mule was still alive, but he didn't have to work anymore — the tongs of all the horse-drawn equipment were cut short and pulled behind the Allis Chalmers.

It was really interesting to tour this old farm. The old-timers enjoyed showing and telling history. The cornfield was last; it was the surprise of the tour. This was a dryland farm with amply spaced stalks. That was the tallest, best-looking corn I have ever seen. Each stalk had two or three big ears.

Beck's big okra.

These uncles were really proud of their corn. When I finally looked down I couldn't believe what I was seeing. The corn was growing in a solid stand of nut sedge. I ask the closest uncle how could they possibly grow a crop in nut grass this thick? The old uncle's answer was simple and short "that's what keeps the soil rich" he said. That was hard for me to believe but there was no way was I going to argue.

I asked the uncles what variety of corn they planted. They said their Mom was of German descent and their Pop was Polish, and each brought a corn from home. One was bloody butcher red and the other was a yellow dent. They planted them together, producing corn with an equal number of red and yellow kernels on each ear.

They told how their dad always selected the best of the best for next year's seed and they had followed pop's example. They said the selection had gone on for the past 82 years.

I asked for some of that seed. They proudly went into the barn and filled me a sack of their finest. Long beautiful ears, no sign of corn earworm and there were 22 rows of seed on each cob.

I couldn't wait for planting season. Just think what I could do in my composted, irrigated, blackland without nut grass. Planting season finally came; those rows got the best of care, and I wouldn't let anyone take roasting ears from that patch. The stalks were beautiful, green and tall.

Finally harvest time arrived. What a big disappointment! I had shucks and cobs but not a single grain had filled out in the whole patch. I got more seed from the uncles for next season, and another disappointment. I have

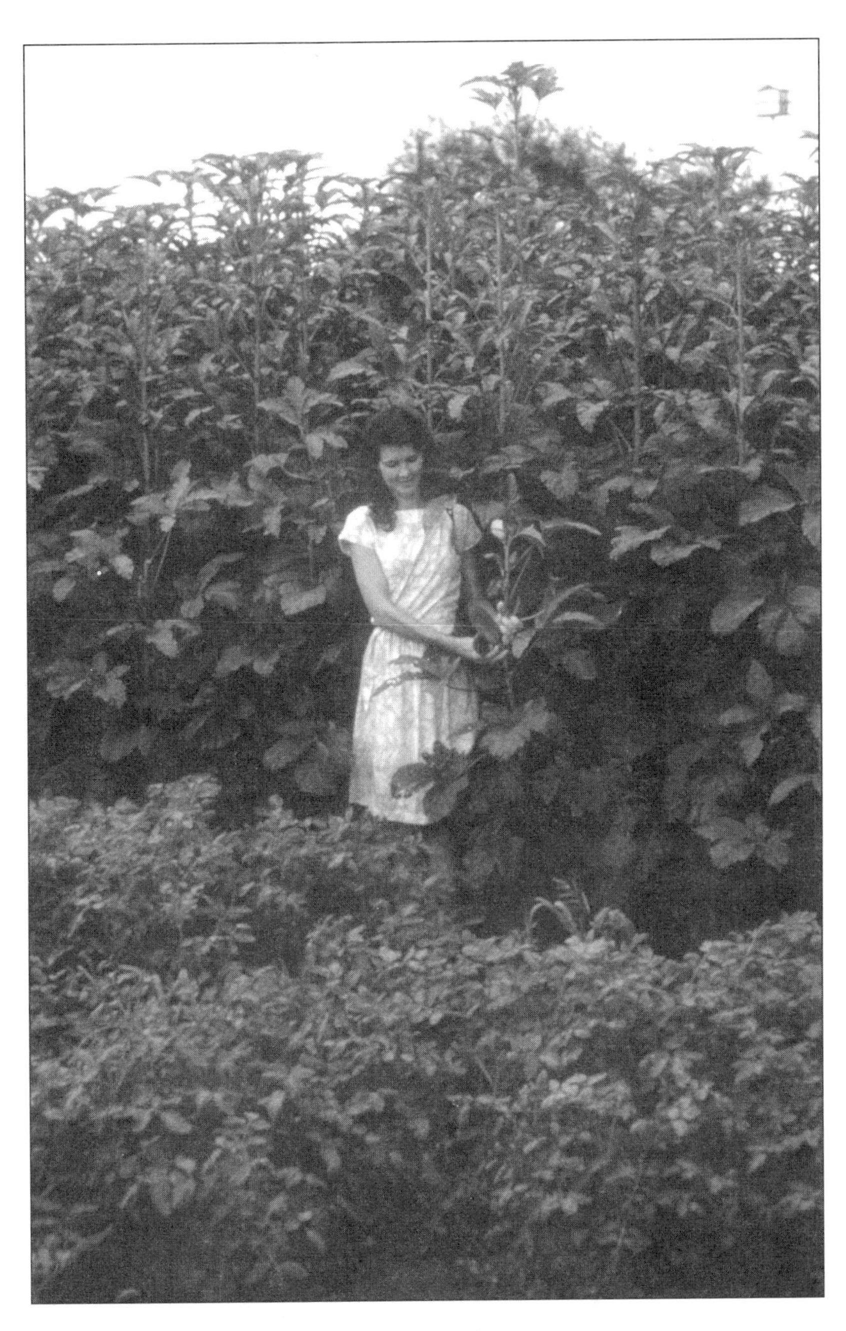

Delphine standing in the Becks' big okra patch.

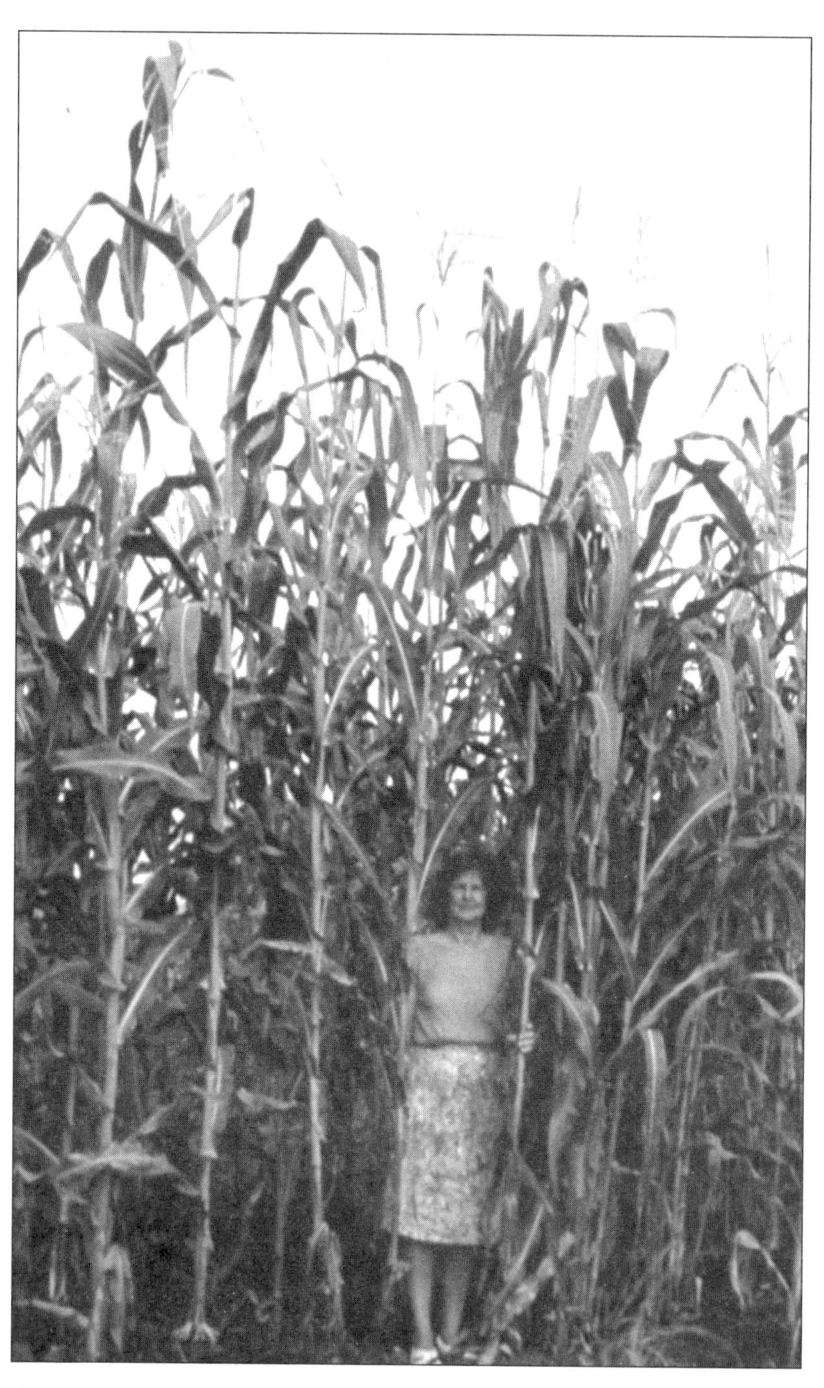

Delphine standing in open pollinated tall corn that is being upgraded through annual selection.

Howard Garrett standing by the same corn earlier in the year.

yet to grow a single grain of that corn. Those many years of selection had developed the perfect specimen for shallow plowing in sandy soil and with no fertilizer. Was the nut grass really helping? Maybe it had some beneficial symbiotic association with the corn.

Years later we visited the Yorktown farm again. By that time, the uncles were up in age and had leased some of their land to my wife's cousins. The cousins had always believed that grandpa's farm must have super rich soil in order to grow the huge open-pollinated corn. They assumed that their excellent hybrid corn would grow to new heights on that old farm. To their surprise, the hybrid, even with fertilizer, did no better there than on any other farm.

The cousins gave the uncles a share of the hybrid corn. Like most old farmers, the uncles had a typical farm — a few old hounds, chickens, ducks, cows and pigs, and of course the corn was used to feed all of them. For the hounds, they ground corn and cooked it with lard. One day they ground the hybrid corn for the dogs, but the dogs wouldn't eat. They took one sniff, then went and lay back down. The next day they still wouldn't eat, and at first they thought the dogs were sick, until one uncle decided that maybe the dogs wanted the old corn. They cooked up a batch of the old corn and the dogs gobbled it up. Boy, were those dogs hungry! They all got a laugh at the dogs, so they decided to see if the hogs would eat the hybrid. Sure enough the hogs wouldn't touch it. Neither would the chickens, nor the ducks unless they were really starved. Animals have instincts that tell them which food is the most nutritious for them to eat. A healthy, well-adapted and well-grown plant will pick all the nutrients from the soil to make it nutritious food animals will prefer. Since humans have lost these instincts, maybe we should pay more attention to the animals.

Since this corn had been grown on the same farm for nearly 90 years, and had been constantly upgraded by choosing seed from the very best ears for the next year's crop, it was perfectly adapted to its particular spot in the world, with nut grass probably helping it somehow.

After so many years of selecting the best from the best on the same farm, that corn would never produce as well anywhere else. On the other hand, in its own place no other corn could beat it.

Wouldn't this be valuable today if all farmers had done their own seed selecting? Farmers could be completely independent of the seed companies. The weed problem could be an asset. The product would be most nutritious. It would be much better than the modern hybrid and genetically engineered seed. And it was all done by Nature without a minute of research or dollar spent. Man can just help speed up the natural process of survival of the fittest.

My wife's family has been saving the seed of a "yard-long bean" for as long as she can remember. They would let the beans get thoroughly dry while hanging on the vine, then on a low-humidity, dry day, they would collect them. They put the beans, dry pod and all, in a jar with a good lid to seal them away from mice and weevils.

When we moved to this farm in the summer of 1968, there was a row of strange okra standing in the garden. We saved the seed and gave some to other gardeners. This okra is a fat and meaty variety which is easy to pick. When it is just right for harvest, it easily snaps off without using a knife. If it won't snap off easily, it will be too old and tough to eat anyway.

I searched all the seed catalogues, but couldn't find a name for this okra. I asked Dr. Sam Cotner, the A&M vegetable specialist, but the okra was unknown to him, too. He sent some to an okra specialist, who said it looked like an okra he'd seen that was not edible, but this okra was delicious.

I asked the lady we bought the farm from how she got that seed. She said a man had given some to her aunt years before, and he'd brought it over from another country. We used this okra as one of the main crops on our farm, and the demand soon outstripped our ability to grow and pick it. Tom Keeter, a noted horticulturist, named it "Beck's Big."

We got a Texas seed company to put it in their catalogue, and that summer my wife and I and the kids harvested a twelve-cubic-yard truck full of seed pods. We hauled the seed to a cousin who had a combine to separate the seeds from the pods. I got a seed cleaner and cleaned and bagged the seed, then loaded my pickup truck full and headed for the seed company. Before much of the seed had been sold, the company went belly up. I never got paid. If anyone wants Beck's Big Okra, you can find it at one of our stores. I always plant some and keep a supply of seeds for friends and customers.

We think we may have finally located the origin of this okra. One day we had several bushels of okra at our packing shed when an elderly gentleman drove up. He introduced himself as a retired colonel interested in buying some organic vegetables. But when he saw the okra, he looked surprised. "Beck, you got that okra! Do you know where that okra came from?" "No," I replied, "tell me."

He said the man who owned the Buckhorn Saloon in San Antonio was touring in Germany many years ago and found that okra. He tried to bring some back, but customs gave him a hard time, so he took the lens off his camera and hid a dozen or so seeds inside. Back home he gave seeds to his friends, and one of those friends lived about three miles from our farm.

Whether or not this okra actually was smuggled from Germany, we can't be sure. All the people involved are long gone, but I have no reason to doubt the old colonel's story.

Okra seed is about the easiest to save. Just let the pod completely dry on the stalk, then cut it off with pruning shears. Store it someplace out of the weather. Mice, weevils, and other critters ignore it, and it keeps almost forever. In fact, I have heard that mixing okra seeds with other seeds while in storage repels weevils and other pests.

Crop Rotation

An old farmer once told me that if I just farmed half of my land and did it right instead of farming fence row to fence row I could produce better crops and make more profit. I didn't really understand what he was talking about until I started truck farming and planted continuous crops of tomatoes and other vegetables. When harvest time came we had a heck of a time getting the vegetables out of the field without driving over lots of good producing plants and causing considerable damage.

The following year I planted all my vegetables in 22-row plots with a 22-row plot of cover crop between it. I continued on with that planting pattern throughout the field. This worked great. The produce wagons or trucks could drive over the cover crop causing no loss of vegetables and we only had to carry the vegetables 11 steps either directions to the vehicle. I used the 22-row spacing because the irrigation sprinklers reached 11 rows each direction. In the cover crop area I planted a legume and a grass such as vetch and elbon rye during the cool season. The vetch was a taprooted plant, which was able to use moisture from deep in the soil and nitrogen from the air, if properly inoculated. The rye is a very strong fibrous-rooted plant that feeds from shallow and takes nitrogen from the soil. The rye is also a good nematode-deterrent plant. The vetch bloomed through the late winter and early spring which invited many beneficial insects such as lady beetles and green lacewings and many other adult beneficials that needed the nectar for energy. The rye would always grow faster than the vetch shading it out so I would mow with a shredder but tall enough not to harm the vetch. This would give the vetch more light and slow the growth of the rye for awhile. Then the vetch would catch up and vine up the rye stalks. Then both grew well and tall enough to help stop the wind from sand blasting the nearby young vegetable plants. In the warm seasons I used a grass cover crop only. We couldn't use legumes because of cotton root rot in the area. Cotton root rot is a problem only when the soil is warm. Hybrid sorghums of any type did well, even corn. Corn stimulates penicillin and trichoderma in the soil to help knock out root rot. Any of these cover crops could have been cut for feed but we weren't in the cattle raising business, and the organic material was more valuable to us as a soil builder.

Planting continuous crops of mixed vegetables posed a problem at harvest time.

Planting 22 rows of cash crop, then 22 or 44 rows of cover crop, solved the harvest problem. We could drive over the cover crops with vehicles to pick up baskets of produce without damaging producing plants.

When planting the cover crop seeds we broadcast with a cyclone seeder over the old vegetable plants, and if we had manure compost or rock minerals to spread in that plot, we would put it out and then drag over it with a disk harrow and blend it all in the top inch or two of soil. Then we irrigated to get the cover started as soon as possible.

As for thickness, the ratio of legume to grass you should plant is up to you. You can base that decision on the cost of the seed. If you want a lot of small plants with a quick cover, you should plant thick. If you want thick stalks and deep roots to break up hardpan, plant thin, which uses less seed per acre.

This rotation from cash crop to cover crop, then back to cash crop, produced excellent results for my vegetable operation. Don't take it as gospel, though — every farm is different!

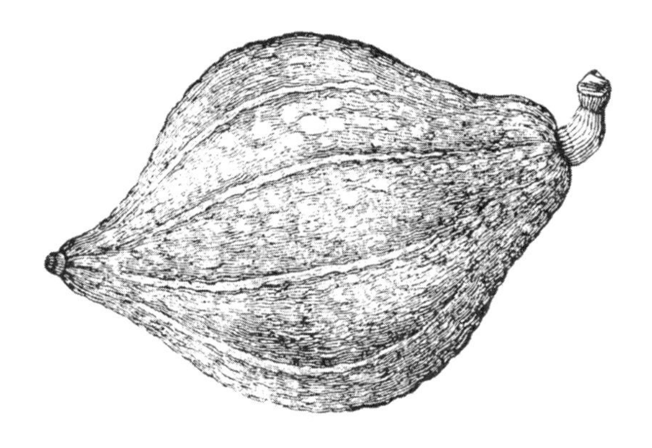

Winter squash keeps better and has a better taste if planting is timed so that the squash matures and is harvested when the weather is cooling off in the fall.

Thinning

Thinning is probably the hardest thing for the beginning gardener to do. It is painful to pull out a plant that you helped bring to life. Even after all these years, I still have thinning withdrawal sometimes. Those little plants look so small and innocent — and healthy! Still, it has to be done. If you planted too thick, all the plants will suffer from lack of sunlight, moisture, nutrients, carbon dioxide in the air, and oxygen at the roots. Plants growing too close together experience poor air circulation, which leads to mold, fungi, diseases, and insect depredations. Fruit will be stunted, small, and poor quality. Furthermore, the roots stay small and very shallow instead of going deep into the earth, so you'll have to water constantly just to keep them alive. There are probably even more problems caused by plants being too close together that I can't think of right now.

Nature, in her wisdom, plants thick like the novice gardener, but she also thins. The reasons Nature plants thick are many. She wants to make sure the soil is protected from erosion and there is ample food supply for all the plant-eating insects and animals. She also wants to make sure that after all of them have eaten, some plants will remain to grow to maturity and supply seed for future plant generations. Those plants that survive insects, disease, and many other hardships are the healthiest and best adapted plants for that particularly environment. As they grow, if there are still too many plants for that location, the strongest and fastest growing will shade out the weaker and smaller, causing them to die and serve as food or a home for the microbes, insects, and small animals. This cycle goes on and on until necessary spacing is acquired for a long, healthy, productive life for each species of plant — whether it is a small flower or a giant tree.

When you understand why Nature plants thick and how she thins through survival of the fittest, you can do the same. Plant more seeds than you need plants in a given space, but you must thin. This gives you an opportunity to remove the smallest and weakest plants and end up with a well-spaced planting of the best in your garden.

Spacing seeds at the distance needed by a mature plant, or only putting one seed in each hill, is worse than over-planting. If a cut worm or bird eats one of your plants, you are left with wasted space, and you are given no opportunity to select the best looking plant. When you thin, don't do it all

View of our farm. Our transplants were put in at proper spacing. The seed planter was set to plant closer than necessary to offset poor germination or other plant fatalities. Later we thinned them to proper spacing.

at the same time. When the seeds first emerge, thin a few of the tiny plants to allow room for growth. A few weeks later, thin again, leaving the biggest and healthiest plants. In some cases, you can thin again a third time if necessary. For example, I plant beet seeds fairly thick since they are sometimes hard to germinate. When they first emerge, I thin them so they'll have room to grow. When they are growing well, I thin again and cook the tender, tasty young greens. This process can happen several times — harvesting baby beets and letting some grow into big hearty roots. At every step, you are helping the crop grow bigger and better.

You may wonder how much to thin. To decide, you must learn about each species' preferences. Some tolerate closeness and may even like crowding. Lawn grass needs to be planted close, but most vegetables need enough space to spread their branches and leaves and collect ample sunlight. Even though some plants will grow in the shade of taller plants and trees, they still need space for deep root growth.

If you can visualize what the plant will look like when it is fully matured, it is easy to figure out the spacing. If not, you will have to rely on the agricultural extension publications, gardening magazines, seed catalogues, and the back of the seed packet. And you have to believe it. Those tiny little tomatoes will really get to be two or three feet in diameter, and those baby pumpkin vines will really sprawl all over the place!

When you pull up these small plants while thinning, they need not be wasted. Many are good to eat as sprouts (health food stores sell bean sprouts), and many others are good in salads or as greens on sandwiches. When you eat the thinnings, you really shorten the time from seed to harvest.

The thinnings that cannot be eaten (squash, cucumber, melons, corn, etc.) can be left lying as a mulch in the garden. They decompose extremely fast and turn into plant food for the plants left standing. So don't feel guilty. Nature thins and thinning isn't wasteful. The remaining plants will show their appreciation with a more bountiful harvest.

The Big Pumpkin

While visiting with Dr. Sam Cotner and Dr. Robert Dewers at the agricultural extension office one day, I was invited to ride with them to visit Tom Keeter, the head horticulturist for the City of San Antonio. I had heard of Keeter in the past, and this visit was definitely no letdown. Lush plants of all types were growing everywhere — in soil, in half-barrels, buckets, and hanging baskets. These ornamentals were beautiful, but they didn't excite me like his garden did. It was about an eighth of an acre filled with almost every vegetable that was in season; there were lima beans on tall trellises, tomatoes in cages, plus green beans, eggplants, and potatoes all beautifully mulched. What really caught my eye was a green pumpkin vine with some bright orange pumpkins bulging out from under the giant leaves. One of them was much larger than the rest. While I was standing there admiring it, Mr. Keeter walked up and asked "How do you like my big pumpkin?"

Dr. Dewers had mentioned to me that Tom's garden was organic, and I guess it was the competitiveness in me that turned my admiration into a little bit of envy. "I can grow one that big!" I answered. Dr. Cotner and Dr. Dewers were standing nearby, and they jokingly said, "Tom, why don't you give Malcolm some of those Big Mac pumpkin seeds and see what he can grow?"

I love a challenge, and since I had popped off in earshot of three of the top agriculture people in the state, this was one challenge I would have to meet.

The following spring I chose a spot in the field close to the house and spread rotting stable bedding about two inches thick on top. Next I chiseled the soil with a sub-soiler in both directions, two feet deep, then irrigated with sprinklers to soak the soil to about that depth. After the soil dried to the correct moisture level (when a compressed hand-full readily breaks apart), I disk harrowed to prepare the seed bed. Then I checked the Llewellyn *Moon Sign Book* for the best planting date, and on that date I raked up beds that were three feet in diameter and two inches high. The beds were twenty feet apart. I sprinkled about one quarter pound of colloidal phosphate on each hill, then pressed ten pumpkin seeds tight to the phosphate-covered soil and covered the seeds and the rest of the hill with one inch of earthworm bedding. I watered each hill with a fine mist until they were well soaked. The mist works because large droplets of water tend to crust the soil, and I didn't want resistance when those seeds were ready to emerge.

After all the seeds were up, I thinned about once a week until the one best plant was left in each hill. After the soil was warm in mid-May, I mulched the whole area with another two inches of compost. Each time the plants needed watering, which wasn't very often, I sprinkled them until they got two inches of water, then foliar fed with fish emulsion and liquid seaweed. I used two tablespoons fish emulsion and one tablespoon seaweed per gallon of water.

The pumpkin vines grew and grew, and after a number of fruit were set, I pinched off all except the biggest and best, leaving one to each plant. The pumpkins were really fun to watch. Each time we went to look at them, they were bigger than before. By mid-July, they were giants and still growing.

The Men's Garden Club had a flower and vegetable show at one of the shopping malls, and our organic garden club also had a show the same weekend. My pumpkins weren't mature yet. It had only been 99 days since planting, and the books say it takes 120 days to grow a pumpkin. I could see that one of my pumpkins was already bigger than Mr. Keeter's, and I couldn't wait to show it off. I cut it from the vine and weighed it. Tom's had weighed 66 pounds, and I beat him by 16 pounds. Had I left it on the vine to mature, I am sure it would have gone over 100 pounds, as most of the rest weighed in the high nineties at maturity.

That season we had other pumpkins and some squash planted in the same field. They were no more than 200 feet away, but they were not composted, and we were in our early years on our new (second) farm, so the soil was not yet built up to high fertility. You could certainly tell the difference between the two pumpkin patches. The un-composted plants were being attacked by squash bugs, aphids, and powdery mildew, while my pet plants were completely untouched. Not a single insect or disease bothered them until after the pumpkins were ripe and the leaf surface was no longer needed.

Some experts still say you can't grow immunity to insects in plants. I wonder if these experts ever grew a really healthy plant? Besides these pest-free pumpkins, I have completely rid pecan trees of heavy infestations of mealy bugs under the bark by mulching heavily with compost. I have reversed gummosis on peach tree trunks with compost — completely cleared the symptoms in one year — and peach trees that looked healthy but had wormy fruit were made to grow fruit without worms as long as I kept them mulched with compost.

Over the years I have seen many times that healthy plants have immunity to diseases and insects. There were times when a seemingly healthy plant was attacked by diseases and insects, but there were other factors involved. Either the plant wasn't adapted to the environment it was being

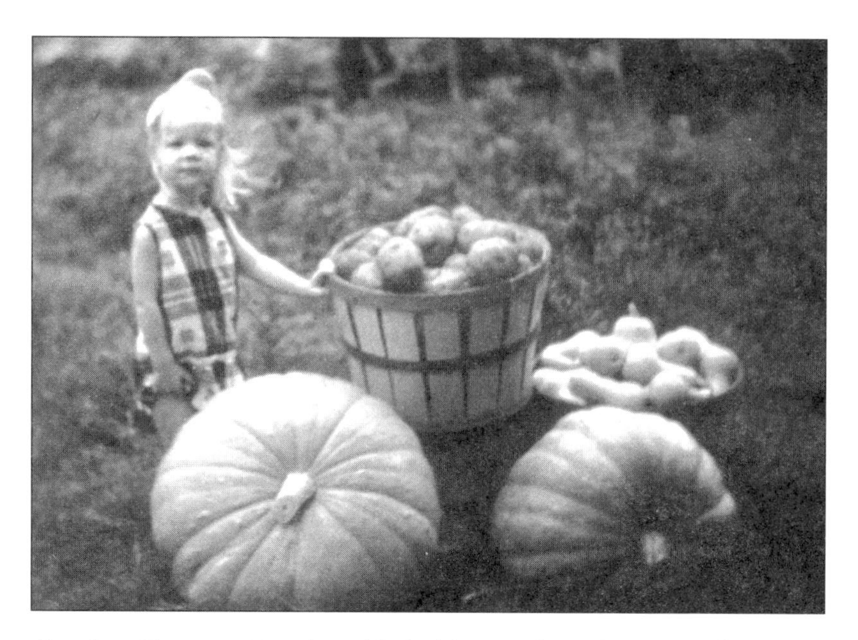

Daughter Kay at age 3 posing with the big pumpkin. The organic farm is the perfect place for children to learn and enjoy Nature, and grow up healthy and happy.

grown in or it was being attacked by a new virus or insect that was imported without its natural checks. Even though the plant being attacked looked healthy, it didn't have the genes that could give it protection from the foreign intruder.

There is always a cause for every problem. Most importantly, don't blame Nature for the things we perceive as problems. Troublesome insects and diseases are Nature's police force with a message telling us that we are in some way bending her rules. Although Nature is very forgiving, if we keep using toxins to kill the police force and ignoring their messages, we get ourselves into more and bigger problems.

Tree Planting Guide

Always plant trees and shrubs that are adapted to your environment. A tree too far out of its natural soil conditions and climate has a poor chance of survival and will attract insects and disease.

The bigger the hole for planting the better, and the more soil loosened the better. The hole must be large enough to accommodate the existing roots without bending or kinking them. It is best to dig the holes ahead of time. This allows the hole to air out, allowing the deep soil gases and carbon dioxide to escape and oxygen to get in. Then beneficial microbial activity will get started and mineral oxidation will occur. The subsoil becomes naturally fertile, allowing better root growth.

Dig a square hole; a round hole tends to push the roots in a circular direction. Place the subsoil (that below six inches) aside, and refill the hole with topsoil from the immediate area. If there is no topsoil available in the immediate area, then use a good topsoil from as nearby as possible, or use a composted soil such as Garden-Ville makes. When backfilling with a really good mixed soil, layer in one-quarter to one-third of the subsoil, no matter how poor it is. You need to introduce the roots to the soil they will eventually have to grow in, otherwise the roots may stay in the hole and mass up as if they were growing in a pot.

Do not plant a tree any deeper than it originally grew. You can look and see where the root turns into bark. Keep the tree at that level. If you anticipate that the soil will settle, you may even plant a little higher because the tree will settle with the soil. The root will form bark, but the bark will not become root. Planting too deep can cause the tree to smother and eventually die.

Do not put fertilizer in the planting hole. It is a good idea, however, to put a handful of natural phosphate (colloidal clay) right below the roots. A small amount of vitamin B_1 is OK, and some people use a few drops of a product called SuperThrive in a drench. A small amount of compost is good, but do not overdo it; mix in about 5 percent compost. Do not use raw organic matter in the hole, especially deep, since it gives off carbon dioxide. The roots also give off carbon dioxide and take on oxygen. Too much carbon dioxide in the hole crowds out the oxygen that the roots must have for growth.

Proper planting determines the health and longevity of any transplanted tree.

When backfilling, use plenty of water and work the soil a little to get out any air pockets and to get better root-to-soil contact. After the hole is completely filled and the tree is at the proper depth, then mulch the tree first with a layer of compost and then a layer of decorative mulch if desired.

Don't pile the mulch against the trunk. Keep it level with the ground. For the first few years keep the lawn grasses away from the tree root zone. Grass competes for the moisture and fertilizer you apply, and it will smother the roots by using up all the available oxygen.

Mulching with compost is the closest thing to a native forest environment, and I have used mulching as the cure-all for most tree problems.

Natural Organic Lawn Care

A deep topsoil of 12 inches or more grows the best lawn (especially for St. Augustine-type grasses in San Antonio-type soil), but a soil of this depth is not always possible. Yet by adding topsoil each year, you soon build it to an undesirable height above walkways, driveways, and the house foundation. A healthy lawn, however, can be maintained in shallower soils if mowed, fertilized, and watered properly.

Mowing

Mow the lawn tall (three inches is ideal), especially in shaded areas because lawn grass needs as much leaf surface as possible to collect the sunlight. Mow often, cutting a little off at a time. Cutting off more than one-third of the blade will shock the lawn because you reduce the food manufacturing surface too much. When you mow often, the clippings will be small and will filter through the soil surface a little at a time. The clippings will then decompose and recycle back into plant food. Thatch will not build up and the lawn will require less water and fertilizer.

Fertilizing

One-half inch of compost applied in the fall and watered in well will do more to keep a lawn healthy than the best chemical program. Even if you feel fungicides and chemical fertilizers are necessary in your situation, the addition of compost will make the chemical fertilizers much more effective and longer lasting. If a fungicide is used, apply compost a few days later. The compost will replace and activate the beneficial soil microorganisms that are killed by the fungicide. If a chemical fertilizer is used, apply it on top of a one-half-inch layer of compost. The compost buffers the release and causes the fertilizer to feed a little slower, preventing quick, weak, disease-prone succulent growth.

Compost acts as a chelating agent, preventing micronutrients, especially zinc and iron, from locking up in our alkaline soils. It has the ability to hold all the fertilizer nutrients in place longer, feeding or releasing them slowly as the lawn needs them, preventing leaching, and making the fertilizer more efficient. Compost can be applied anytime as long as the grass is not smothered during the growing season, and it needs to be watered in immediately after spreading. A good composting program will make chemical fertilizers and fungicides unnecessary in no time at all.

Watering

Always water in the early morning before the day gets hot. Sprinkling in the heat of the day can cause up to a 40 percent loss to evaporation, and if certain salts are present, they can cause burning of the grass blades.

The amount of water needed, and how often the lawn needs watering, depends on the depth of the soil the lawn is grown in. Lawns with really deep top soil can be watered less often, as seldom as once every two weeks if two to three inches of water is applied each time. However, most lawns do not have the luxury of a good deep soil and will require watering more often, but with less quantity. Each lawn owner, through trial and error, can determine what is best for the soil condition of that particular lawn.

A good rule to follow is that deep watering less often is better than shallow watering more often.

Fungus in the Lawn

If you have a fungus in the lawn, such as brown patch, there is a new, simple, organic discovery that cures it almost instantly — cornmeal. Cornmeal from a feed store is best, from the grocery store is OK. Sprinkle it over the affected area until you start to see the soil turn yellow, then water it in. It works beautifully. The corn grows a good microbe called Trichoderma that destroys the bad fungi. As a bonus it feeds a few birds and adds a little organic fertilizer to your lawn. Cornmeal can be used around all flowers, bedding plants, in a greenhouse, or anywhere a fungus may be a problem. People have even cured toenail fungus with cornmeal.

Weeds in the Lawn

Weeds are symptoms of weak, poor lawn growth. Weeds are pioneer plants; they can tolerate bad soil conditions and thrive. As they grow, they bring the soil to better condition by breaking up the hardpan with their strong roots. These roots grow to a great depth, collecting and assimilating minerals that the grass roots could not reach. When the weeds are mowed down and die, these minerals and organic matter are deposited in the root zone of the lawn grass. Weeds, especially the nitrogen-fixing clovers, can do a great deal toward correcting poor soil conditions.

Clover is a legume. Its roots have nodules containing bacteria that collect nitrogen from the air. Clover is an annual. It dies out each summer, leaving a deep-reaching root to decay into nitrogen-rich humus for the lawn grass to feed on the next season. The tunnel left from the decaying clover root also allows rain and irrigation water to quickly soak into the soil instead of running off. These tunnels allow oxygen to get into the soil and

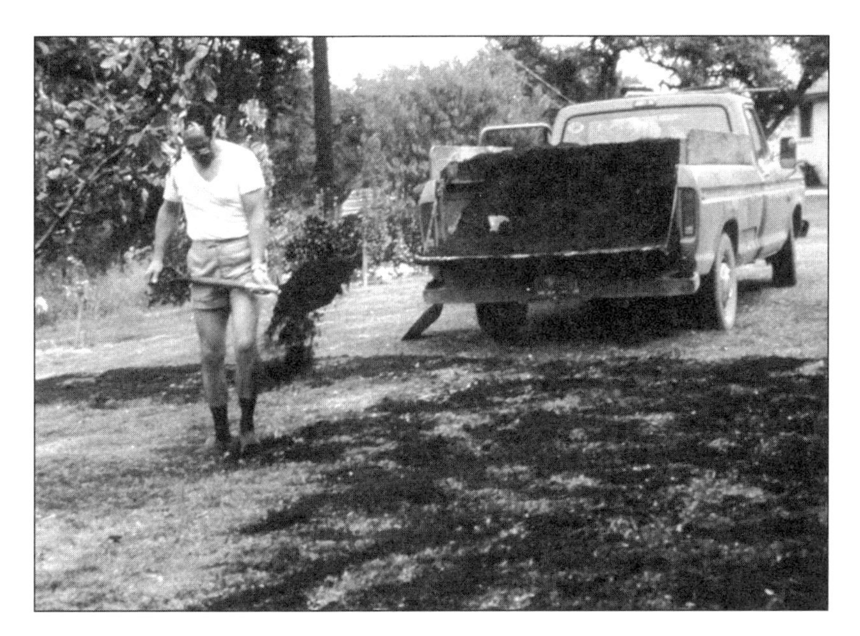

Spreading compost on the lawn.

soil gases to escape. The grass roots eventually follow these tunnels down and it too becomes deeply rooted.

For an inexpensive soil-building, aerating, fertilizing program, I even suggest planting clover in a poor lawn. You could buy a quicker lawn-building program, but it would not be as good as what clover will give you for free — all it costs is patience. So, if you don't mind the appearance, don't herbicide the weeds, especially the clover. When you kill weeds, you are only treating symptoms and ignoring the cause of a poor lawn — usually poor soil conditions.

Follow good watering and mowing practices, ignore the weeds, and sooner or later they will build the soil up to a condition where the lawn becomes so healthy it crowds out the weeds.

Mulching the Lawn

Nature has forever been mulching the earth with dead grass and leaves, fallen limbs and trees, even dead animals and insects. As this expired life lay on the surface of the soil, it kept the soil moist and at a favorable temperature. When these dead things decomposed, they built the soil to higher fertility than before.

Mulching is therefore the most natural and beneficial of all gardening practices. The rewards are many and are still being discovered.

We have learned to copy nature by mulching our landscape plants and gardens, but few people mulch the lawn, which could benefit just as well. Naturally, you wouldn't use bark or wood chips to mulch your grass, but letting clippings lay and even shredding up leaves from the surrounding trees into the lawn are two good ways to mulch.

If the lawn is in poor health and quicker results are desired, compost works wonders as a mulch material. One cubic yard spread over 600-1,000 square feet is the best rate. Wheelbarrows full of compost dumped around the lawn, evenly spaced and then spread with a "comealong," work best. The comealong is a long-handed tool that looks like a rake without any teeth. It is used to smooth concrete but works great for smoothing compost into grassy lawns.

After the compost is spread, it should immediately be watered well into the thatch to prevent nutrients from leaching into the air and compost from smothering the grass. When you water the compost in well, the nutrients go directly into the soil and are available to the plant's roots. What remains on top serves as a light blanket to maintain a balanced temperature and capture rainwater when it falls.

Compost can be applied at any time, but the best time is after cool weather has slowed or stopped the grass from growing. Think of mulching as putting a blanket over the roots for winter protection.

Over the years we have delivered compost to thousands of lawns, to homes, to big institutions with lawns covering many acres, and to numerous sports fields. In fact, the first two high school football fields that were composted were the site of State Champion Class 5A games. A soccer coach that had his soccer field composted reported that, for the first time ever, he

Buffalo grass is considered very water-conservative but usually not thick enough to crowd out weeds. This is a buffalo grass lawn divided by a sidewalk. The dark green side had a half-inch of compost spread on it in November, and the photo was taken end of July. Neither side was watered that year.

has not had a single knee injury or a shin-splint. He attributes this lack of accidents to the healthy, soft, thick turf.

Not all composted sports turfs have resulted in championships, but all are reporting needing less fertilizer, pesticides, and herbicides as the thick turf grass chokes out weeds. All compost users report they need to water less often. From 30 to 50 percent less water is needed to maintain the turf.

Mulching the lawn with compost in the fall is the closest thing to a cure-all there is. Although it is some work to spread the compost, I know of no one who was ever disappointed with the results.

The Effect of Soil Cover on Soil Temperature

A study of soil temperature under various covers was conducted at Garden-Ville from 1991 to 2003. Soil temperatures were taken at various locations to determine the variation of temperature as a result of various soil covers. Temperatures were also taken of soil that had no cover (soil in full sun), soil under a grass cover (soil under turf), soil under trees and soil under a mulch.

Soil temperature was taken at 9 a.m. once a week at the same location with a Tel-TRU thermometer at the depth of four inches throughout the test.

The trees involved were deciduous. The turf was a home lawn. The location in full sun was plowed field. The mulch was three to four inches deep, depending on the decomposition of the mulch before it was replenished. Mulch products of leaves, shredded tree branches, or pecan hulls were used depending on the availability of the materials.

Soil in Full Sun

The soil in full sun is directly affected by atmospheric conditions. It rises during the day and cools again as the sun goes down in the evening. It is also affected by a sudden rain, cloud cover and soil moisture or the passing of a cool front. The soil temperature reached a low of 36 F on February 5, 1996, and a high temperature of 96 F on July 27, 1996.

Soil under Mulch

Soil under an organic mulch is warmer than soil in full sun during the winter. In the spring, in March or April, the soil under the mulch and the soil in full sun equalize. At this time the soil under mulch becomes cooler than the soil in full sun and remains cooler during the summer. In the fall, usually in November, the soil temperatures under mulch and in full sun equalize again. The soil under mulch then remains warmer than the soil in full sun in the winter.

In the afternoon when ambient temperature was 104 F, bare soil ¾ inches deep was at 120 F.

Under four inches of mulch, the soil was only 85 F. Most beneficial soil life prefers 80 to 85 F. A mulch can help maintain proper soil temperature.

The greatest effect of a mulch cover is the insulation of the soil. There is little fluctuation of temperature under mulch throughout a season and from morning to evening. There is little change from a sudden rain or the passing of a cool front.

The highest temperature recorded under mulch was 80 F; the lowest temperature was 43 F. On July 27, 1996, the soil temperature in full sun was 80 F in the morning. It rose to 96 F by 3 p.m. that afternoon. This is an increase of 17 degrees during the day. The temperature under mulch on the same day was 79 F in the morning and remained 79 F at the 3 p.m. reading.

Stabilizing the temperature with an organic mulch and insulating it against atmospheric fluctuation allows plant roots to continue to function throughout the summer and winter. In addition, soil moisture remains at a more constant level.

Soil Temperature under Deciduous Trees

The soil under deciduous trees was the coolest soils in the study. The tree canopy protects the soil in the summer and keeps it from becoming too hot. Since the trees are deciduous, the canopy has little effect on soil temperature during the winter months.

The soil temperature increases during the day proportionately with the ambient temperature, however, the fluctuation is not nearly as great as soil in full sun. The highest temperature taken under trees was 78 F. On July 27, 1996, when the soil was highest in full sun, under the trees the temperature was 70 F in the morning and 74 F in the afternoon. This is an increase of only four degrees compared with the increase of 17 degrees in full sun.

Soil under Turf

A turf cover modified the soil temperature only slightly compared to a mulch or tree cover. The greatest effect of a grass cover occurs in the summer. The soil temperature increases during the day proportionately with the ambient temperature. The grass offers less protection than the trees, but much more than the soil in full sun. On July 27, 1996, the soil temperature under the turf was 71 F in the morning and 80 F in the afternoon, an increase of nine degrees. The turf had little effect on soil temperature during the winter months.

From our study we can see that bare soil is the most susceptible to temperature variations. Mulch keeps the soil warm in the winter, cool in the summer, and keeps the temperature relatively constant throughout the seasons and throughout the day. Mulch conserves moisture and allows roots to continue to function with little interference from atmospheric conditions. Trees cool the earth by shading it in summer, and a grass cover assists in moderating soil temperature during the summer.

W.L. Schumann, horticulture consultant at Garden-Ville, conducted this study and reported its results.

Sterility of Potting Mixes

You have probably heard that potting mixes should be sterilized to avoid losing a large number of seedlings to a fungus that causes damping-off. One of the reasons people give for turning away from compost, sand, and other local materials in favor of peat moss, vermiculite, perlite, and rock wool is that those products are sterile. In fact, peat is rarely sterile. It is even possible for vermiculite, perlite, and rock wool — which emerge from sterile furnaces — to be contaminated later. When Penn State University tested 50 samples of potting mix sealed in plastic bags and advertised as sterile, they found that all of them had disease spores.

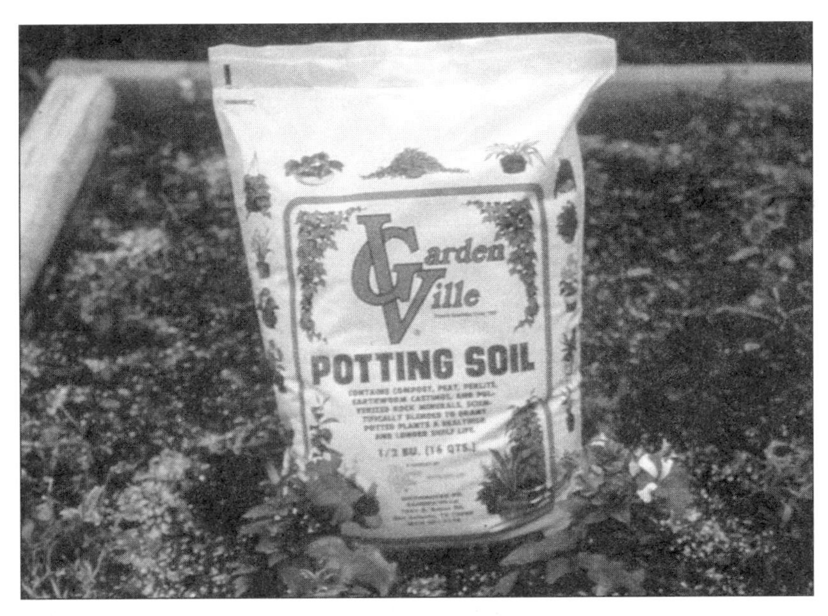

A good potting soil should contain beneficial live microbes that are found in worm castings and well-cured compost. Beneficial microbes contribute to root health and keep harmful pathogens in check.

In fact, potting mixes should not be sterile. A sterile mix is a biological vacuum waiting to be filled. Whichever organism finds it first takes over. If the first-comer is a disease, then problems can be expected.

Rather than heat a mix to 212 F to sterilize it, use a lower temperature that kills disease but leaves the beneficial soil bacteria and fungi alive. The damping-off fungus dies at 125 F, and many other diseases cannot stand temperatures over 140 F. Tests have shown that a mix heated to 140 F for half an hour can be reinfected with damping-off fungus and still be safe for seedlings. Evidently the disease is kept in check by beneficial microorganisms. Those fungi that do survive the 140-degree heating process may occasionally produce mushrooms in a potted plant mix, but aside from being unsightly, they do no harm.

There are many types of fungi, bacteria, algae, and other microorganisms that live in soil, helping to make it fertile. Since they form the bridge between inert minerals and plant and animal life, life on this planet as we know it could not survive if they were all suddenly to die.

The microscopic soil life in Garden-Ville Compost, Potting Soil, and other composted soils is stabilized through the heat of its own composting action. After the soil is mixed, the temperatures hold for weeks at a time at 140 F to 160 F, assuring the survival of all beneficial soil life and the destruction of all damping-off fungi and other harmful organisms. This process is called pasteurization.

The Organic Greenhouse

While attending a greenhouse conference at Texas A&M, I became interested in greenhouse growing and visited many growers to learn techniques. In my travels, I noticed that none were as successful as Rosco, my co-worker, who allowed me to experiment in his greenhouse with cedar flake mulch. After studying his operation, it appeared to me that he was breaking all the rules. He didn't use cooling pads or heaters with fans. For cooling, he opened up north and south walls, and for heat he burned used crankcase oil from railroad locomotives.

He needed no insecticide or fungicide. If a few plants got leaf mold on the lower leaves, he just pruned them off. For fertilizers he tilled in chicken manure from a nearby poultry farm, and he found some fermenting fish emulsion that a fertilizer company threw into the local dump. He added the

This disease- and insect-free greenhouse is easy and fun to maintain.

fish emulsion to irrigation water before it was pumped to the greenhouse. Neither the fish emulsion nor chicken manure was measured precisely. Rosco applied it by feel, from past years of growing experience. Rosco didn't realize it at the time, but since he stopped using Vapam to sterilize the soil, his tomatoes qualified as organically grown. He made a bumper crop each year with very few culls. At least he did until a tornado destroyed his greenhouse.

In 1972, my wife and I built a small 24' x 36' greenhouse mainly to grow our vegetable transplants for the farm. She always managed to find room for an assortment of hanging baskets and other tropical plants she collected. That greenhouse is now more than 30 years old. Everything we grow is in pots or some container; the floor is covered with four inches of cedar flakes to walk on and support the large growing containers. The fertilizer we use is fish emulsion and liquified seaweed. We don't have cooling fans or wet walls; we simply open the doors and gable vents for air circulation and cooling. We have grown thousands and thousands of vegetable transplants and many other types of plants and to this day have never had a troublesome insect or disease of any kind in our greenhouse. Besides containing balanced nutrients for the plants, the fish emulsion also seems to have an insect-repelling effect, especially when sprayed on the leaves as a foliar feed. It leaves a slightly oily deposit that the insects don't like. Possibly the cedar aroma also has an insect-repelling effect, much as a cedar closet repels moths. I believe the plants' immunity to insects and diesease in these greenhouses was because of the abundance of carbon dioxide being released from the decay of the organic floor and fertilizers. Our only problem has been freezing. Twice we ran out of propane during freezing weather.

Why Weeds Grow

After a long winter, when spring finally arrives, gardeners and farmers just can't wait to get out and start planting. However, they soon discover plants sprouting from seeds they didn't plant. These plants, like greedy strangers, soon become unwelcome, and the dictionary calls these unwelcome plants "weeds." Like troublesome insects, weeds take some of the enjoyment out of gardening.

You can read through the gardening magazines and farm journals and find much written about weeds, but little of it is praise. You are told how to prevent, outwit, and even poison them. Have you ever read anything good about weeds?

Weeds are Nature's greatest and most widely dispersed group of plants. Man has often condemned weeds and considered them his enemy. Mention weeds and most people think in terms of control. They rarely think of why weeds grow.

Have you ever wondered why weeds seem to grow everywhere? Or have you ever thought of how desolate and bare the earth would be if the only plants growing were those we planted?

I also fought weeds with much dislike, until one day I asked the above questions. After much thought and study, I discovered some obvious, but usually ignored facts. I found that weeds weren't the enemy I accused them of being.

The weeds aren't all bad, and I feel they deserve at least a fair amount of recognition in the plant society. Weeds are here for a purpose and they have a job to do. They are here to insure that the soil of our planet always has the protection of a green blanket, and little does man realize the importance of this cover. Our fertile soil, man's greatest natural resource, which took Nature centuries to build, would erode away without the protection of a plant cover.

The profusely growing weeds are part of the Creator's plan because man, with some of his bad cultural practices, would lose much of his valuable top soil if the weeds didn't move in to help prevent it. Weeds take no chances; they soon invade and protect any soil left bare.

If it weren't for weeds, mostly unwanted weeds, the topsoil of many farms would have eroded away years ago, gone from our farms forever, gone to muddy our rivers and fill our lakes and eventually end up in the ocean. Weeds are said to rob our crops of moisture, sunlight, and nutrients, but they shouldn't be unjustly accused. The weeds don't rob, they only borrow, as eventually it all returns to the soil for future crop use.

Weeds are not given the protection man gives his domestic crops from insects, disease, and other adverse growing conditions. This forces weeds, or wild plants, to maintain their hardiness. Rarely do you find weeds destroyed by insects or diseases.

Some weeds are pioneer plants, able to grow in soil unsuited for edible or domesticated plants. As the pioneer plants grow and decay, the soil is improved. Nature gave these plants a means of protection, such as a bitter taste, thorns, or even made them poisonous so they wouldn't be eaten by animals. This is so they could continue the soil-making and building processes until finally good soil is made. Then the edible plants can move in and take over.

Weeds are indicators of certain soil deficiencies. For example, scientists have found that wild daisies grow in lawns that are deficient in lime. The daisies somehow collect or manufacture and store lime in their tissue. When the daisies die, the lime is deposited in the topsoil. This continues until the lime becomes sufficient for the lawn; then the wild daisies disappear.

Daisies are rarely found growing around the area in which I live because the soil, having been made from limestone rock, is already rich in lime. Many of the wild plants tell us other conditions of our soil. Some grow only where the soil is waterlogged; some grow in soil that is acid, and others only in alkaline soil.

There are times when weeds are even good companion plants. Some have insect repelling abilities, while others with deep roots help surface feeding plants growing next to them to obtain moisture during dry spells through capillary attraction. Water moves up the outside of weed roots from the deep moist soil toward the surface, and shallow rooted plants make use of this moisture.

Properly controlled or spaced weeds also give a certain amount of beneficial shade and humidity. When the weeds transpire, the air becomes more moist and there is less moisture loss from domestic plants.

Weeds are easily grown and make an excellent cover crop. The successive growth and decay of weeds lays down an absorbent mat on the soil which prevents erosion from rain runoff and wind. This absorbent mat of growing and decaying weeds traps the rain water and causes it to soak into the soil for future needs. The water soaking into the soil keeps the springs flowing, which feed our rivers, keeping them crystal clear and running at an even rate instead of flooding after each rain. This insoak also feeds the wells from which many people get their water supply.

If it wasn't for the weeds in this over-grazed pasture (opposite the tall grass pasture) the soil here would have eventually eroded away.

Because the decaying weeds hold the rain on the soil and let it soak in, and the growing weeds take up and store soluble plant foods in their tissue, the wasteful leaching of phosphate, nitrate, and other minerals is prevented. This helps prevent the pollution of our water with an excess of these nutrients.

Weeds are a vital link in the soil fertility and food chain. Farmers should realize the value of weeds toward soil building and conservation and take full advantage of them.

When vigorous weeds become too numerous in the fields and gardens, however, controlling them does become necessary. Not realizing the dangers of spraying chemicals into the environment, many farmers and gardeners use powerful herbicides to destroy weeds. Some of the herbicides are hormones so powerful that one ounce distributed over 35 acres of cotton will seriously injure the entire crop. Some herbicides persist in the soil for years, and they upset or unbalance the necessary harmony of the soil organisms.

There are safe and non-polluting weed control methods available. Mulching with organic materials smothers weeds while also conserving moisture and helping control soil temperature. The old reliable method of hand weeding, hoeing, and timely cultivation with adapted equipment is still the safest, most widely used, and most effective method.

The most important thing in weed control is to stay ahead of them, especially if permanent control is desired. The weeds must not be allowed to re-seed. In a fertile soil, rich in humus and beneficial soil organisms, weeds are not such a problem because the rich soil will compost and digest some of the weed seeds, preventing them from sprouting. The result is that weeds don't become too numerous where they aren't really needed.

Are you beginning to see that weeds are not just an accident, but were planned and have a purpose?

Besides protecting the soil, weeds and wild plants perform still other services for man. Plants are the bridge of life between the mineral kingdom and animal kingdom. Plants alone have the ability or power to use the energy from the sun to convert the elements of the earth into food for man and animal. The plants are the bridge between the soil and you because all the food that nourishes your body, sustains your life, and makes you grow comes directly or indirectly from plant life.

The delicious vegetables we eat today were nothing more than weeds centuries ago before people started cultivating them. Even today a lot of the plants we call weeds are cherished by many people as delicacies.

For centuries, certain weeds have been valued for their therapeutic powers and medicinal value. They are no longer called weeds but are given the respectful name of herbs. If you search through the folklore medicine journals you can uncover a natural herb remedy for almost every ailment, and from these much of our modern medicine has advanced. Aspirin and many of the other pain relievers doctors use originated from plants. Penicillin, which is a drug of nearly miraculous effectiveness against a number of dreaded diseases, is obtained from a primitive plant of the fungi group.

Plants have the power to convert man and animal waste products back into useful materials. The carbon dioxide we exhale while breathing is converted back to life-sustaining oxygen and a food element — carbohydrates. The pollutants from automobiles and factories are filtered from the air by plants. Without these services, we would soon suffocate and starve.

The algae and fungi that feed on garbage, manure, and dead plants and animals, cause your compost pile to transform waste into valuable fertilizer. These plants are very small or microscopic but serve a vital link in the continuing life-cycle of birth, growth, death, decay, and rebirth.

Wild plants also furnish fiber for clothing, building material for our homes, and make homes for most of our wildlife.

The fuel we use to warm our homes and run our automobiles is energy from the sun's rays captured and stored by plant life many years ago. Each plant, be it domestic or weed, is still today operating as a perfectly efficient factory, capturing the sun's rays to be used now or stored for future use. As they capture and convert the sun's energy, plants prevent the air and the earth's surface from being overheated by the penetrating sun's rays. You might say that plants are air conditioners — they keep us comfortable.

Because of plants, especially wild plants, Nature is never boring, but always beautiful and fascinating. When plants bloom, they add sweet fragrances to Nature. They attract and feed the fluttering butterflies, and the bees make honey from the wildflowers. The grasses and flowering weeds beautify our roadways. They hide the trash and litter thoughtlessly thrown there, as well as the bare rock and dirt.

We could probably go on and on finding good things to say about weeds. If you are wondering, I still hoe, pull, and cultivate to control weeds when necessary, but it's with a different frame of mind. Mainly, I have learned to use weeds to my advantage. Here we might add that weeds help a gardener get plenty of exercise between planting time and harvest.

Even though few people love them and they are always being destroyed, weeds are very generous. They keep coming back, as their seeds are usually impatiently waiting in the soil to sprout forth. Weeds take no chances — they produce many seeds to insure the survival of their kind so there will always be plants to clothe and protect the earth.

Organic Weed Control

At one time I had a vineyard; most of the vines were grafted onto a prolific rootstock. The vines kept sprouting under the grafts. It was a constant chore to keep the suckers pruned off. I knew there had to be a better, quicker way! I tried the strongest vinegar. It did little good so I got a 98 percent acetic acid and diluted it with water to about 20 percent acid. Bingo, it worked great. I noticed that wherever it drifted onto weeds under the vines, the weeds were burned.

After a few days of experimenting it turned out to be the perfect product. It would only kill green growth. It had absolutely no effect on one-year-old wood. You could kill weeds and grass that had grown in between the stems of multi-trunk plants such as rose bushes. The only thing it killed were green leaves.

Vines enjoying the benefits of acetic acid used as a sucker and weed control.

When using it on grass or weeds, you must spray while they are still young and still tender. It doesn't work as well on old tough weeds and perennials. It has little effect on weeds and grass that have rhizomes and nut grass, but if you keep using it on them, they can be weakened and eventually will die.

The only problem I have found with acetic acid is that it is very volatile. Always spray with the wind to your back. I have found that adding a couple ounces of molasses or orange oil to each gallon helps to lessen the volatility and even kills the weeds a little faster.

This mix is completely non-toxic to soil life and even beneficial, especially in alkaline soils.

Corn Gluten: Organic Fertilizer that Controls Weeds

Gluten meal is a golden yellow powder that is extracted from corn. Because of its high protein content, it is an excellent product to increase the value of dog, poultry, fish and cattle feed. Corn gluten meal is 60 percent protein, which converts to almost 10 percent nitrogen by weight, which makes it a very good plant food as well.

Corn gluten meal also contains an organic compound that inhibits the root formation of seeds after they sprout. The result is that if it is applied on annual grass and leafy plant seeds, they will never grow into nuisance plants. With proper timing of application, corn gluten meal can serve as a fertilizer and weed control — a totally organic "weed and feed!"

To use the meal to control weeds, apply 20 pounds per 1,000 square feet one to three weeks before weed seeds are expected to sprout. Rake in slightly on bare soil or apply directly over lawn grass. In either case, water the ground to encourage the weed seeds to sprout. Once they have sprouted, let the soil dry for a week or more. If the ground is kept continually wet, some seeds may be able to develop roots in spite of the corn gluten meal.

If you are using corn gluten meal as a fertilizer, apply it only to well established plants or after your garden seeds have well established roots. Apply up to two pounds per 100 square feet or 100 feet of row when your plants show a need for nitrogen. For trees, apply one pound per inch of trunk diameter around March 1 and again around October 1. These application dates are also generally a good time to use the product as weed control. To existing lawn grass, apply 20 pounds per 1,000 feet mid-April and mid-October. Since corn gluten meal is an organic fertilizer, timing is not as critical as it is when you use chemical fertilizers. The release of the nutrients takes place over a longer, more sustained period of time.

Corn gluten meal is good for fertilizing and controlling weeds in perennials such as strawberries, grapevines, orchards or around any established plants. The seed root-inhibiting effect will only last about three weeks in good, rich garden soil that is kept moist. The microbes in the soil will completely degrade and digest the meal by the fifth week. In dry conditions, however, or in poor soil, the inhibiting effect can last much longer. Keep this in mind when you plant seeds in the vegetable and flower gardens.

Corn gluten meal is a completely non-toxic weed control agent that provides the extra benefit of being an organic fertilizer. Nick Christians, Ph.D. at the Department of Horticulture at Iowa State University first discovered that corn gluten meal worked in this fashion in the late 1980s. In the early 1990s, Dr. Christians was issued a patent for this revolutionary discovery. This discovery proves once again that if we just ask, Mother Nature will give us perfect answers to all our gardening problems.

Critters: Friend & Foe

Pest Management

The greatest number of living creatures on this planet are insects. Some we call "good" bugs, the others pests. The pests seem to reproduce at a fantastic rate and have varied and excellent means of mobility. Have you ever wondered why they haven't destroyed all vegetation?

Organic growers believe that plants growing in their preferred environment and soil balanced to suit their needs will be healthy, and healthy plants do not attract destructive insects. Because of the healthy plants' immunity, the few insects that may get on them do not quickly multiply to damaging numbers. Their many natural enemies are able to hold these pests in check, hence the "balance of Nature."

This philosophy of destructive insects acting as a censor to cut out the unfit and unhealthy plants is really just a basic law of nature, unfortunately ignored by many. Skeptics will scoff at this philosophy, but that is their role, and I respect it. Organic growers understand and work with these natural laws with success, and they aren't all small operators either. Some farm hundreds of acres and enjoy production levels beyond what their chemical neighbors produce.

When insects (and diseases) attack a plant and are able to damage or destroy it, the organic grower asks why and searches for the cause. The non-organic grower ignores the cause and just treats the effects with pesticides which may eventually worsen the problem.

The discovery and understanding of these natural laws is nothing new. Sir Albert Howard, a soil and plant scientist in England, spent most of his life researching and proving these natural laws. His best-known book, *The Soil and Health,* was published in 1947. In this country another brilliant scientist, Dr. William A. Albrecht of the University of Missouri, spent 25 years researching the same subjects. His many scientific papers have been compiled into a series of books, *The Albrecht Papers,* published by Acres U.S.A. I also think the book Howard Garrett and I put together, *Texas Bug Book,* is very helpful in identifying and working with insects in Texas. We tell how to recognize and distinguish between pests and pals in the insect world, and help you learn how to benefit from the hard work of these small gardening friends.

Pest management does not mean knowing which chemical to use but understanding and recognizing why each species is here on earth, such as the beautiful fly in this photo. In the adult stage it is a great pollinator. In the larval stage it feeds on aphids.

These books should be must reading for every grower and student of agriculture. In them, the authors tell how they grew healthy, bug-free plants right beside diseased and bug-infested plants. The only difference was balanced soil.

I myself have used compost and natural fertilizers to grow pumpkins bug-free, while improperly fertilized pumpkin plants nearby were heavily infested with squash bugs. I have pecan trees that were severely infested with mealy bugs, and after being mulched with compost, they were completely clear after two years. I completely wiped out nematodes in one year from a tomato hot bed used to start seedlings with the use of compost and earthworms. On a peach tree which had the whole trunk oozing with sticky sap caused by the larvae of the peach bark beetle, mulching with compost overcame the problem. I have also learned that weather conditions can put plants under stress and open them to attack from insects and disease, but plants in the balanced, fertile soil were not affected by stress as quickly and usually held on until better growing conditions returned without being unduly affected.

Here again, the skeptics will argue, "But we don't have enough compost for all the farms in America." For that reason, the really big organic grower doesn't always use compost. Instead he grows cover crops for additional organic matter, tests for elements needed, and adds them to balance the soil. Mainly he is careful not to use toxic pesticides or any chemical that may destroy the living factors of the soil. The beneficial microbes and earthworms are essential in making a soil fertile enough to grow healthy plants.

If your soil isn't yet fertile and your plants are being attacked, there are acceptable methods of control. *Bacillus thuringiensis,* a bacterial organism that is used on cabbage worms, webworms, and many other worms, is very effective and safe. It kills the bad bugs only and not the good ones. Also available is Sabadilla Dust made from lily seeds. It is nontoxic to man but works well on squash bugs, harlequin bugs, and other members of the stink bug family. It too is fairly specific in what it kills.

These are good control materials because they leave the beneficial insects unhurt, and you are really using nature's own control methods. There are other safe materials, methods, and techniques for insect control and more are being discovered. It is important to remember, though, that insects and disease should be considered symptoms and not causes of unproductive and failing plants. The bad bugs may really be good bugs in disguise, trying to tell you all is not well with your ways of growing things.

Lady Bugs — A Lesson in Nature

One evening many years ago while resting on the porch thumbing through a farm magazine, I ran across an article about the Colorado potato beetle and all the losses it was causing. The article told of a poison being used to control the beetle and went on to tell the range of that troublemaker, which included Texas.

After reading the article, out of curiosity I went to inspect my potato patch. Sure enough, while walking down the rows I noticed that there were beetles crawling all over them, even though there were no holes in the leaves and the plants looked healthy.

Early the next day I got the recommended poison and was out dusting when a friend walked up and said, "Beck, stop! You are killing the lady bugs." He was too late. I had already dusted the whole patch. My friend described the difference between lady beetles and potato beetles. I thought, "So I poisoned a few good bugs, so what?" He also told me that lady bugs and lady beetles are the same critter with two different names.

A week or so went by, and I was out looking over the field again and saw no potato bugs — also no lady bugs. The plants, however, didn't look so good; they looked sick. The leaves were cupped and curled and weren't that healthful green they had been before. On closer inspection, I discovered why. Plant lice (aphids) were all over the stems and undersides of the leaves. The plants looked terrible and I began thinking, "What do I do now? Maybe I'd better call my friend who said to stop killing the lady bugs."

My friend informed me, "The lady bugs were there feeding on the aphids and keeping them in check. The poison killed potato bugs, aphids, and lady bugs alike. The aphids, however, reproduce extremely fast, a generation a week, while lady beetles are much slower. It will take the lady beetles a while to come back in numbers large enough to get the aphid population back in control. Now you will probably need to use more poison because you upset the balance of Nature."

Lady beetle feeding on aphids.

Then I began to feel upset, not only because I killed the good bugs and the bad bugs were destroying my garden, but because I, a country boy, was being told something I should have known by a city boy.

I asked my friend how he knew all about good and bad bugs. He replied he had been reading a magazine called *Organic Farming and Gardening.* He gave me some back issues, which I read. All through the magazines the editor tried to sell the idea that adapted plants in their proper environment, in a soil balanced in minerals, rich in organic matter, with an abundant, balanced soil life — meaning earthworms on down through the microscopic soil life — would be strong and healthy. Nature's censors, which include many of the destructive insects, would not be attracted to them, or be able to destroy them, and we wouldn't need a lot of toxic materials to grow the food we eat.

Then I read more in my modern farm magazine, and all through it the idea was being promoted that we need poison and chemicals of all kinds to grow our food and be profitable farmers.

I thought for a while on this chemical philosophy and then on the organic philosophy, pondering which idea was really modern or the best. The question kept coming back: why should we need toxic materials to grow the food we eat? Was Nature designed that way? After more thought, I decided gardening or farming could be more fun, a lot more challenging, and even just as profitable if we followed the natural or organic laws, and the food we ate would be more healthful too.

The Colorado potato beetle. These insects started me on my lifelong study of Nature.

I really became a student of that organic magazine, and in it I noticed an ad selling lady bugs: a whole gallon (or about 75,000) for $12.50. Since I had killed some, I felt maybe I should order some replacements.

Soon the mailman dropped the lady bugs off at the mailbox and blew his horn to let me know of the perishable delivery. All excited, I picked up the container, ran out to the garden, took out my pocket knife, cut the package open, and the lady bugs crawled out by the thousands — all over me. Then they flew up in the air about 15 feet and headed west, right back to California. It was then I read the instructions: Be gentle when handling them and first release only a few late in the evening. If they crawl about searching as if hungry, release the rest. If they only want to fly away, close the container and put it in the refrigerator for a few days, then try releasing again.

Lady bugs are the best known and most valued of our predator insects. In the larval and adult stage, they are the chief enemy of the troublesome aphids. There are about 350 species in this country. The young unmated adults hibernate through the winter, and these are the ones that are sold to gardeners. You may need to keep them in the refrigerator a while because they need to use the food they've stored as fat for hibernation. Otherwise they won't be hungry and will only want to return to hibernation.

The benefits of lady bugs have long been known but sometimes need rediscovering. In 1922 a group of citrus growers in California banded together to eradicate the California Red Scale by chemical methods. They tried, unsuccessfully, until 1961. Then they switched to a total program of biological control. They bred and released parasites and predator insects on 8,000 acres. They proved a big success at controlling the scale, with a savings of about $40 per acre. The lady beetles were a big part of this control program.

Almost all gardeners recognize the lady beetle in the adult stage, but it is also important to know it in the larval stage. So many times I catch people destroying them through ignorance. The larval stage is the growing stage, and that's when their appetite is the greatest and they eat the most aphids.

Here in Texas we have many different species of the lady beetle. Most are shaped like a Volkswagen bug. They are solid colors — orange, white, black, or red — no spots to 12 spots or more. Spots can be black or various colors. Buying and releasing more is fun and sure can't hurt anything, although it isn't always necessary. Most important is that you don't destroy those you may already have. Nature will build and keep the population balanced in numbers that your garden environment will support. But the main thing is not to mistake them for potato bugs!

Understanding Insects

People save money for months, spend weeks preparing, and then travel for hundreds or thousands of miles to enjoy the wonders and beauties of Nature — all the while overlooking some of the most interesting and fascinating wonders that Nature has to offer. A few of these wonders may even be found in your house, and many are found in your yard, especially your garden.

The number of these wonders is great. They are slapped at, sprayed, stomped on, dusted, trapped, feared, played with by little boys, shrieked at by little girls, and cursed at by grownups. However, if observed closely and studied carefully they are never boring.

Despite their small size, insects are among the most interesting and fascinating creatures known to man. Yet most of them are looked upon only as a nuisance. Few people understand their reason for being here.

The number of insect species is estimated to be in the millions, and scientists find most of them to be beneficial to man in some way. Only one percent are considered pests, but because of these few, over 1.9 billion pounds of pesticide are sold each year in this country. That means that if you loaded 100,000 pounds per box car, your pesticide train would be 19,000 cars long!

Scientists tell us that destructive insects could destroy all crops and vegetation regardless of the volume of poison we could use — if it weren't for natural, biological checks and controls. Chief among these natural checks are the insects themselves, the predatory and parasitic species commonly called "good bugs."

When people use poison to eradicate insects, they often end up destroying both the good and the bad, predator and prey. The laws of Nature do not allow a predator or other natural check to eradicate a species; they only control it or keep it in balance, and there are reasons for this.

Every living thing on earth is interdependent upon other living things for its existence. In Nature, everything eats and is eaten; the weak, the sick, the old, the dying, and the dead are used as food. Every living thing has a natural enemy, but every living thing also has a means of defense. Only when that living thing is in prime condition will its defenses keep it out of the clutches of its enemy.

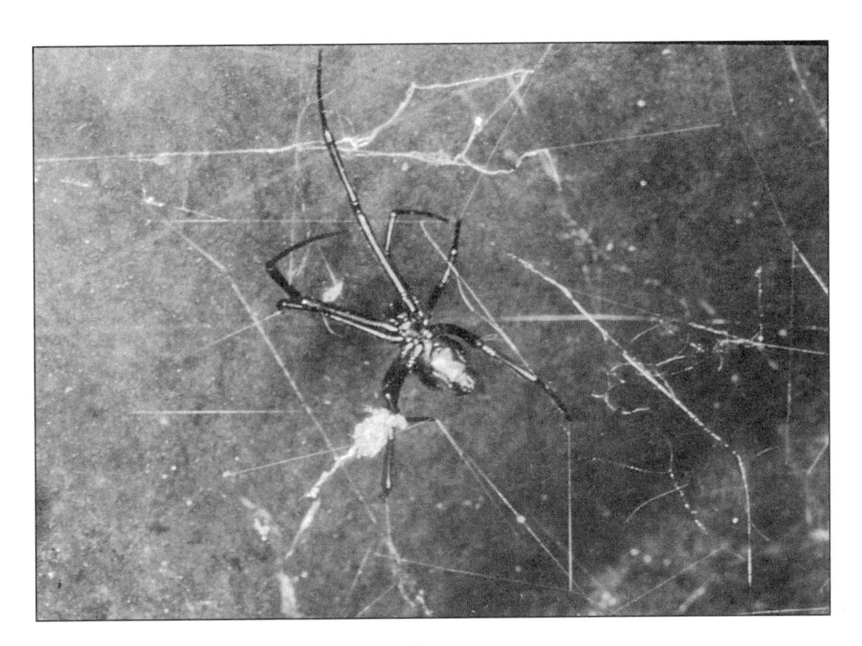

All creatures have their job in Nature.

In a natural environment (where a pest hasn't been introduced without its natural check), there is a perfect balance between the predator's ability and the prey's defense. The predator animals catch the weak and the sick; the insects are attracted to and destroy the plants that are unhealthy and unfit. This serves a useful purpose, since only the best adapted, healthiest, and strongest of each living species have been able to survive through the centuries.

Silk-making and pollination are some of the services that insects provide, but when they eat our crops we look upon it as a disservice. Could the insects be showing us that our crops are being grown improperly and are under stress? Research has shown, and I have seen it proven again and again, that properly grown, healthy plants are not susceptible to insect attack and damage.

This proves that destructive bugs are here for the purpose of censoring, and the many good bugs are here to help Nature keep the number of censor bugs in balance so they only do their job sufficiently and not overdo it. When the insects become a problem, it usually because man has violated a law of Nature.

When using insecticides we are only treating symptoms; we are not getting at the cause. The plant may not be adapted; the soil may be out of balance, or perhaps the plant is stressed because of bad weather conditions. Using insecticides of the wrong type or at the wrong time may upset the prey-to-predator balance and create a need for still more insecticide. Soon we have a plant that has been doused many times with poison, then we eat the plant — one that Nature saw unfit and was trying to destroy-and wonder why we get sick. Have you ever wondered why we should need poison to grow the food we eat? Was Nature designed that way? I can't believe it was.

Oil of mint repels rats and mice.

Ant Lion

As a small child, I spent many hours playing with bugs. The ant lion, or "doodlebug," as it's called by many people, occupied many of those absorbing and intriguing hours.

Actually, it is the larval stage that is best known — as a child I played with them for hours. The doodlebug was friendly; it didn't run away; it didn't bite. It would also catch all the ants I threw into its sand funnel. If the ants tried to escape, the bug would throw sand at them and they would slide to the bottom where the bug would catch them.

I often purposely messed up their sand funnel, and without showing the least bit of anger, the bugs would patiently start rebuilding by going around and around flipping sand until the funnel would again be perfect.

The little sand funnel ant lions make for catching their prey.

The ant lion will catch and eat any insect that is dumb enough to crawl or slide into its fine sand funnel. Most often ants, including fire ants, are its prey.

The ant lion was easy to catch. I carried them around in my pockets and played with them all day. When I finally put them back in their sand homes, they would still be there the next day, as if waiting for me to take them out to play again.

I have always said that Nature put the doodlebug here so children would have something to play with on a long summer day!

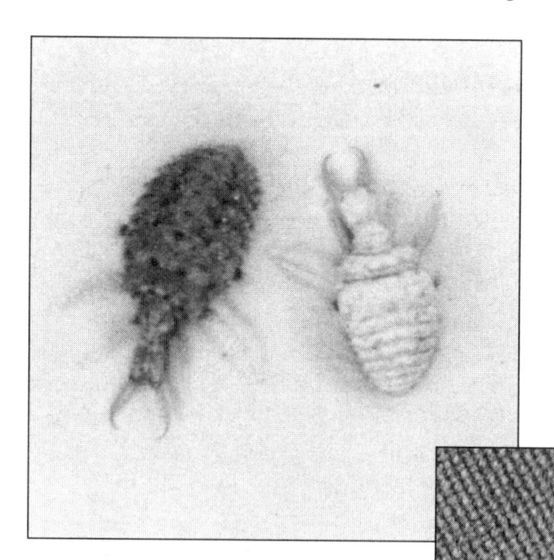

Two ant lions in the larval stage. One of them appears to be an albino — the only one I have ever seen. As a child I spent many hours playing with these little creatures in dry sand.

The adult ant lion.

Lightning Bugs

Because of insects, childhood was never boring. Summer days were spent playing with doodlebugs and other critters. But evenings were for watching and chasing after the flying bugs with the blinking lights called lightning bugs, fireflies, or glow worms. I used to imagine that they were little fairies, enchantingly dancing around, flashing their Lilliputian lanterns and saying, "Come follow us to fairyland!"

In the adult stage, lightning bugs definitely add beauty and fascination to summer evenings. The larval stage is equally beneficial. They are meat eaters and dine mostly on snails and slugs.

There are more than 130 species of lightning bugs in this country. In some species, the female doesn't have wings, but she and the larvae and even the eggs glow in the dark. The lightning bug poses a problem for scientist, who have not yet revealed its secret method of making cold light.

Sad to say, my grandchildren don't get to follow the little blinking lanterns to fairyland. We can no longer enjoy this evening-time fantasy, because in our area we no longer have lightning bugs. Are we guilty of poisoning our environment and making it unfit for their survival? What other reason could there be? Certainly the lightning bugs did their part to keep the world clean and enjoyable.

Giant Beetles

Among the most ferocious-looking creatures in the insect world are the giant beetles. The rhino beetle, Hercules beetle, and ox beetle are all large and scary-looking bugs. The larvae may be up to three inches long and adults can exceed three inches. Most have horns on their heads.

Despite their unfriendly appearance, these beetles are actually harmless to people and beneficial in the garden. Collectors prize the adults, and in Japan they are sometimes kept as pets. Sold in stores, these big beetles have been known to bring as much as $3,000 for a giant, perfect, shiny adult. The beetles are kept in cages and fed a special diet. They can live as long as two years under these conditions. In the U.S., giant beetle larvae are prized as catfish bait.

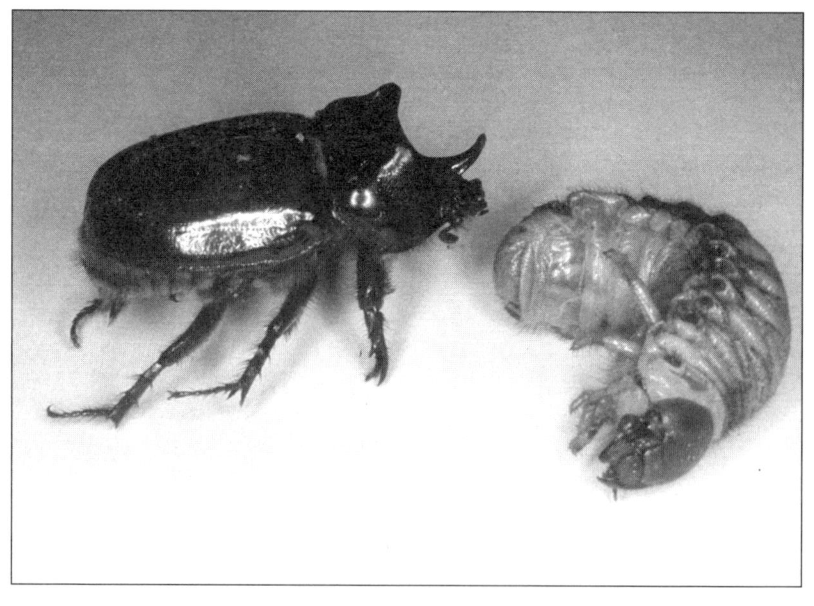

They look ferocious and are thought to be destructive, but nothing is further from the truth. The grubs feed on old rotten wood and make compost out of it. The adults feed on small, troublesome insects.

Ounce for ounce, these giant beetles are the world's strongest animals. A scientist glued weights on a rhinoceros beetle's back and found it could carry up to 100 times its own weight. It did get tired, however. With only 30 times its own weight, it showed no signs of fatigue after walking half an hour. That is comparable to a 150-pound man walking a mile carrying a Cadillac on his back!

If you are lucky enough to find giant beetles in your garden, enjoy them! They are predatory bugs that eat pest insects such as aphids and other small plant-sucking bugs. Their larvae are often found in compost piles where they are totally beneficial. Their life cycle moves from egg to larva to pupa to adult.

The Perfect Product

Every now and then something comes along that at first you put no faith in and shrug off as useless in the garden, but later it turns out to be a real blessing. The fine mesh or webbed cloth that lets sunlight and air through to plants but screens out insects is just such a product.

I was introduced to this cloth in 1987 by a persistent saleslady, but wouldn't even try it for a year. First marketed under the trade names Ree-May, Agri-Net, and Grow-Web, Garden-Ville now markets it under the "Plant Shield" label with fuller instructions. I first used the material sewn into a tube and fitted over tomato cages. I tried it on four plants as soon as they were transplanted in the garden. Lo and behold! They started growing so fast that they were soon twice, then three times, the size of the uncovered neighboring plants. The blooms and fruit were also greater in the same proportion.

I couldn't wait to tell Dr. Jerry Parsons, the agricultural extension vegetable specialist, about my discovery. I guess I was too excited to be credible. My story must have sounded as unbelievable to him as the saleslady's story did to me the year before, because he just shrugged it off and didn't bother to try it right away either.

Determined to see if the material would continue to give these extremely good results, I tried it in the spring and fall gardens. I got three friends from the Men's Garden Club to also try it. All of us experienced double and triple growth and fruit set on our tomatoes. After hearing so many success stories, Dr. Parsons decided to try it, and like the rest of us, he became a true believer. He's talked about it in his newspaper columns and on his radio and TV shows so much that almost everyone in the area knows about it now.

This net or web works by preventing the plants from being stressed in several different ways.

It slows down the wind. Research has shown that when wind speeds exceed 15 mph, plants are stressed enough to stop growing. It traps carbon dioxide and concentrates it around the leaf surface to aid in photosynthesis.

It also gives some frost protection but does not overheat the plants as plastic does when it is not removed in time. The material screens out many troublesome insects. It provides protection from hail. In my garden, the

The Grow-Web, or Plant Shield. After further testing, Dr. Jerry Parsons made the statement, "This is one of the best products to ever come along for the home gardener."

cover was riddled from hail but the tomato plants under it survived with little damage while those in the open were cut off at ground level by the damaging hail storm.

Also, if the material is put on the plant as soon as it emerges or when it is transplanted, it will prevent the plant from getting one of the numerous virus strains that can stop plant production. Viruses are usually spread from a carrier plant — usually a weed — by little sucking or chewing insects. If you are careful to cover the plant well, leaving no openings for the insects, virus prevention on clean plants is 100 percent.

This material also works better than netting to prevent bird damage to grapes and fruit. It tends to hide the fruit in the first place, but even if the birds do find the fruit, they can't peck through it, and the branches of the grapevine or fruit don't grow through it as they do netting. This makes the material easier to remove at the end of the season than traditional bird netting is.

Finally, although Dr. Parsons doesn't yet agree with me on this point, I think the material helps photosynthesis by defusing and reflecting sunlight all over the plant in moderate amounts, instead of being too hot and intense in one spot or from one angle.

Usually when something this good comes along, there are also some bad points, and this product is no exception. One drawback, of course, is that the material is not free, but if you are careful not to tear it, it will last several seasons. Second, it is an extra gardening chore to put it on the plants. I have found that wooden clothes pins work well to hold it tight around cages, and they are easy to remove later without damaging the web or the plant. Another minor drawback is that in extended cloudy weather, the material doesn't speed up the growth of the plant as well as it does in bright sunny weather. I like to use big cages covered with the material and leave it on until the plants start to bump the top and sides. By then, the tomatoes are getting close to ripening, and viruses can't do much damage to these large plants. If your tomato plants are not in all-day sun, however, you may want to remove the web a little sooner, especially if fruit is not setting. Even if you remove it sooner, you still benefit from early insect control and virus prevention while your young plants are establishing themselves.

This material works well for crops like lettuce and other greens as a row cover. You have to weigh down the edges to make sure insects can't crawl under and the wind can't blow it away. You can use rocks or boards to hold it down, but a little soil works best. Even when using it around cages, I use a little soil or sand around the bottom to seal the area. When covering row crops, stretch the material over a horizontal pole to form a little tent. This gives the plants more room to grow and you can keep the net in place longer. Vegetables and fruit that need insects for pollination — melons, cucumbers, squash — will have to be uncovered as soon as the female blooms open.

The retail price for this product is around 8-10 cents per square foot, depending on where you buy it and what size you buy. I think this is a small investment, considering that it can be used again and again and it can make the difference between big success and complete failure. It also insures that you won't need to even consider using any insecticides.

Earthworms

The earthworm is nature's plow, chemist, cultivator, maker and distributor of plant food. It is extremely valuable to man because it enriches and aerates the soil. Its tunnels allow rainwater and oxygen to penetrate deeply into the soil, thus promoting the growth of helpful microorganisms.

The earthworm tunnels as deep as six feet, bringing up minerals from that depth. In comparing worm castings with the surrounding soil, they are found to be five times richer in nitrogen, twice as rich in calcium, twice as rich in magnesium, seven times as rich in phosphorus, eleven times as rich in potassium — with all these minerals readily available for plant use.

When earthworms are present, the beneficial soil microorganisms are increased seven times, while the harmful bacteria and nematodes are destroyed as they pass through the earthworm. The earthworm's digestive processes also neutralize soils that are either too acid or too alkaline. Under normal conditions, the earthworm can turn up, digest, and add 12 tons of castings per acre per year to the topsoil.

Many insecticides and chemical fertilizers destroy earthworms. In fact, a very common fertilizer, ammonium sulfate (21-0-0), is even used to kill earthworms on golf greens. Organic farming methods promote their growth and increase their number by making soil conditions favorable for them.

After 50 years of study, Charles Darwin concluded that without earthworms, the vegetation in many parts of the world would degenerate finally to the vanishing point. To encourage earthworms to live in your garden, follow organic practices using compost and mulch. If you want to introduce earthworms, dig some from the local area or your neighbor's garden. You need only a few to get started, but don't buy fishing worms as you may get an imported species that won't survive in your environment.

Squash Pests Outflanked

Summer squash — yellow, zucchini and white scalloped — were always part of our garden and one of our main vegetables on our truck farm. Squash was second only to tomatoes in sales at the farm stand.

On a farm with a large planting of squash, the squash vine borer doesn't exist. For some unknown reason, the squash vine borer will not attack large plantings, but they will get every plant in a home garden and shorten the lifespan of the plants. Squash bugs are another big problem for the home gardener. Squash bugs are also there on the farm, but so scattered that they do little damage. Powdery mildew is another problem the gardener and farmer have to contend with, especially during humid, rainy and cloudy weather.

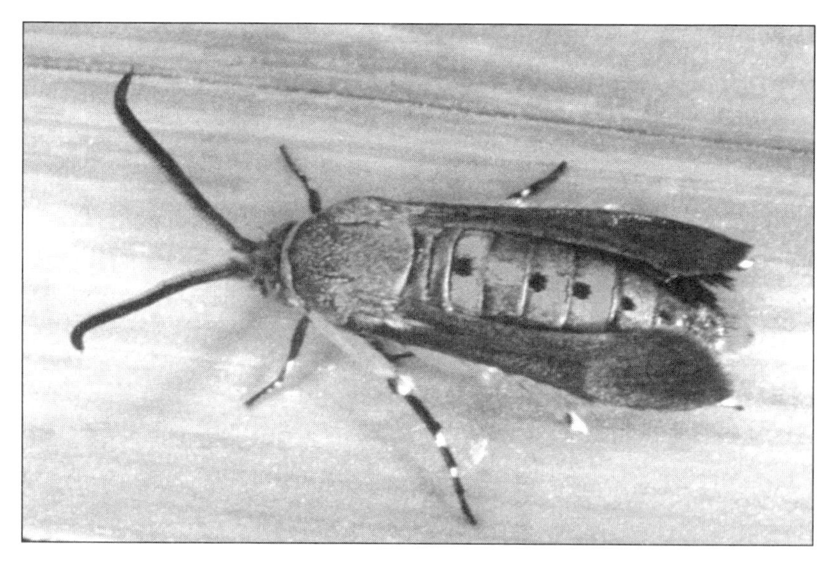

The colorful adult squash vine borer moth looks more like a wasp.

On our organic farm, the good fertile and healthy soil helped overcome all of these conditions. If you build your soil and keep the plants watered and well-fed, they will be much more likely to withstand any disease or insect problems. Hand-picking will usually reduce the numbers enough that they are no longer a problem.

There is one squash variety that is delicious to eat and immune to all of the problems that plague other varieties. Tatume, a perfectly round green squash, is best harvested when about the size of a baseball or slightly larger. If left on the vine it will turn into a six to eight-inch golden pumpkin.

Plant this squash, using plenty of compost early in the spring, and if kept watered it will provide you with squash until the first frost of autumn. Tatume is a vining squash that is not bothered by the squash vine borer, the squash bug or mildew. In fact, I have never had any problems with this variety.

That is unless you consider huge vines a problem. Tatume squash grows and grows. We have had one plant cover an area 29' x 29'. We ate all we could, gave away all we could, and fed the rest to the goats.

'Trich-ing' the Pecan Casebearer: Control with Trichogramma Wasps

The twenty pecan trees on the small farm we purchased in 1957 produced a bumper crop, and we thought we had a bonanza on our hands. The second and third years, however, turned the bonanza into a bust. The tree produced few nuts or no nuts at all. Throughout the summer I watched the nutlets turn black and fall off the trees.

The extension service gave me the bad news: I had nut casebearers. Left alone, the casebearers could destroy 50-90 percent of a pecan crop. Furthermore, they told me, the only way to get rid of them was to spray with arsenate of lead. That was against my organic farming principles, but sometimes principles get in a shoving match with economic realities. We needed that money from the pecan crop to make ends meet.

I went ahead and bought the poison. Then a new problem occurred to me. All our farm animals, including the milk cow, grazed under the pecan trees. Another call to the extension service told me I'd have to fence the animals away from the trees until after a rain. That bit of information gave my principles the little nudge they needed to win out. I returned the poison.

I still had the problem though, and I kept thinking there must be a safe, natural way to control those casebearers. A friend mentioned an ad he'd seen in *Organic Gardening* magazine. It advertised a microscopic wasp called *trichogramma* that was parasitic to moth eggs. He also told me that the nut casebearer might be the larva of a moth.

Once more I turned to the extension service. Yes, they said, the casebearer did turn into a moth. Furthermore, they knew that the adult moth deposited eggs between May 1 and May 6. They didn't know anything about the trichogramma wasp, so I called the man who was advertising the Trich-O. While he didn't know anything about casebearers, he did tell me about the success others had had with the tiny wasps' controlling the cotton boll worm, another moth larva.

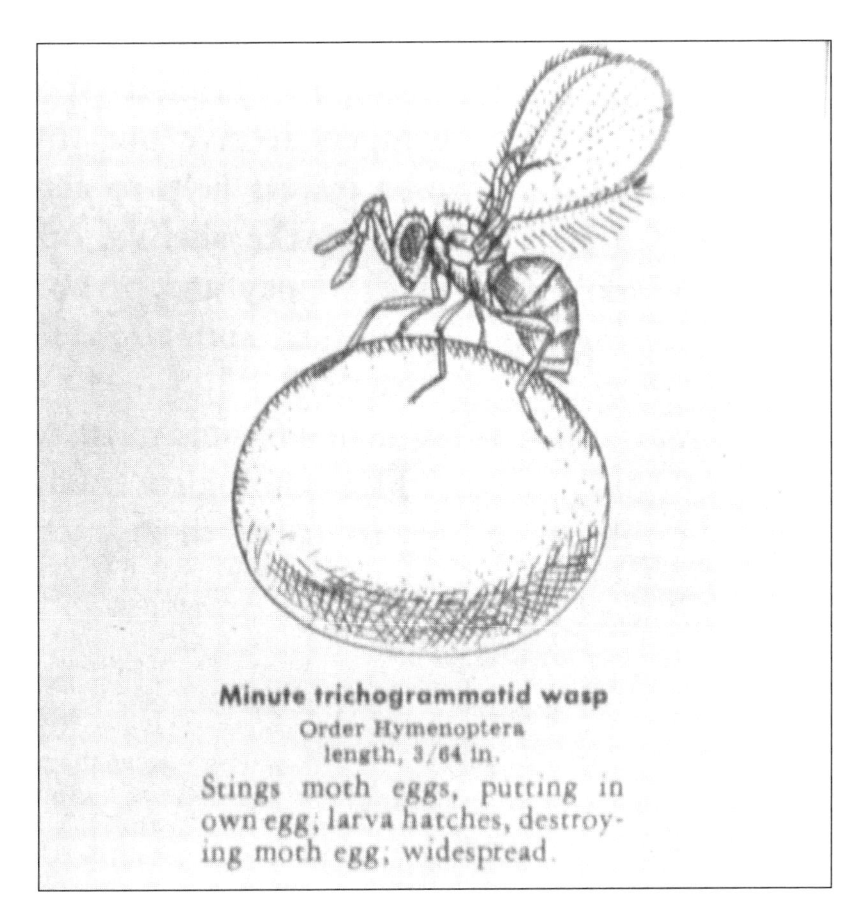

A microscopic trichogramma wasp setting to work on a moth egg.

It was the middle of April, and I was excited and impatient to see if I'd found a solution to my problem. I immediately ordered and released a batch of the wasps. Since I knew the moth was going to deposit eggs around May 1, I ordered another batch to be released then. I kept an eye on the trees and that year the nut crop was greatly improved. Maybe the little wasps were doing their job!

Every year after that I released a batch of wasps in the middle of April and another on May 1. I never lost more than ten percent of a crop, and I wasn't the only one. Soon word got around that there was a safe, easy method to control the casebearer. Friends and neighbors tried the wasp, and all reported a measure of success.

I felt pretty proud of myself for making this discovery, but not everyone was quite as impressed. One day I told a friend in Gonzales, Texas,

Small pecans destroyed by a casebearer moth larva that didn't get parasitized.

about my natural casebearer control. He was an extension entomologist, and all the time I was talking he was shaking his head. "Charlie," I asked, "don't you believe the wasps work?" "No," he said. He'd tried them and just couldn't see good enough results. He released 50,000 wasps per tree on the day the casebearer moth released its eggs.

I left Charlie's office puzzled. Then it occurred to me that I was making two releases instead of one, and probably as a result getting better coverage and allowing for the moths who deposited eggs early or late.

During one of his visits, I told Robert Rodale about my experience and he asked me to write it up for *Organic Gardening* magazine. As soon as the article was published, phone calls and letters from all over the South flooded in, requesting more information. I still get calls and letters from people who have solved their casebearer problems with an almost invisible wasp. I have used the Trich-O since 1962 on two different pecan groves, and in all that time, I've never had more than 10 percent loss due to the nut casebearer.

I believe my continued success is due to using totally organic methods on both farms. I have a stable environment. As opposed to those who use chemical pest control, I never upset the natural predator-to-prey balance. Furthermore, in the two weeks between April 15 and May 1, the wasps have a chance to reproduce in the area. They destroy other moth eggs, and when

A small pecan with a white casebearer egg on the bloom end. Even though they're so small you can barely see them, trichogramma wasps do a tremendous job of controlling this pest.

the casebearer deposits her eggs, there is a bigger army of Trich-O wasps to attack the eggs and keep them from hatching into damaging larvae.

My experience and the experiences of others with the parasitic wasp and other parasite and predator insects show that these "good bugs" are a powerfully effective and completely safe method of pest control. They must, however, be a part of an organic whole. If they are used in a totally organic environment and applied with the best method and at the proper time, they will help Mother Nature do her stuff. The wasps are not like toxic insecticides to be applied once for a quick cure. Harmony and balance are the goal, and achieving the goal requires an overall organic program of providing what is needed when it is needed to sustain Nature's great system.

Webworms & Wasps

"Why don't you have webworms, Beck?" was the question always asked by friends and visiting farmers. We had eight acres scattered with 20 big pecan trees growing around the house, in the cow lot, the chicken yard, and around various buildings. We didn't have a single webworm colony and never had since purchasing the place seven years earlier. It wasn't because they were scarce. Webworms were thick, especially during those years, all over the state, and I knew that I wasn't blessed with the good fortune that webworms couldn't find me or were nice enough to leave me alone.

There had to be a reason my trees were left alone all those years. I did read that wasps preyed on larva such as webworms, and on several occasions I actually saw wasps attack and carry off green loopers. I believed the wasps were doing the job, but I wasn't sure. However, I soon got proof.

Having been an abandoned farm for several years, with lots of old unpainted buildings and a water hole nearby, our place was a perfect environment for wasps. The big yellow-and-black, black-and-rust, and rusty wasps had nests built everywhere. One day my two younger brothers came out when I wasn't home and spent the day knocking down wasp nests with their slingshots. The wasps never bothered me and I never bothered them, but the temptation was too great for the boys. The nests were the perfect target for a challenge, and they only missed one or two. The boys' timing must have been perfect for knocking out future wasp generations, because to this day few of the wasp nests have been rebuilt. The very next year we had a webworm problem.

The wasps are interesting social insects, but they are not very prolific. The males and young queens arrive or hatch in late summer. Workers, males, and old queens die with the approach of winter. This leaves only the young queens who hide in cracks, crevices, and bark of trees throughout winter to emerge in the spring to start new colonies.

Other people have also found the wasp interesting and helpful. Once, when giving a talk on natural gardening to a group, I mentioned the wasp and a man in the crowd got all excited. He said, "I have a machine that will spray 100-foot tall trees. That's what I do. I go up and down river bottoms and spray trees for people. One day, while getting the rig ready to spray, I

Fall webworms would not be a problem if we stopped killing the paper wasp.

noticed a webworm colony in a low-hanging branch. A wasp flew in, captured a webworm and flew off. I got interested and instead of cranking up the spray rig, I just watched. Within 20 minutes, the wasp carried off every webworm."

About three years later, while talking to another gardening group, I told of my experience and the sprayer's story of the wasp. Again there was an old gentleman in the crowd who wanted to tell his story. He said, "I learned long ago the wasps were beneficial and preyed on webworms. But I noticed the wasp had a hard time getting through that web. So one day I decided to help them by taking a stick and tearing the web open. Sure enough they would clean up a web a lot faster after I tore it. For years now I have been tearing the webs open for them. For a while it took 15 to 20 minutes for the wasps to find the opened web; later it took them five minutes to find it. Now I can just walk out of the house with a stick and here they come!"

We all laughed at his story's ending, but entomologists that study wasps claim they are the intellectuals of the insect world. They seem to have an ability to learn. The entomologist captured wasps and put them under a glass dome with a small escape hole. The wasps escaped, and each time they were caught and put back into the dome. They always looked for the opening and escaped again. No other insect would learn or remember the escape hole.

I, too, find them pretty smart. While photographing them with a close-up lens, I got within eight inches of a big nest. As I took my time to get focused properly, they didn't bother me or fly away. In fact, only one of them seemed to notice me. She watched for a while, then reached over and with a front leg tapped a neighbor on the back as if to draw her attention to me, then they both stared at me. I got the message and moved on.

More about Wasps

Wasps will sting. The stings are painful and can be dangerous because of allergic reactions. I have been stung, but only when I bumped a nest and moved too fast and they took my action as a threat against them. Through studying, observing, and actually playing with wasps, I have learned that they only sting when they sense their nest is being threatened. Don't threaten them, not even mentally: they can sense your feelings.

One day a neighbor came over to borrow a cyclone seeder that was stored in a shed. When I reached down to pick up the seeder, I turned and bumped a very large wasp nest hanging on a chain. There must have been at least 60 wasps on the nest. As soon as I realized what I had done, I froze. It took all the nerve I had, but I stood very still as the wasps flew around me and bumped into my face and bare arms. Still, I didn't get a single sting. I waited a couple of minutes until they were all settled back on the nest, and then I slowly moved on.

Another time, the wasps decided to build their nest hanging from the seal above our back door. That door is used dozens of times each day by the children, grandchildren, my wife and me. Because we are pretty tall people, the nest was only a few inches away from our heads every time we went in or out the door. Yet, they never bothered us. They kept enlarging their nest until a wasp or two was knocked off every time the door was opened. My wife kept warning me that sooner or later someone would get stung. Sure enough, they got her first, but she said it didn't hurt very much.

I did plan on moving the nest, but I kept putting it off. One day I let the screen door slam and knocked several wasps off the nest. One wasp came and gave me a warning shot on the hand. It didn't hurt much either — not as much as I knew it could have. It seemed like a warning to me, and I finally took heed. I promptly got a bucket of water and splashed it on them; it knocked all the wasps to the ground and with their wings wet they couldn't fly. That gave me plenty of time to break the nest loose and fasten it with a thumb tack about 14 inches higher. In a few minutes, the wasps dried out, flew back to the nest, and went about housekeeping as if they had never been moved. Over the years I have moved many wasp nests, never got stung, and the wasps went back to the nest. The only time that didn't

Small nest of paper wasps early in the spring. These are your friends. Treat them as such, and they will be friendly.

happen was when I moved one from the shade to the sun. They don't like direct sun rays on their nests and wouldn't move back in.

Around our place of business we always have lots of wasp nests. If the nests are low or positioned so a customer or employee can accidentally bump into them, I move them. The porch across the front of our office usually has a wasp nest in all four corners. One day a lady came into the office and said she got stung by a wasp out by the Coke machine near the corner. She said it didn't hurt as much as stings usually do. I asked her if she threatened the wasp in any way and she said she hadn't even noticed the nest. Her tone of voice let me know that it seemed to her I was more concerned about the wasps than I was the customers.

About a week later, an employee also got stung while at the Coke machine, and he too said it didn't hurt much. But I wondered why those wasps were aggressive. I got a stool and sat out on the porch and just watched the wasps for a while. It didn't take long until I saw the reason for their aggression. A spider had built her web across the corner of the porch. A wasp came flying in toward the nest and momentarily got entangled in the web. While she fought to get loose, she must have sent out some kind of distress signal because all the rest of the wasps left the nest in search of a possible enemy. I moved the spider web and no one has been stung since.

Realizing how beneficial the wasps are, I have protected them for more than 35 years. They seem to have become friendly toward us. Even when someone does accidentally bump a nest, they usually don't sting, and when they do it is very light.

A young landscaper was loading his own material from a storage shed one day when he raised his head directly into a wasp nest. Five wasps stung him in the face. He came running to the office scared, but not half as scared as I was after I found out what had happened. I offered to take him to the hospital. He said that it had scared him but didn't hurt. I made him rest in the office for a few minutes to make sure there wouldn't be an allergic reaction. After just a few minutes there wasn't any pain, swelling or any sign that he had been stung. I wonder. Are the wasps getting less poisonous or can they actually govern how badly they want to hurt us? Do they recognize us as not being a threat to them?

We now have 270 pecan trees here on the farm and the wasps keep the trees almost completely clean of webworms. Our neighbors have more webworms in one tree than we have on the whole farm.

When the wasps catch a webworm or other troublesome worm, they rip the worm open and dig out balls of meat to feed their young larva. The adult wasp is a vegetarian and eats very little, usually nectar from flowers. In the process, they do a little pollinating as well. They often get blamed for damaging fruit such as peaches and plums, but in fact they are only drinking juice at a hole in the fruit that a bird pecked.

All wasps are beneficial, and like most all other wild creatures in Nature, only become aggressive if they feel their nests and young are threatened. Then the sting may only be as severe as they consider the threat. Treat them as friends and neighbors, and they will return the favor.

Webworms & Our Favorite Tree

The pecan tree is my favorite and probably the favorite tree of most Texans. It is the one tree that offers beauty, size, shade, and delicious food — a nut that is eaten and enjoyed by almost everyone, and preferred by the confectioner and the baker alike.

Even though the pecan is our state tree, many people are reluctant to plant it because of one unsightly, troublesome pest: the webworm. This is a shame, because with just a little study and understanding of Nature the webworm need not be a pest.

The webworm has many natural enemies, among them certain birds, but most of its enemies are in the insect world. Wasps are great at controlling the webworms, but they are not alone. One day we saw a praying mantis in a webworm colony, holding a webworm in each forearm and eating on both of them. She must have stayed there and really enjoyed the feast, because later I found she had deposited her egg cluster on a twig right in the center of the webworm colony and only a few worms were left.

While looking out the kitchen window one day, I noticed a webworm colony on a low-hanging pecan branch. Usually I tear these out and throw them on the ground, step on them a few times, then let the fire ants finish them off. But this time, as I started to reach for it, I noticed a member of the assassin bug family, a giant wheel bug, sitting on the outer edge of the webworm colony with a webworm stuck on the end of his snout as he sucked the juice from it. Naturally, I didn't destroy that colony but left it alone so the wheel bug could have a picnic.

Later that day a gardening friend came over, and I took him around the house to show him the assassin bug in action. When we got there, there were two assassin bugs, one on each side of the colony, and each had a webworm stuck on the end of its snout. Again the next day, about noon, an old grandma came over. She and I always enjoy discussing Nature, so naturally I had to show her the wheel bugs, but when we got there they were all gone, and so were all the webworms — except one. "I wonder why they didn't eat that last webworm," I remarked. She replied, "Well, they left it for seed."

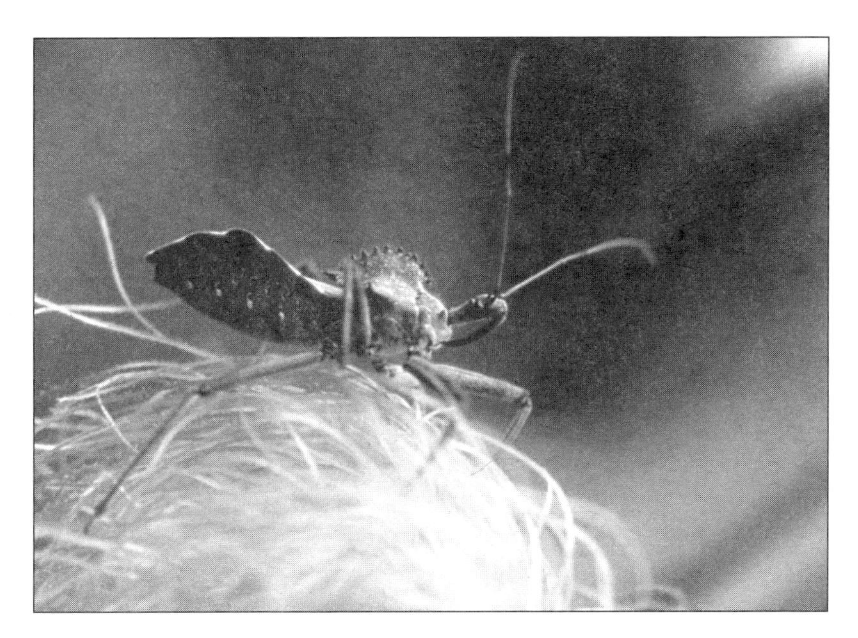

A giant wheel bug, very beneficial. I have never seen a giant wheel bug feed on a beneficial insect.

Whether they actually left it for seed or not, we don't know. However, the assassin bugs are very interesting and helpful creatures.

As a child, I always played in the shade of pecan trees and climbed them, too. During the season, my pockets were always full of nuts to munch on. I remember seeing an occasional webworm back then, but never the problem we have every year now. The webworms started becoming a problem in the '50s, at least in our area, and that was about the time people were learning to spray or were becoming prosperous enough to own spray equipment.

I believe spraying with the wrong thing, a poison that kills too many beneficial insects, caused the webworm to eventually explode into a nuisance. I don't approve of persistent broad spectrum insecticides, but I do believe there is a time and place for dusting and spraying, and a heavy webworm infestation is one of those times.

The adult webworm moth deposits large clusters of eggs, and without some natural check, their populations really multiply. The webworm's natural enemies aren't nearly so prolific as they once were, and years of spraying with the wrong materials have really allowed the webworm to gain a big lead. This makes us want to spray more.

Without man's interference, and given enough time, Mother Nature always corrects herself and puts the proportion of prey-to-predator insects back in balance. But man is here and will always interfere, so Mother Nature, in all her wisdom, gave us a product to spray with: Bt.

Bacillus thuringiensis (Bt) is a natural organism that destroys only the webworm and other larvae of the same species. It does not harm you, the wasp, the assassin bug, the praying mantis, the birds, or any of the rest of Nature. Bt is being widely used in agriculture, and if properly used, works excellently on webworms.

The first time I tried it, it didn't work very well. I sprayed at about 10 o'clock on a bright sunny day. I didn't realize that the webworms were all just hanging asleep in the web and wouldn't be feeding until dark. They must eat it before it will affect them, and by nightfall the Bt must have mostly degraded. So now I spray either late in the evening or on a damp cloudy day, and it is 100 percent effective.

In its natural environment, which covers most of our state, the pecan tree has very few other problems, and with a little study and understanding of Nature's ways, all can be corrected. So there is no need to hesitate. Plant your favorite tree now. The squirrels have planted them without a shadow of hesitation for centuries.

The Giant Wheel & Potato Beetles

My first ever experience using poison was on potato beetles (or what I thought was potato beetles, see page 238). Every year, potatoes were a large part of our vegetable crop, and some years the potato beetles were bad enough to warrant some control. Since I wanted to stay organic, I really wasn't sure what to do. I remembered when I was a child at home, our dad made us pick the potato beetles by hand, but I never could understand how that could help because we only picked while Dad was home to watch. As soon as he left, my brother and I would end up throwing them at each other until we figured it was time to go swimming. But I do remember that the potato beetles didn't destroy the crop.

Now that I owned a farm and had responsibility, I figured I better find an answer. I just couldn't believe picking a few beetles was the answer I needed. I bought a bug book and learned that the first potato beetles to appear in the spring were the young un-mated adults that hibernate through the winter. If you get them before they deposit eggs, you have knocked them out for the season. But I still didn't see how you could pick them all or even pick enough to do any good. But the few my brother and I picked back home did seem to do some good, so I decided to hand-pick some anyway.

One thing I remember from picking the beetles as a child is that the beetles didn't seem dumb. A lot of them would see us coming and fall to the ground and play dead. We didn't bother to pick them off the ground then, but now I wanted to destroy as many as I could. To kill them I squashed them between my fingers. Every now and then I found one on the ground, but there was no juice in it and I got to wondering why those young adults were all dried up. As I continued down the row, I soon found the answer: a giant gray bug with half of a cogged wheel sticking up on his back and a long snout. The snout was used to stab the potato beetle and suck its juices. It wasn't long before I found several more of these big wheel bugs that had captured and were sucking potato beetles.

The giant wheel bug deserves having her photo in this book twice. This bug, with the help of children, eliminated the potato beetle problems on both of our farms.

About that time a neighbor walked up and said, "Malcolm, I see you got potato beetles too. I used an insecticidal dust on mine, and there is still some left if you want it." I answered, "No thanks, I don't think I'll need it." She seemed a little puzzled at my answer, and I didn't bother to explain.

After that I didn't bother to pick any more beetles. Almost daily I watched the potato beetles decrease in number. The lady beetle population remained strong and kept the aphids from getting a toe-hold. One day I decided to go over and visit the neighbor and her potato patch. She did have the potato beetles under control, but there were also very few lady beetles, and the aphids were taking over. I couldn't find a single giant wheel bug.

From then on, every year I hand-picked a few potato beetles as soon as they appeared, and each year there were fewer and fewer of them. By the sixth year, they were so few of them that it wasn't necessary to pick, and by the eighth year they were completely gone.

I think that gradually improving the soil each year may have given the plants some immunity, and by hand-picking and not using poison, I didn't kill any of their natural enemies such as the giant wheel bug. Each year I watched the giant wheel bug and never did I see it capture a beneficial insect. In addition to the potato beetle, they captured striped and spotted cucumber beetles and moths — all serious pests.

We stayed on that small farm for 11 years, and the potato beetles never came back. On our new farm, our potato patch was bigger, and with the first planting the potato beetles came in droves. My two oldest sons were eight and ten, and I decided it was time they learned about potato bugs. With the size of the patch, however, I figured they would need help, so I recruited two little neighbor girls. I took all the kids out into the field and explained the good bugs and bad bugs and their life cycles. The kids found it fascinating, then I said I would pay them a penny for each bad bug they picked.

I gave them each a can with soapy water to drop the bugs in and explained how soap alone would kill the bad bugs. The kids picked with enthusiasm about as long as you would expect, then they came to the house to show me and count their bad bugs. Surprisingly, none had picked good bugs. Together, I owed those kids almost five dollars.

The next day the little neighbor girls were back, asking if they could pick bugs again. One of them said she wouldn't even charge me if I would let them pick. My two boys didn't offer, but it took much less persuasion than I thought it would, even for them. Each year thereafter, the kids had their bug-picking party. Just like on the first farm, each year as the soil was built up to better and better fertility and we only killed bad bugs and protected the good ones, the potato beetles became less and less of a problem. Eventually they were gone completely.

This experience proves again that if we work with Nature and employ her help, toxic materials aren't necessary to grow the food we eat.

Ants Away from Home

In all the talks and presentations I give around our part of the country, there is one question that never fails to be asked: "What can we do about fire ants?" The imported fire ant showed up on our farm in the mid-seventies. Right away we noticed they were having an effect on some of our troublesome pests. My wife said she wasn't finding ticks on the kids any more just about the same time we stopped losing transplants on the farm.

Every spring we transplanted thousands of tomatoes, bell peppers, and eggplants, and in the fall we planted cabbage, broccoli, and others. We always planted 10 percent more seedlings than we needed because we could depend on the cutworms to destroy about that much of the crop each season. The few mounds of imported fire ants we had then were welcome guests because they helped control the cutworms and ticks. Before their arrival, we had native fire ants, but they didn't do the complete job of stopping ticks and cut worms that the imported ants did.

I didn't see a need to control the ants as long as they were helping me out. But they didn't stop with the ticks and cutworms. They went on to destroy things that weren't pests. Our native fire ants were disappearing, and the red harvester ants were growing fewer in number. Quail, which we always had an abundance of, were almost gone, and I haven't seen a single green lizard or horned lizard since 1977. Both were plentiful before the imported fire ants arrived.

When the food supply of other predator insects is depleted, the predator population drops to match the supply of food. The population of the predators rises and falls with the supply of insects they feed on, but not so with the imported fire ants. When their insect prey was depleted, they turned to eating plants. They developed an appetite for okra, tomato, cabbage, eggplants, and any other young, tender plant if it was the only thing nearby to eat.

I could tolerate the ants as long as they left me alone, but now they had attacked something I value. It's hard to tell what attracts them. They got into an outside extension phone and plugged it so tight with dead ants that it was ruined. They got into an expensive circuit breaker and ruined it, then the water pump pressure switch, and finally every light socket and base plug they could get to. They really seem to like electricity.

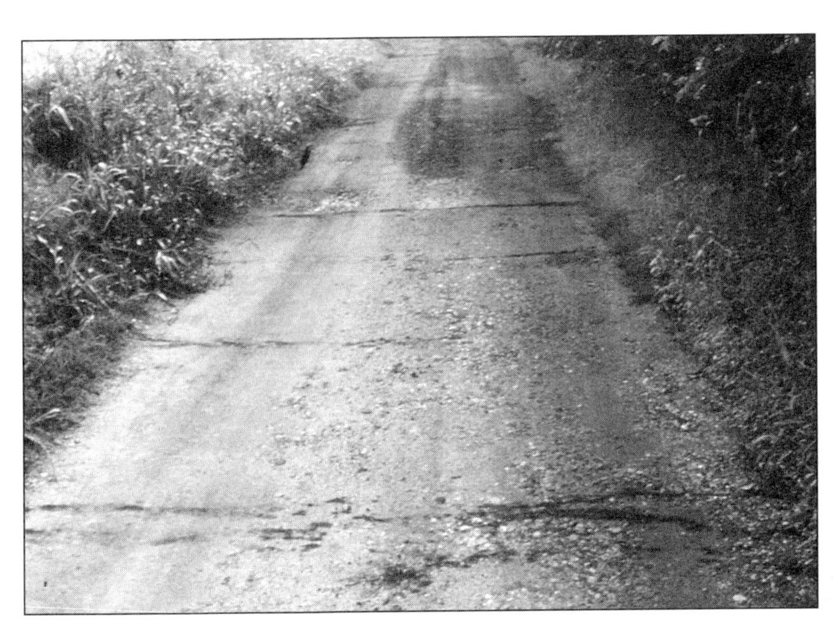

The ants, as a colony, are probably the most intelligent of all the insects. This photo shows evidence of several fire ant colonies crossing a lane; they tunnel for protection from the auto traffic, and they always go straight across, never at an angle, for the shortest distance through the hard surface.

When the imported fire ants were first discovered here, they had one queen per mound, and a logical way to control them was to kill the queen, thus ending their reproduction. A very small amount of poison bait worked fine at first. I even used it around my buildings to protect the electrical units. I put out a good distribution, and it completely stopped the ants for a while. During that time we had the worst explosion of ticks ever. You couldn't walk from the house to the barn without being covered.

After a few weeks, the fire ants came back and again wiped out the ticks, but this time they weren't so welcome. I try to keep them under control with the least toxic methods. The Garden-Ville Fire Ant Control (known as Auntie Fuego) works well in our garden.

The poison baits designed to kill the queen aren't very effective anymore since the ants have retaliated by having multiple queens per mound. I suspect they soon will catch on to the hormone baits also and develop some kind of immunity to them.

If we did nothing toward their control, Nature would sooner or later balance them out, put them back in line, but that may take much longer than we care to wait. One thing is for sure, they are here to stay. Even if we could wipe them out, we would find ourselves in big trouble. We would have nothing to stop the hoards of ticks, cutworms, and other pests whose numbers might explode.

In Nature, every living creature has a purpose or a job to do, and it continues to fill that purpose or do that job without quitting, or even stalling, until something interferes. We need to go back to the ant's original home to find the natural interference — that natural police force — that kept them in check. I am sure it isn't a poison bait or even a hormone. Probably it is a combination of many things, including diseases, insects, and animals with each one of these having its own police force to keep it in balance.

While giving a talk once, I said, "Give Nature enough time and she will put them in their place and they will no longer be a big problem, but I can't estimate the time that is needed." At a lecture on fire ants, a University of Texas scientist, Larry Gilbert, stated that his research had led him to a similar conclusion: "If we had done nothing and not used poison that destroyed many of their natural enemies, especially our native fire ants, the imported fire ant would no longer be a problem."

A Natural Fire Ant & Insect Control

Of all the many products that were developed and sold by Garden-Ville, the Fire Ant Control is probably the very best. It resulted from the observations of myself and my good friend Sabino Cortez. Sabino owns and operates a hydro-cyclone machine that separates the liquids from dairy cow manure. He noticed that wherever he sprayed the liquid, the fire ants disappeared. I noticed that wherever I spray cow feed molasses, the fire ants also disappeared. We mixed the two together and found that it even killed a few other pests. A friend of mine who owns a chemical company suggested we add orange oil, a food-grade product pressed from orange peels. He gave us some to mix with the molasses and manure tea, and *bingo*! We found that if we coated the ants with the mixture blended in water it would kill them within a few minutes. After many months of research, we finally nailed the correct ratios and had a product with good shelf life that could be used to control any troublesome insect.

We put out many samples for trials with gardeners, housewives, farmers and college professors. They all loved the way it worked and the way it smelled. An agriculture Ph.D. liked it so well that he sent us a letter saying it would be his product of choice because it was completely nontoxic, made from agricultural waste products, killed fire ants as well as any other product, and also seemed to leave a beneficial residue to keep the fire ants from repopulating a treated area. It wasn't long before we had stacks of testimonial letters of how well it worked on every troublesome insect they doused or sprayed it on.

We approached the Texas Department of Agriculture for permission to market the product. After we explained how it worked and what it was made of, they said to go ahead. A nontoxic product to kill fire ants and all other pest insects was badly needed, but they couldn't give us written permission.

In a short time we had orders from all over the state. We were selling it as fast as we could make it. And more calls and letters came telling us of the good control people were attaining after using it on troublesome insects.

A gallon jug of the fire ant and insect control made from agricultural waste products.

It kills insects three ways: When mixed with water, it is gooey. If you are able to coat the insect, it has a smothering effect. The orange oil is an organic solvent and works to dissolve the exoskeleton. The molasses feeds the decomposition process and microbes that soon completely devour and destroy the pests. Then it all turns into soil conditioner and fertilizer. It is also a foliar feed for plants when used to control insects feeding on the leaves.

Here we had a product that could eliminate the need for all toxic pesticides, and it fertilizes plants as it controls the bugs. It was working too well. It was pushing diazinon and orthene and other toxic pesticides off the shelves. No way could the big pesticide companies stand for this! They had the EPA put a stop-sale order on it in all the small stores around the state.

I called the Texas Department of Agriculture, and they were very apologetic. They said they wanted the product on the market, but it was out of their hands if we sold it as a pesticide. If we couldn't get an EPA pesticide registration, they suggested we sell it as a Soil Conditioner, which didn't need a registration. So we relabeled it: "Auntie Fuego Soil Conditioner," but sales dropped off. Without being able to give instructions on using it as an insecticide, it is hard for customers to know what to do. We are not even allowed to mention the word "pesticide" while making a sale of it in stores.

I knew it would be hard to get an exemption or an EPA registration number, but I tried anyway. The first person I worked with at the EPA was really excited about this nontoxic product and tried her best to help, but she was soon told she had to turn me over to a higher-ranked employee. He too was excited about the product, but he turned cold and didn't want to talk with me after a while. I was then told I would have to work with a new person. This time is was a young woman. She loved the product and said she'd have it back on the market within a few weeks with an exemption. She tried but someone kept throwing roadblocks at us. After several months, this young lady finally said to me, "Mr. Beck, don't you see what is going on here?" I told her yes and thanked her for trying to help.

During the six months of trying to get an exemption or a number from the EPA, they were trying to get me to change the formula and only buy products from companies they recommended. They also wanted numerous tests done to see if it actually worked, if it was toxic to humans, and if it had any harmful microbes in it. I offered to have all the tests done, but they said they could only be done by the people they recommended. They would need three tests done for each perceived problem. Each test would take up to a year or longer, and each would cost between $50,000 to $1 million. I told them to send the paperwork and I would try to find investors to get the money. I never got a single form, name, or paper of any kind from the EPA to get the testing started. Someone is determined to keep our product off the market. Which only proves its ability to make toxic insecticides obsolete. That would obviously affect the profits of many large chemical companies — especially since we didn't patent the product and we freely give out the formula so anyone can make it themselves.

Diatomaceous Earth

Diatomaceous Earth (DE) consists of the sedimentary deposits formed from the skeletal remains of a class of algae *(Bacillariophyceae)* that occur in both salt and fresh water and in soil. These remains form diatomite, an almost pure silica that is ground into an abrasive dust. When the tiny razor-sharp particles come in contact with an insect, they cause many abrasions, resulting in loss of body fluids. DE is the secondary ingredient in a variety of insecticides. DE is harmless to mammals and birds and is digestible by earthworms. DE is found to be beneficial in conjunction with grain and seed storage and as a deodorizer on fecal and other waste around barns, kennels, and garbage cans. Both USDA and state departments of agriculture have information on using DE.

Although all diatomaceous earth is made up of these tiny skeletons, there are some variations among packaged brands of DE. Each company mines their DE from a particular place and the size and shapes of the skeletons depend on the locale. Some brands also contain larger amounts of calcium carbonate, which increases the weight of the product without increasing the number of diatoms. Through experimentation, we have found that some brands are more effective than others because the skeletons are sharper and they contain smaller amounts of calcium carbonate.

DE as an Insecticide

Over the years I have done many tests using DE to control insects. Sometimes with good results, other times it didn't work at all. I finally realized that humidity was the controlling factor. In low humidity, it would kill most any insect if you gave it a good dusting, but in high humidity it was of little use except on some small soft-bodied insects.

DE Test on Fire Ants

Will DE kill fire ants? It was a question I heard frequently, but could not truthfully answer without doing my own testing. I had heard strong arguments both ways.

For a test, I got two one-quart fruit jars and put one teaspoon of DE (Brand A) in one jar and one teaspoon of DE (Brand B) in the other. I took my jars and found a healthy fire ant hill. I put a heaping tablespoon of ant hill, including very mad ants, into a jar. Then I put another tablespoon into the other jar. I kept alternating jars until each jar had six tablespoons of ants and ant hill in it. I was forced to stop then because the ants were racing up the spoon handle and stinging me. I quickly replaced the lids tightly on each jar, and I shook each slightly to mix the DE in the soil, to make sure the ants would come in contact with it.

This test was made about four o'clock in the afternoon. At nine that night, I checked the jars and found all the ants to be healthy and active. At nine the next morning, the jar containing DE Brand A was full of dead ants. The jar containing Brand B had healthy and active ants. At three o'clock, the ants were still alive, but by eight the next morning, all the ants in the second jar were also dead.

Now I knew that DE will kill ants, but I wanted to know exactly how long it took to kill them. I decided to take the ant samples early in the morning so I could watch them all day. I used the same procedure as before, except that this time I used a third jar without DE mixed in with the ants. I placed all three jars on my desk, so I could watch them throughout the day.

Days went by and nothing happened. The ants were still all alive and appeared healthy. On the ninth day, something finally happened, but not what I expected. The ants in the control jar — the one without any DE — were all dead. Not until the 13th day did I notice ants beginning to die in the other two jars. By the 16th day, the ants in Brand A were finally dead, and on the 18th day, the ants in Brand B were dead.

Great! Now I was really puzzled. Instead of proving that DE killed ants, I had proved that it prolonged their lives! More tests were definitely called for, but how?

After much study, I decided it must have been the difference in the moisture in the jars that caused the difference in the two test results. The first test was taken in the afternoon when the ant hill moisture and humidity were low. The humidity was high in the morning when the second test was taken and the ant hill contained much more moisture. Perhaps the moisture kept the ants from losing body fluids and somehow they received energy from the DE to help them survive longer. Another test was needed.

In the third test, I again used three jars, but all contained different brands of DE. All samples were taken from the same mound. I was very careful to get all exactly the same and with as little moisture as possible. The samples were taken on a hot, dry afternoon. By the fifth hour, all the ants in Brand A were dead. The ants in Brand B died by the ninth hour, and those in Brand C were dead by the 11th hour.

From this test, I learned that DE would kill ants in a low humidity in jars within five hours. But how fast would they die in only dry soil in jars? Back to the drawing board. I used two jars with equal amounts of soil and ants from an ant mound. I shook one jar as if I were mixing in DE and the

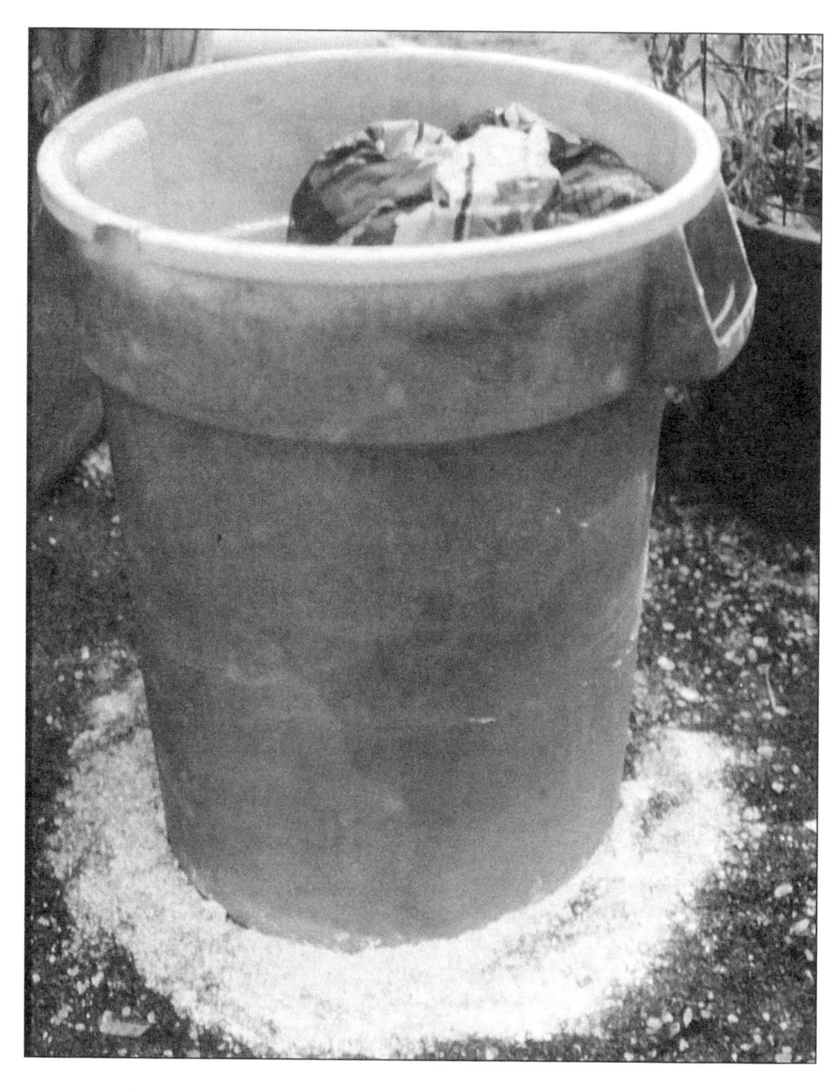

DE spread on the floor around this feed container completely stopped ants for months. Another product from Nature, found in natural deposits, that has so many uses.

other one I disturbed as little as possible. The disturbed ants were all dead in two and a half days. The undisturbed ants took a day longer to die.

All of the jars in all of the tests were kept in the office out of direct sunlight at temperatures between 72 and 82 degrees.

I was ready for one more test to find out if DE alone would kill ants in the field. I found a single big healthy ant hill that had no other hills nearby. I applied about four ounces of Brand A and then took a stick and scratched it into the mound well. I applied the DE in the afternoon when the humidity was low. The next day at noon I checked the ant mound and found no live ants. Furthermore, unlike many insecticides, the DE appeared to keep other satellite mounds from appearing later. No new mounds appeared in the area.

Summary

All brands of DE tested do kill ants, although some kill faster than others. The method of killing must include dehydration since high humidity seems to limit the effect and even cause beneficial effects. It seemed to me that if given a choice the ants definitely will stay away from DE.

"Brand A" has worked best for me in all my tests. Its name is Celite #392, and it's the kind we sell at Garden-Ville. The diatoms in this brand, which can be seen under a microscope or powerful magnifying glass, are various shapes and extremely sharp. It also contains less calcium carbonate, so is less heavy and therefore more economical than some other brands. Other brands, however, do work in the same way that this one does since they are all made up of the tiny skeletons that have an abrasive effect on insects.

Using DE as a Repellant

I use a 20-gallon trash can for storing fish food and have always had ant problems. The fire ants loved that stuff, and I had heard that fire ants were toxic to fish, so I was particularly anxious to keep them out. To see if DE would help, I spread a pint of DE on top of the soil around the trash can. After several months, the DE has spread and worked its way into the soil some, but there are no fire ants in the fish food. I keep the food in a greenhouse where I raise tropical fish, so the humidity is always high. Still, there hasn't been a single fire ant in the fish food since the day the DE was applied.

Some people also set their pet food dishes in larger dishes of DE and report that it keeps the ants out of the cat or dog food.

Good Guys in Disguise

Aphids, one of the most prolific insects, are considered one of our biggest pests. They may produce up to 50 generations per year. They can produce several generations without mating. The females can lay eggs or give live birth; those that are born alive already have within them developing embryos constituting the next generation; they are born pregnant. The young quickly grow wings if they need to migrate away from a natural enemy or to a better food supply. Their life history is very complex. The life cycle varies widely between different species and may vary widely within the same species in different geographical locations.

With all of the life- and generation-sustaining abilities, you would think that aphids would soon destroy all vegetation. But they don't. They have lots of natural enemies in the insect world, but more importantly, healthy, well-grown and adapted plants have some immunity to them. The aphids flourish and multiply fastest on plants that are sick, weak, and stressed. Lady beetles and many other beneficial insects prey on them, but many times I have watched the aphids multiply faster than their predators or parasites can destroy them. This always happens on a weak plant. At times I can correct the stressing condition by giving the plant more sunshine, moisture, or missing nutrient. If the plant isn't too far gone it will bounce back, build up immunity, and aphid reproduction will slow until the beneficial insects can control them. There seems to be a fine line between the aphids' ability to destroy a plant and the good bugs' ability to hold them in check.

You could call the aphids censor insects. They seek out and try to destroy any plant that is a misfit, weak, or sick. The aphids and many other troublesome insects should really be classified as "good bugs." We have overlooked their importance to keeping the plant world healthy. Since the beginning, they have only allowed the best plants to reproduce and furnish food for the animal kingdom. We are indebted to the aphids for not only improving our food stock, but probably keeping much of the plant world from degenerating away to the vanishing point.

We can see the importance of aphids and other so-called bad bugs, but this doesn't make the lady beetles and other well-known predators and par-

Aphids on a branch. We should always ask why the aphids are attacking certain plants and not others.

asites any less important. The censor insects could quickly overdo their job if Nature didn't have a police force to hold them in line.

This police force of predator bugs seems to prefer patrolling on the healthy plants with few aphids rather than neighboring sick plants loaded with aphids. I have witnessed this for years. At first I considered it a coincidence or my imagination, but I have noticed this too often. Researchers explain it this way: "No respecting lady beetle would want to eat an imbalanced aphid that grew on an imbalanced plant. The lady beetles, like cows, have nutritional instincts luring them to feed on the most nutritious food supply and this has genetically caused the aphid population to prefer imbalanced plants." I call it "more of the wisdom of Nature."

To keep cats out of flower beds and sand boxes, sprinkle in some ground Cayenne pepper. The cats always sniff first and it will burn their noses. They will go elsewhere. You can buy large containers of cayenne pepper in the spice section of the grocery, in some garden centers, or you can grow and grind your own peppers.

A Helpful Fly

She almost looks like an ordinary house fly, but inside the house is the last place she would choose to be. The first time I met her was while inspecting our tomato field. Everything was calm and quiet except for one plant that had a large branch shaking vigorously. Curiosity drew me over for a look, and I found a big tomato hornworm on the branch with a common-looking fly that kept attempting to land on the worm. Finally she learned to land between vigorous wiggles, and each time she succeeded, she left behind a small white egg.

Right away I got out the bug books and learned that we call this bug a tachinid fly. The books also said there were more than 1,400 of her species described. They are considered an important parasite and are credited with saving the sugar cane industry in Hawaii.

The second time I met her was years later on our new farm. We had a bad infestation of walnut caterpillars. They were doing more damage than I cared to stand for. That was before I found out about Bt, *Bacillus thuringensis,* and I didn't know of a natural control for the caterpillars. A trip to the extension service only offered me toxic materials which I was tempted to use, but decided to wait a few more days. It was a good thing I did! While working under an old truck, I noticed a fly buzzing around near the ground. I saw it light on a walnut caterpillar, deposit an egg, fly off in a circle, then come back again. Over and over again, the fly deposited her egg on the caterpillar, then flew away only to return. I noticed she always deposited them close behind the head of the worm. Each time the worm would reach back and try to knock the egg off, but couldn't bend his body short enough to dislodge the eggs just behind his head.

I began inspecting and noticed all the walnut caterpillars-and there were plenty of them-had tachinid fly eggs deposited on them. I went and telephoned my friends at the extension service and told them I didn't think we would have to worry about the walnut caterpillar next year because their natural enemy had caught up with them. Sure enough, it has been over 30 years since then, and we have yet to see the walnut caterpillar return in damaging numbers.

The tachinid fly. She looks like an ordinary housefly but is way too helpful to be insulted as such.

If I had been impatient and sprayed, I could have killed enough tachinid flies to widen the predator-to-prey gap. Some caterpillars would have escaped the toxic spray and would probably have come back in damaging numbers the next year. Sometimes the only help Nature requires of us is patience.

Nematodes & Cedar Chips

A railroad co-worker of mine grew greenhouse tomatoes for extra income. His greenhouse was 6,000 square feet, and he allowed me to mulch a double row of tomatoes in the center of the house as part of our cedar flake research. His tomatoes were already planted and standing about 18 inches tall when I put a one-inch layer of cedar mulch around the plants. The rest of the house was left without mulch. I saw this co-worker often, and each time he told me that the cedar-mulched tomatoes were no different from the rest. One day late in the season, however, he said he had tomato plants beginning to droop all over the house because of root-knot nematodes — except in the mulched row. He told me that it was his fourth year growing tomatoes in the same spot and that the experts had said that by the sixth to seventh year it would be impossible to continue growing because of the nematodes, even if he fumigated with a toxic chemical each year to sterilize the soil.

A nematode is a very small worm-like insect, sometimes called an eelworm, that moves around in the soil and feeds on and lays its eggs in plant roots causing knots to form which causes the plant to lose nourishment and become stunted. Not all nematode species are harmful. Some are even beneficial. There are predator types that destroy other harmful insects, including the troublesome nematode. Even the troublesome nematode in very small numbers can be considered beneficial. They seem to stimulate extra production in plants. Several times I have seen a plant grow bigger than its neighbor, and upon inspecting its roots I noticed a few nematode knots where the neighboring smaller plants had none. All through Nature, researchers have found that a small amount of damage from any insect seems to increase plant growth. The secret is balance and control.

In the greenhouse, I thought maybe the mulching effect just helped the plants with their moisture needs, so we cut off the irrigation line to the mulched row to test my theory. The plants still didn't droop. This seemed strange, so when the season was over I helped clean out all the old plants from the greenhouse. We inspected the roots of each plant and found the mulched row had 90 percent less nematode damage than any other row in the house. This was a very exciting discovery, so I called the tomato green-

My railroad co-worker Rosco Jordan's tomato greenhouse, where the cedar flake/nematode test took place. Rosco didn't realize it, but his tomatoes were organically grown. Rosco learned to be thrifty growing up on a farm. For fertilizer he used partly composted chicken manure, for cooling on hot days he had the north and south wall hinged to completely open up, and for heat he used smudge pots vented through the roof in which he burned waste crank-case oil from the railroad diesel locomotives. It was the most productive and profitable greenhouse I've ever seen.

house Ph.D. at A&M to discuss it with him. He had no explanation, but he did invite me to a greenhouse growers conference at College Station.

During the conference I struck up a conversation with the person having breakfast across the table from me and told him about my mulching experience. Immediately he brightened and introduced himself as a Ph.D. from Mississippi. He said he would be giving a talk at two o'clock that afternoon on that very subject. He said he always suggested that growers put wood chips on the floor of the greenhouses to walk on. The chips kept the soil from packing when walked on and their feet wouldn't get muddy. As the chips decayed they gave off carbon dioxide to feed the plants. He noticed that in the mulched houses, the nematodes were much less of a problem, and in some houses, the nematode population was almost eliminated within seven years.

After his talk, he asked me to elaborate on my experience in the tomato greenhouse. Everyone in the audience wanted to know how wood chips deterred nematodes. The Mississippian didn't know, but suspected it must be a phenol or aromatic in the wood. I thought it was some biological action because I had read in a Rodale publication of a beneficial fungus that destroyed nematodes. There were lots of experts there, but none had heard of a nematode-destroying fungus. One grower at the meeting who was having big nematode problems decided he would grow in pure cedar flakes. He put down plastic sheeting film to separate the infested soil from the cedar, then planted his tomatoes. I visited him about the time the tomatoes started ripening. He said, "Malcolm, something is wrong. I have got the worst nematode infestation I ever had, and I don't understand it."

This grower didn't realize it, but he proved the nematode deterrent wasn't chemical; it had to be biological. All of his tools and watering equipment probably had nematodes or their eggs on them, and he accidentally re-introduced the nematodes into a sterile environment. The cedar flakes are sterile from the steam cooking and void of any beneficial fungi or other competing soil life, and the nematodes had nothing to hold them in check.

Now, years later, you can go to Texas A&M and they will show you pictures of two different fungi attacking nematodes. One loops around a nematode and pops its head off; another grows into the nematode and devours it. In order for these beneficial fungi to flourish, they need a fertile, aerated, balanced soil, with a supply of carbon to use as energy, and cedar flakes are a good energy source.

There are many types of microorganisms that aid in decomposition. They each take a turn feeding on and decomposing carbon products such as cedar flakes. Bacteria usually start the process, and their populations explode to high numbers and then subside. Other microorganism populations — actinomycetes, algae, and fungi — explode and then subside. Each species takes its turn at dominating. The nematode-destroying fungi are probably late in the dominating cycle, and since cedar flakes are slow to decompose, there is still energy left for the nematode-destroying fungi. This is one explanation of how the cedar flakes help control destructive nematodes.

Spiders

It was the spiders that fascinated me most during my childhood. There were so many different types, sizes, and colors, and they never ate our plants. Instead, they ate the bad bugs that were eating in our garden. They built all kinds of webs to snare their food. Some I saw flying through the air like kites, making their own string as they went. Others were black, jumping spiders that hung around the windowsills in our house. They had big, green eyes that looked friendly and always right at you. They were welcome, and my parents wouldn't let anyone harm them. They were probably the bug that gave me the biggest thrill, because in the blink of an eye they could jump and catch a fly.

As a child I had very few toys, and they had to be shared with all my brothers and sisters. But I didn't care; the insects were more amusing anyway. There was one spider my mother taught me not to play with. I don't believe I would have anyway because of her deadly looks. This spider was shiny black with a bright red hour-glass on her underside. Her web was silky but ugly because it had no pretty pattern like other spider webs. My mother said she was the black widow and deadly poisonous. She was so mean she'd kill her husband after mating.

Later on in life I learned that there are only two dangerous spiders in this country. The other one is called the brown recluse. I have seen them in pictures. They have the outline of a violin on their back. I have never seen one in Nature; they must really live up to their name. The black widow is more common. During high school, I worked for a plumber for a couple of summers. Many homes then were built on piers and the plumbing was underneath the house. If the house was fairly new, I always found numerous black widows. For some reason, I never saw them under old houses. They seemed to prefer new structures.

My wife, Delphine, loves Nature as much as I do. I guess that's why we have a good marriage. When she had time, she liked to keep bees. One day a new swarm came out, and she asked me to clean up a bee box that had been in storage. When I took off the top of the box, I realized I had torn open a mud daubers' nest.

A beautiful and beneficial garden spider named argiope.

I knew mud dauber wasps caught spiders, but I didn't know how many or what kind. The first thing I did was get my camera and take pictures of the nest. Then I got a tooth pick and started separating, identifying, and counting the paralyzed spiders.

When the mud dauber wasp catches spiders, she doesn't kill them. The sting paralyzes the leg muscles so the spider can't move. She then caries them to a mud chamber, lays an egg with the spider, and seals the chamber. Her egg hatches into a wasp larva; the larva crawls among the spiders, eating

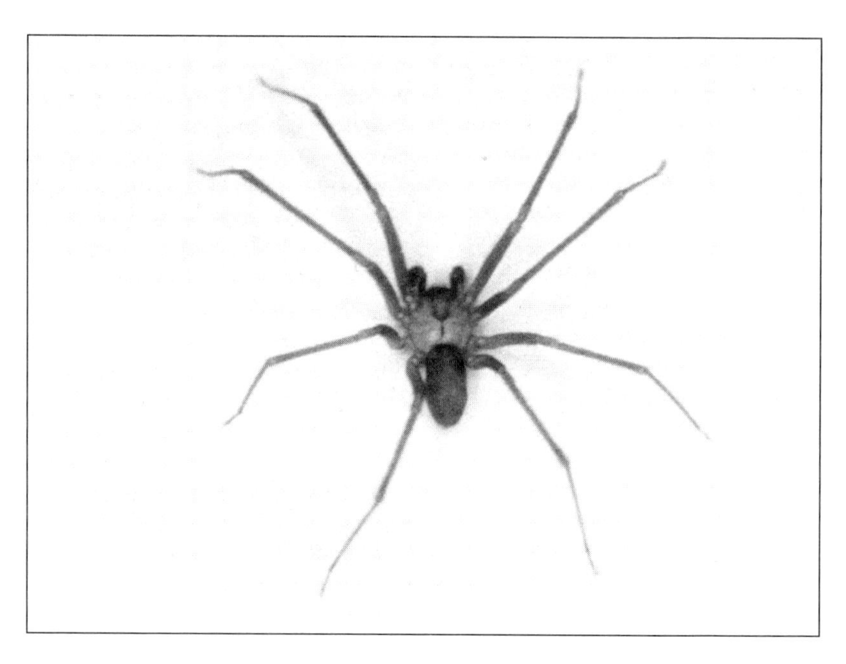

A brown recluse.

their leg muscles first. The larva doesn't feed on the spider bodies until last, so the spider remains alive longer.

When I got through counting and identifying the spiders in this one nest, they totaled 77. Of those, all but eleven were black widows.

I am sure Nature gave us the black widow for a reason. One use we have already discovered is that her web is extremely strong for its thickness, and it makes good crosshairs in rifle scopes. But Nature, in her wisdom, realizes that we don't need a lot of black widows, so she put the mud dauber here to keep that poisonous lady under control.

Once when I gave a presentation on insects and talking about spiders, a lady in the audience told us she was an entomologist who studied spiders. She said she once opened a mud dauber's nest and found it stuffed full of brown recluse spiders. Nature puts her checks and balances in place. Our job is to not upset that balance.

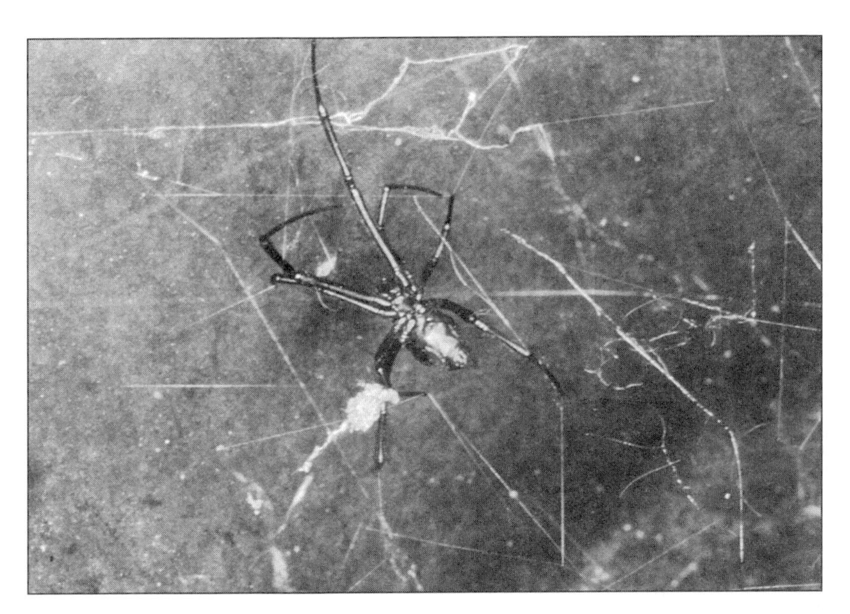

A black widow. The brown recluse and black widow are the only known dangerous spiders in this country — and even they have something beneficial to offer us.

The Birds & the Bees

An old gardening friend from the city visited my wife and me one day in 1957. After I showed him around my little farm, he told me it would be the perfect place to keep honey bees — especially since I didn't use any poisons. It wasn't long before he had brought a dozen or so hives and put them on the farm. Besides being good for pollinating the garden, the bees were fascinating to watch. Del and I were learning a lot about the art of beekeeping, since our friend had been at it a long time.

The beekeeper always gave us some honey each time he robbed the hives. We enjoyed the sweet amber bonanza and everything was going great until he came out one day and discovered that I had put up a big purple martin house, where several pairs of birds were already in residence. The beekeeper was pretty upset at seeing those birds patrolling the sky. He said I'd better take down the martin houses because he was afraid they would eat all of his honeybees.

By then I was already attached to the friendly martins, and they must have been attached to us too. They acted as if they belonged to the family; they never flew away when we walked near their house, instead giving us a friendly chirp. I just couldn't see taking down the house where our friends were living. Besides, I couldn't believe that such a beautiful and beneficial creature would attack and eat such a beautiful and beneficial insect.

I didn't remove the martin houses, but I did promise to pay the beekeeper for any hive that was lost. As time went by, the martins and bees seemed to be getting along well with each other. One morning on the way to the barn to milk the cow, however, I noticed a martin flying toward its house with swift and erratic maneuvers. It looked like something was chasing it, and it zoomed right into the house at full speed. I can't imagine how it stopped without slamming into the inside wall of the house.

On several occasions, I noticed this same flight pattern by the purple martins and was puzzled. One morning I was close enough to understand. The honeybees were escorting the martins home whenever they accidentally flew through the bees flight pattern.

Since that discovery, I always watched for the escort bees. Usually there would be three bees, one on each side of the martin about a foot away and one directly behind the bird at about the same distance. I never saw more

A purple martin house containing many martin families that patrol our farm and garden. Entomologists have told me we didn't witness honeybees chasing purple martins because martins are much faster flyers than honeybees. Evidently they have never timed a mad bee in the draft of a scared, erratically flying purple martin.

than three bees, but occasionally there would be only two, one on each side. I'm sure the martins didn't enjoy the escort service, but it really was fun to watch. The bees flew at the same speed the martins did, and regardless of any evasive move the martins made, the bees kept up and always remained in perfect formation.

I knew from then on that I wouldn't be paying for any lost bee hives, at least not because of anything the martins did. We have always had martin houses on our farm, and my children loved them. The birds always perched on their front porch and looked down at the children and chirped to them rather than flying away like other birds. One beautiful shiny male became our special friend. When we walked out into the barnyard, he would fly high in the air, then fold his wings like a diving hawk and dive directly at one of us at full speed until he was about six feet above our heads. Then he would spread his wings and flutter to a halt, with a lot of wild chirping sounds as he flew back up into the air. Most evenings he was ready to put on his show. Usually he came from the direction of the setting sun and tried to sneak up and startle us.

My kids named this dive-bomber "Old Dover," and every spring they couldn't wait for him to come back home. He returned at about the same time each year for five or six years. We were all sad to be without him when he didn't return, and no other martin has learned to play like Old Dover did.

The purple martins are the friendliest of birds, and I think they are also the most masterful in the art of flying and gliding. Along with the industrious honeybees, they add a lot of beauty and fascination to Nature.

Outwitting the Thieves

After years of working to build the soil and then following the six organic rules, I can finally produce beautiful fruit and vegetables. Each year, I just can't wait to taste the first fruit — but I'm not the only one. The birds can't wait either. Usually they eat only a small portion, and with the amount I planted, we were glad to share with these neighbors because we enjoy their company.

The birds always find the first ripe peach, but I make them share it with me. Usually I am watching and steal it back away from them before they make more than a few peck holes. With my pocket knife, I can cut out the holes and then eat the rest.

The birds and I got along well until I put in my vineyard. We put in many varieties of grapes for testing. We are in the process of thinning down to a few of the best varieties. One variety named Mars does well. It is a soft-skin, seedless, delicious table grape that is the first in the vineyard to ripen.

I planted ten Mars vines, and by the third year they were producing heavily. I impatiently waited for them to ripen, but so did the birds. Weekly, I checked on them and after they started getting good color, I figured that in three days they would be perfect and ready for picking.

On the third day, I drove out to the vineyard with buckets and baskets, anticipating a good harvest. You can imagine my disgust when I found that some thief had beaten me to every single grape. They didn't even leave me one to taste! I was so mad that I planned revenge. I kept a close eye as the other grape varieties ripened and discovered it was the mockingbirds, our state bird, who were helping themselves to my grapes. With the law on their side, using a shotgun was out of the question.

First, I put out "Big Eyes," a balloon that scares the birds away. It worked for a while — a very short while — then the birds discovered it was harmless and went on with their grape harvesting. Then I put out silver and red streamers; they worked for a day or so too, but were soon ignored.

Nets, if put on properly, give fairly good protection, but they are a nuisance, especially to take off. If you leave them on for any length of time, the vines grow through and tangle in the net, causing problems when you try to remove the net. Fine mesh web works better than netting since it hides the

Grape vines grown and shaped as a shade tree. These are New York Concord grapes. When I planted these the experts guaranteed me they would be dead within two years of Pierce's disease. They are now eight years old, they produce a heavy crop of disease-free grapes every year, and the birds do not get a single grape.

grapes from the birds and doesn't let branches grow through, but it is some trouble to put on and not inexpensive.

Since I had varieties ripening over a long period of time, I could see that I needed something that would scare the birds away for good. I thought that if I could catch them and scare them, they might move on. Then I remembered the sticky glue traps that are used to catch mice and insects.

This year I waited until the Mars grapes were just beginning to show a little color. I got out my gallon of bulk glue and put a little on top of each steel T post that held up the trellis wires in the vineyard. I also made some perches of rebar and coated the surface with the glue. I put these into the ground near some exposed grape bunches.

It worked great! The glue doesn't hurt the birds, but when they land on it, they immediately sense danger and attempt to fly away. They are able to fly after a few seconds of fierce struggle, but they often lose a few feathers in the process and end up with a badly bruised ego and loss of dignity.

I watched the birds struggle, then fly away, with great satisfaction. After all, I was willing to share. They were the ones who were greedy and wanted the whole crop to themselves. I was pretty proud of myself. I concluded that once the birds experienced the fright of lost freedom caused by the sticky glue, their survival instincts would override their taste for the grapes.

But I didn't give their instincts enough credit. The sticky glue worked perfectly — for two weeks. I can imagine that they had a big mockingbird meeting over in the next field and discussed that annoying sticky stuff old Beck had put in the vineyard. They voted to go ahead and finish the grape harvest, being very careful to avoid the posts and glue. So, once again I am disgusted with the birds but in awe of the magnificent adaptability of Nature. Nature can always find a way to accomplish its ends. Birds, ants, roaches, weeds — they all constantly change and adapt as situations change.

When imported fire ants got here, each colony had one queen that was the heart of the mound. We developed ways to kill the queen and therefore wipe out the colony. What did the ants do? Did they quietly die out and leave us alone? No way! They began multi-queen colonies. Now each mound has twelve or fifteen queens, so if one or two get poisoned, no problem. Life goes on as usual. Or think of cockroaches. We've been developing new and better poisons for them for centuries. Has the population declined? Are roaches extinct? You know better. As we change poisons, they adapt and become immune, and tougher than ever.

We notice the adaptability of pests and are not always happy about it, but we also need to notice that all of Nature is constantly changing and adapting. Without that wonderful ability, we'd be in very poor shape indeed. Plants and animals have been able to adapt to the stupid things man has done to Nature. The bees buzz through polluted skies to pollinate crops and make honey. Plants continue to grow on depleted soil, giving at least minimal sustenance. We ourselves continue to adapt as situations change.

We sometimes think we're awfully smart, but whatever intelligence we have comes from the great wealth of ingenuity and adaptability to be found in Nature. We may be smart — but so far, not smarter than the mockingbirds!

As time went on I was determined to outsmart the mockers. One year there was a bumper crop. I tasted the grapes daily. When I considered them perfect I went out just at daybreak with my pickup truck full of clean buckets. As I approached the vineyard a giant flock of brown/gray birds flew away — not a single grape was left. The mockingbirds beat me again. The mockers couldn't eat all the grapes the mature vines were producing, so they recruited the cowbirds to get revenge.

I finally did learn to grow grapes without sharing with the birds. Instead of training the grapes on two horizontal wires, I grow each vine up a single post with a cross at the top and prune the vines to the shape of an umbrella. Picking the grapes is a little harder, but the birds will not touch them in this hidden position.

The Bats

The purple martins get glory by day
As insect eaters while they glide and play

But in the dark of night
Many bad insects are in flight

Troublesome bugs of all type
Moths, beetles and mosquitoes that bite

All feel free to fly about
Bugs know when the birds are not out

But when the light of day fades away
Many hungry bats come out to feed and play

All night long they fly and eat
While the martins are fast asleep

They can catch bugs by the pound
While they navigate using high-frequency sound

But at light of day they hurry on back
To a dark, deep cave or spooky old shack

And rest up for another night
Of catching bad bugs while in flight

And return the skies of day
To the martins that glide and play.

Twenty million bats emerging from the Bracken Cave. Each night they consume over 250,000 pounds of insects. Their favorite food is the corn earworm moth which is also the tomato fruit worm and cotton boll worm. The bats are the farmer's best friends.

In the San Antonio area bats can outnumber martins as much as a hundred to one. They fly up from their winter home in Mexico at about the same time that the martins arrive, but the bats stay three to four months longer in the fall.

Bats detect flying insects and find their way around in the dark by echolocation. They can detect objects as fine as human hair, so it is very rare that a bat will accidentally run into something.

Bats don't mate until they are two years old or older, but they are able to fly and eat bugs within three to four weeks after birth. The gestation period is six to eight weeks. The nursery caves are filled with mother bats raising their young. Bats raise only one young per year and can live to be thirty years old.

There are many different species of bats. The smallest bat is the size of a bumble bee, and the largest has a six-foot wing span. Seventy percent of the bat species are insect-eaters. The rest eat fish, frogs, fruit or blood. There are only three species of vampire bats, and they all live in Latin America.

Bats are important to the ecosystem, particularly in controlling insects. One bat can eat 600 mosquitoes in an hour. Twenty million bats return each year to just one Texas cave, and that colony in a single night will eat a quarter of a million pounds or more of flying insects. Those insects are the ones that would otherwise prey on farmer's crops, homeowner's gardens, and the homeowners themselves!

Bats are also important pollinators to many different kinds of plants, especially those in tropical rain forests.

Bat guano is also an important resource. It is full of beneficial microbes. Garden-Ville uses it to inoculate their organic fertilizers, and because of the many good species of microbes and nutrients in guano, it is also used in bioremediation to break down toxic waste. In Peru, the Incas valued guano so highly that they would punish anyone with death for harming the bats. Guano tea can destroy fungus on plants, and guano can destroy harmful nematodes in the soil.

There are many reasons to protect bats. They are helpful in every respect and rarely harmful. You can learn more about bats from Bat Conservation International, P.O. Box 162603, Austin, Texas 78716.

Harvesting Bat Guano

Garden-Ville has been using bat guano on the farm and in the garden since 1959. We've been selling it in our store since 1970 and doing our own harvesting from the Bracken Cave, which is only a short distance from Garden-Ville, since 1982.

The Bracken Cave is the largest active bat cave in the world. Every year on the third of February 20 million mother bats fly up from Mexico to the Bracken Cave to give birth to their young. While they are there they will deposit between 85 and 100 tons of guano in the cave. In order to generate this much guano the bats, along with their young, will consume up to 200 tons of insects each night.

I have researched the Bracken Cave going back to 1896, when it was first harvested by the Marbach Family. Some of the family still live in this

Every other year in January, Garden-Ville harvests about 200 tons of guano from the Bracken Cave.

area, and they say that "No one has ever gotten sick from working in the cave and handling the guano — in fact, the cave workers seemed to be immune to even the common cold." This was hard for me to believe until I started harvesting the guano myself. Sure enough, none of the harvesting workers ever got so much as the sniffles while they were working in the cave.

When the Marbachs first worked the cave they shoveled the guano into gunny sacks and hung the sacks out on a cable. Later they dug a shaft down to largest area in the back of the cave and hoisted the bags out with a rope over a pulley. By the late '70s, large vacuum equipment had become available, and it has been used ever since.

The bats don't give us very much time to do the harvesting. Some years they don't leave for their winter home until a really cold spell sends them on their way, which is usually November or later. Then we have to wait another ten days to two weeks for the guano beetles to finish their job of digesting the guano and any dead bats into a fine, better smelling product. Actually the product we harvest is more beetle poop than bat poop.

The shaft in the back of the cave, and the harvesting, has made the cave a better habitat for the bats. To show their appreciation the bats swirl up, each night, in enormous columns with a spectacular show. And when they are away on vacation they allow us to take from their summer home tons of the very finest plant food.

Seven Laws of Success

Whether you are composting for your own garden or on a commercial scale, whether you are a serious farmer or a weekend gardener, you will find that working with Nature has many rewards. I have found that following these seven laws in every area of life helps me live more fully and more contentedly. They have grown from my experience with life and Nature. I share them with you in the hope that they will bring you the satisfaction they have brought me.

1. Do Not Abuse Your Body

Keep your body and mind in the best of health. A stressed body cannot be fully productive or nourish a creative and sound mind. Hate and negative thoughts of any degree destroy the mind and the body.

2. Use Your Talents

Pursue an occupation that you enjoy, regardless of what it is, as long as it is good. Every person on earth has a God-given talent to do something beneficial that he or she can enjoy and prosper from. The only difference between work and play is the degree of enjoyment you have while doing it. It is easy to have fun and a good attitude doing a job that you like. Don't let an impressive pay scale drive you into an occupation you will not be happy in. All successful and prosperous people are doing work they love.

3. Study, Study, Study

If you want to accomplish something, you must look at a question or problem from every angle and point of view. Read books; go to school. Discuss your ideas with other people. Even if you think the person you are talking with knows nothing about the subject, talk about it anyway. The other person may spark a thought that leads to success.

4. Ask God for Help

And most importantly, have faith that you will receive the help you need. The help may not come in the way you wish, but you will receive what is best. From my earliest childhood I had dreams of the many things I wanted to do and to have, and I put these dreams into my subconscious without the slightest doubt that they would come to me. At the right time, they all materialized — the jobs, the wife, the children, the business, the knowledge, the accomplishments, the awards, the acquaintances, the house, the farm, the big trees, the big trucks and tractors, and even patents. I cannot think of a single dream I didn't get by following these seven positive laws.

5. Think for Yourself

Accept the word of others as neither true nor false. Listen and store what others think, then see if or how it fits and is proven by your own ideas and experience.

6. Don't Give Up

See the big picture, consider setbacks and hardships as necessary learning experiences. Always think positively, and never, never think negatively. There is some good in every person and something to be learned from every event. The good only needs searching for.

7. Thank God

If what you wish for is good, and you have faith, it will come. And when you share your beneficial knowledge and discoveries, you will prosper much greater than if you selfishly kept them hidden. Knowledge and discoveries don't belong to any one person; they are eternal. They are written for all by the Master Designer. Just feel honored to be a chosen messenger. And if you wish for future requests to be granted, you must not forget the last law of success — and that is to tell God, *thanks!*

The Destruction & Survival of a Beautiful Planet

Communications and speed of travel has squeezed our beautiful and life-sustaining space ship down to neighborhood size. With modern electronics we can speak to, look at and spy on anyone around the globe as if we were visiting across the yard fence.

Instead of using these miraculous inventions to study, improve and protect his environment and generate neighborhood fellowship, humans are constantly quarrelling, warring, and killing each other because of jealousy, envy and greed.

There are uncountable numbers of live species on earth. All of these species are programmed to only be what they are and do what they do. But man has a free will. Free to work or play, be happy or sad, be trim or fat. He can also be productive or destructive.

Man has the thought and brain power to learn, design and invent — and even discover how the Earth is designed. But, with all of this vast knowledge man does not seem to understand the very system that supports and makes his life possible on this planet.

Soil, the very earth man walks on, supports all life. The quality of the food we eat, the water we drink and the air we breathe is determined by the quality of the topsoil. But, man mostly ignores the soil and treats it like dirt.

Twenty percent of our planet is dry land, but only eight percent is suitable for agriculture. That eight percent is the most abused part of Nature. What is not being paved over is dumped full of chemicals and then overtilled, which exposes the microbial soil life to sun rays that destroy more of them. The soil life, from earthworms to microbes, is what keeps the soil healthy, plant life thriving, which in turn keeps water pure and air clean.

Only healthy plant life can collect carbon dioxide from the air and process it into energy-loaded carbohydrates that furnish food and energy for all other life forms. Dead and decaying plants are just as important.

Our planet. From a distance she is beautiful, but here at home we are beginning to see her ills and feel her pain.

They furnish the energy and environment to the soil life that creates the good soil structure so badly needed for soil and water conservation.

Six percent of the earth is covered with ice; the remaining seventy four percent is covered with water. But, of all that water, only three percent is fresh — the rest is salty. The supply of that three percent is getting less and less each year.

The average annual rainfall has even gone up some in the past 100 years, but the structure of the topsoil is so poor from the lack of organic matter that the soil can't properly accept and hold soaking rain. Then the water rushes off, in raging floods, carrying topsoil with it to join the salty sea.

If man, with his free will and supposedly intelligent but sometimes arrogant brain, doesn't learn to be neighborly, stop warring, and start respecting the dirt under his feet, he will destroy the planet for himself and most other, species. Then planet Earth will be returned to lowly soil creatures. The microbes will once again start Earth on the path to becoming fertile, beautiful and habitable.

Pushing up Daisies

Nature designed life. Nature designed life to increase and multiply. Nature then designed death to make room for new life.

Walk into the woods or meadows and visit with Nature. You will be in the presence of much life. There will be plants and animals, large and small. There will be life in abundance.

Now take a closer look. There is an equal amount of death. There will be dead grass and leaves, fallen limbs and trees, even dead animals and insects.

When a plant or animal dies it will eventually be eaten by the decomposing microbes. They will decay or disassemble it and put it back into the soil.

This life-death-decay-life cycle has built the thin layer of fertile soil that covers our land. It nourishes and grows our plants, which are the bridge of life between the soil and man.

The laws of Nature demand that all expired life be recycled back to the soil to serve as food and energy to support future life.

Nature did not exempt the human body from this cycle. Should not it too be recycled?

Mutilating the human body by embalming is a grave injustice to the natural laws. Embalming consists of draining the liquids, plugging the orifices, wiring the jaw shut then pumping the body full of toxic chemicals that could someday pollute the Earth.

To further the injustice, the body it is then sealed in a plastic, fiberglass, metal or concrete box or tomb and buried beyond the reach of the decomposing microbes.

The graveyard where the body is placed is taking up land that could be used for food production, playgrounds or other useful needs. Many times the graveyards are not well kept and become an eyesore.

The casket and tomb the body is placed in are made from raw materials and energy, which are both becoming short in supply. The manufacturing process, along with digging the grave, uses more energy, which still creates more pollution.

There has to be a better way to lay a body to rest. A way which is more respectful and in tune with natural laws.

In Nature, all plants and animal bodies are disassembled, consumed, and returned to the Earth by the decomposing microbes. These microbes can detoxify poisons and destroy harmful pathogens as they maintain and build soil fertility.

Wouldn't this also be a more respectful way to handle our deceased? The large compost companies around the country have discovered that large animals completely disappear within a few weeks when placed in an active compost pile. Even a full-grown horse or a 2,000 lb. bull is completely consumed. All that is left are horseshoes or a plastic ear tag if the bull had one. No teeth, no bones, hide or hair are left behind. Just the memory, elements and energy contained in the compost.

If human bodies were composted that person could literally push up daisies. The remaining compost could enrich the soil in flowerbeds, gardens or farms.

By composting the body, the laws of Nature are not violated and the cycles of life could continue.

How to Lay My Body to Rest

I want my body dressed in a white linen or cotton gown and then, if necessary, held in cold storage until I can be gently placed on a warm bed of compost that no longer has a foul odor but is still microbially active.

Then my living relatives and friends could use shovels and buckets to cover me with a thick blanket of more warm, active compost. During this laying and covering process the religious rituals would be performed.

This composting process could be done in a container decorated with silver and gold. For proper composting aeration, the bottom, sides and top could be made of fine mesh stainless wire cloth. This container could be placed on a trailer or have wheels of its own. It could be pulled behind white prancing horses or a shiny black automobile.

At the location my body is to be returned to Nature, such as my farm, gardens or meadow, the container will be parked until my body is completely consumed. Then the container would be opened so my elements and energy can be distributed over the land to start the timeless cycling journey through higher and higher forms of life. Then finally, once again, the highest form of life.

Eternally,
Malcolm Beck

The Old Farmer's Prayer

Time just keeps moving on
Many years have come and gone
But I grow older without regret
My hopes are in what may come yet
On the farm I work each day
This is where I wish to stay
I watch the seeds each season sprout
From the soil as the plants rise out
I study Nature and I learn
To know the Earth and feel her turn
I love her dearly and all the seasons
For I have learned her secret reasons
All that will live is in the bosom of Earth
She is the loving mother of all birth
But all that lives must pass away
And go back again to her someday
My life too will pass from Earth
But do not grieve, there will be other birth
When my body is old and all spent
And my soul to heaven has went
Please compost and spread me on this plain
So my body Mother Earth can claim
That is where I wish to be
Then Nature can nourish new life with me
So do not for me grieve and weep
I did not leave I only sleep
I am with the soil here below
Where I can nourish life of beauty and glow
Here I can help the falling rain
Grow golden fields of ripening grain
From here I can join the winds that blow
And meet the softly falling snow
Here I can help the sun's warming light
Grow food for birds of gliding flight
I can be in the beautiful flowers of spring
And in every other lovely thing
So do not for me weep and cry
I am here, I do not die.

— by Malcolm Beck with Robert Tate

Appendix

Below is a drawing of the kind of compost container I recommend. It is made of lightweight wire and is easy to handle.

Examples of moveable holding units: wire, snow fencing, and drum.

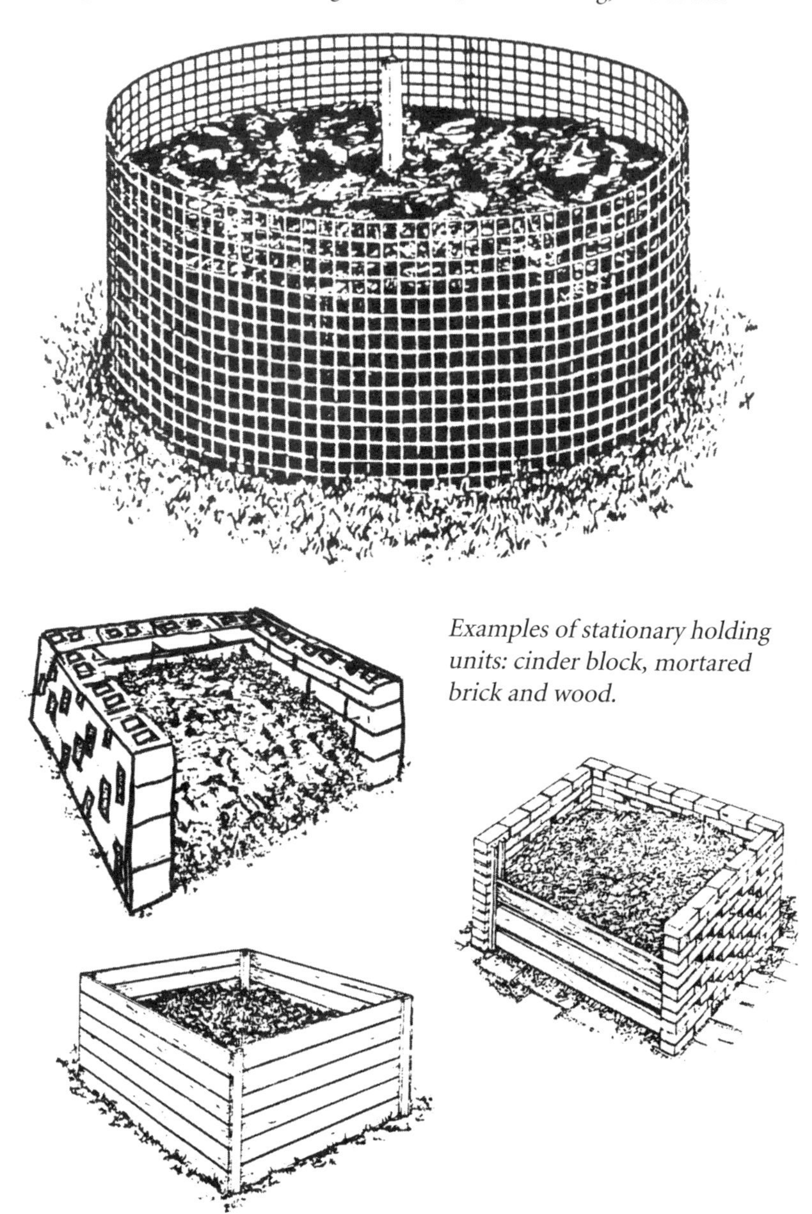

Examples of stationary holding units: cinder block, mortared brick and wood.

Piles of grass clippings, leaves, and other material can also be made without an enclosure by simply choosing an out-of-the-way corner and layering the material with soil or manure. The pile should be turned or moved periodically just as enclosed piles are. The appearance of the pile may be less tidy, but the results are the same.

Pest Control Alternatives

Pest	Natural Control*
 *Aphid*	Insecticidal soap (1 ounce compost tea, 1 ounce molasses, seaweed in 1 gallon water, sprayed at night), predators, especially lady beetles.
 *Colorado potato beetle*	Eliminate with handpicking, removing eggs from plants, row covers, heavy mulching, predators, especially giant wheel bug.
 *Harlequin bug*	Plant at proper time in fall so the plants mature when days are shorter. Row covers, control weeds; plant trap crops of turnips near main crop, pyrethrum for heavy infestations, Garden-Ville Auntie Fuego.
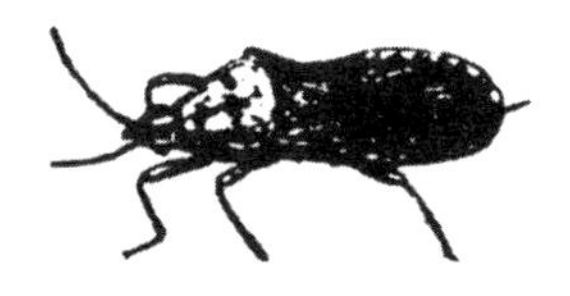 *Squash bug*	Handpicking, row covers, clean cultivation, Garden-Ville Auntie Fuego. Plant tatume squash.

***The *best* natural control resides in adapted, healthy, well-nurtured plants.**

Pest Control Alternatives

Pest	Natural Control*
 *Red spider mite*	Mix 2 tablespoons seaweed and 1 tablespoon molasses per gallon of water and spray the entire plant in the evening or on a cloudy morning every 5 days.
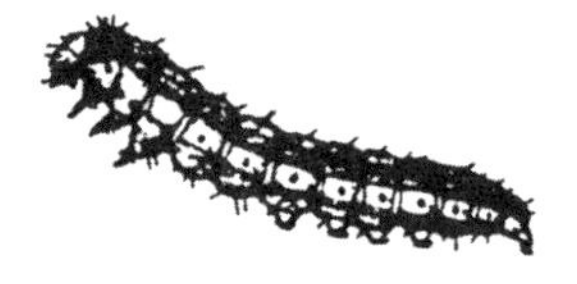 *Corn earworm*	Half a dropper of mineral oil applied to corn silk, Bt for infestation of other vegetables.
 *Cutworm*	Paper collars around seedlings and transplants, diatomaceous earth. Handpick at night with flashlight.
 *Tomato hornworm*	Handpick; if larva has papery cocoons on its back, natural parasite has already doomed it, so do not kill.

***The *best* natural control resides in adapted, healthy, well-nurtured plants.**

Suggested Organic Fertilizer Applications

	COMPOST	MANURE	COTTON SEED OR BLOOD MEAL
Trees, Shrubs & Bushes	Use 2% to 5% in backfill when planting new trees. On established trees, use 1-3" as a mulch, starting at the trunk, going out beyond the drop-line of branches.	20 to 50 pounds per 100 sq. ft. spread over root zone and raked into top one inch of soil, or covered with an organic mulch.	2 to 5 pounds per 100 sq. ft. raked in one inch deep over root zone, watered in or covered with an organic mulch.
Lawn Grasses	New Lawn: 1-2" tilled in 4-6" deep, then plant sod or seed. Established Lawn: 1/2" raked in, apply late fall.	New Lawn: 20-50 lbs per 100 sq. ft. tilled in 4-6" deep, then plant sod or seed. Established Lawn: apply 3-10 lbs per 100 sq. ft., raked and watered.	New Lawn: work in 5-10 lbs per 100 sq. ft. 4" deep, then apply seed or sod. Established Lawn: 5-10 lbs for 100 sq. ft. watered in.
Vegetable & Flower Gardens	1-2" tilled in 4-6" deep any time before planting. 1-2" as a mulch around plants after soil is warmed up in late spring. Use thick layers in walkways at all times.	20-50 lbs per 100 sq. ft. tilled in 4-6" deep, 6 weeks before planting.	5-10 lbs per 100 sq. ft. tilled in 4-6" deep, 4-6 weeks before planting.
Comments	Nature's own fertilizer, it increases the beneficial microorganisms and destroys the harmful. It is the closest thing to a cure-all available, since it heals nature's wounds. It is the gardener's most useful product.	Manure, the oldest fertilizer known to man, is well-balanced with major and minor elements, organic matter and microorganisms. But it should always be composted with bulky carbon materials before being used.	Two good sources of nitrogen with small amounts of phosphorous and potassium and trace minerals. Cotton seed meal is acid-forming, and the blood meal gives extra iron.

Suggested Organic Fertilizer Applications

	Fish Emulsion & Seaweed	Bat Guano	Bone Meal	Rock Phosphate Colloidal Clay
Trees, Shrubs & Bushes	Dilute and use as on vegetables. Spring growth responds best to foliar feeding.	5-10 lbs per 100 sq. ft. raked in 1" deep over root zone, watered in or covered with mulch.	New planting: use 1/4 to 1/2 lb mixed in each cubic foot of backfill. Established trees: 1-2 lbs for each 1" of trunk diameter in holes 8" deep in circle around tree at outer canopy limits.	Apply a good handful to each cu. ft. of backfill at planting time. Established trees: 1-2 lbs for each 1" of trunk diameter in holes 8" deep in circle around tree at outer canopy limits.
Lawn Grasses	Mix 2 tablespoons fish emulsion and 1 tablespoon seaweed per 1 gallon water and spray in morning. For a perfect lawn use as often as once a week.	5-10 lbs per 100 sq. ft. evenly spread and watered in.	NOT RECOMMENDED. Use rock phosphate at planting time only	5 lbs per 100 sq. ft. tilled in 4-6" deep before placing sod or planting seed. NOT RECOMMENDED ON ESTABLISHED LAWNS.
Vegetable & Flower Gardens	Mix 2 tablespoons fish emulsion and 1 tablespoons seaweed per 1 gallon water. Foliar feed plants in the morning; soak root areas any time of the day. Fast-growing plants, use weekly. Slow growing, monthly.	5-15 lbs per 100 sq. ft. tilled in 4" deep two weeks before planting.	10 lbs per 100 sq. ft. tilled in 6" deep. Apply once every 5 years.	5-10 lbs per 100 sq. ft. tilled in 4-6" deep once every 5-8 years. Best results are achieved when a small amount is used on seeds or the roots of transplants at planting time.
Comments	A natural 4-2-2 fertilizer used for foliar as well as root feeding. Contain a balance of all nutrients needed for healthy plant growth. Considered by many to be nature's finest.	A natural fertilzer of the highest analysis; a 10-3-1 formula with all the needed trace minerals.	A natural, high-analysis form of phosphate, 0-10-0, which helps develop sturdy roots and beautiful blooms. It is used by the serious bulb and rose growers.	The most economical source of phosphate in a natural, non-burning form. Helps develop sturdy roots, bloom & fruit. A favorite of the big farmer, it is rich in trace elements.

Conservation Tillage — Benefits & Controversies

Nature, left to her choice, never allows bare, exposed soil. She prefers a continuous cover of diverse plants that are good for food, forage and thousands of other uses. If we overgraze or somehow destroy the good plants, she then grows a less desirable plant, putting in place a lesser plant until there is nothing growing except hard-to-control bitter, poisonous and thorny plants. Nature is determined to protect her soil. Soil is the foundation to the whole environment. That is why she designed weeds, cactus, mesquites and junipers. These so-called pest plants are in fact pioneer plants. Give them enough time — and it may take centuries — and they will restore the soil to perfection. However, if we abuse the soil to such a degree that the weedy plants can't grow, then the land will be lost to desert forever.

Holistic Resource Management is a method developed by Allan Savory. It teaches us to research every plan, product and action to see what the ripple effect will be. How will it affect the environment, our children, our neighbors and the future? Ranchers who follow HRM teachings seem to have a good handle on animal grazing and ranching that meets Nature's approval. Conventional agriculture definitely does *not* apply HRM practices.

The poor farming practices of modern agriculture can destroy the soil and turn farmlands to desert even more quickly than overgrazing. Conventional agriculture is falling way behind the HRM ranchers in soil and water conservation. The land grant universities should be guiding the farmers, but I find little evidence of it — although there is a super website to help existing no-till and wannabe no-till farmers at <www.no-tillfarmer.com>. It is committed to providing no-tillers with latest in no-till ideas, inventions, techniques and industry news. It also has a question-and-answer section and a chat room.

Agriculture need not be destructive to the soil. There are better ways to grow food and fiber. We don't expect conventional agriculture to quickly change to organic or no-till, but it must happen eventually. With guidance from HRM for ranchers, USDA and resources such as the no-till website, it could happen soon.

Let's take a look at agriculture nationwide: There are 455 million acres in cropland and 578 million acres in grassland pasture. Of that, a very tiny proportion is farmed organic. There are quiet a few farms already in low-till or some type of conservation tillage, but most of our agricultural land is still being plowed, wasting water and carbon while polluting the air.

The farmers I know all work long hours. Some work 60 to 70 hours a week. Even when they are not on a tractor, their brains are working. They are always planning and thinking about some farm-related problem, be it labor, weather, money, price, equipment, whatever. They can't go home and leave their job and its problems back at the office. At the end of the year, after profits are tallied, most don't make a parity wage.

The only reason most farmers haven't left the farm for a 40-hour-a-week job is that government subsidies and/or crop insurance pay enough to allow them to stay on the farm. Farmers like to be their own boss and do what they love. Almost all the farmers I have visited tell me that without subsidies and crop insurance they couldn't survive. Some of these are large farms. One family I visited farms 28 "sections" (square miles), they have 34 center-pivot sprinkler systems. Many of the systems are the large half-mile type — one complete circle covers a full mile. Each system has several wells feeding it. The farmer agreed they were pumping the Ogallala Aquifer dry to grow corn that has a poor market and brings less dollars per bushel than it costs to grow.

The big center-pivot, circular irrigation systems leave a plot of land at each corner unirrigated. The government allows the farmers to put this acreage in the Crop Reserve Program, along with a certain amount of other tillable acreage. Once acreage is put into the program, it has to stay there for 10 years. This would be fine if they allowed the farmers to concentrate on building the health and organic content of this soil — but they can only do what the government program permits. The farmer with the 34 center-pivot systems, for example, had a whole square mile in CRP. He was told to plant Old World bluestem, a climax plant that is not a very good soil builder, and he was required to keep it sprayed with a broadleaf herbicide to keep out weeds. Weeds would even be a better cover crop, as they ***are*** good soil builders. This farmer showed me a section he had just taken out of CRP — the corn growing on it was poorer quality than the section next to it that had been in continuous cultivation. We need to change from CRP to a Soil Building Program, which would use legumes in rotation with different grass/grain crops.

Farmers and ranchers should get subsidies for *building soil health,* not for destroying it. Is this ignorance or stupidity? Getting paid each year for the percentage of increased soil organic content would be a much better farm program. It would raise the quality of the crop, the farmer could get a better price, production costs would drop, water would be saved, the air would be less polluted, and soil would still be there and in good health for our children and future generations.

The big farms owned by corporations are usually in worse shape than family farms. Their workers probably only work 40 hours a week, and all they care about is the paycheck. The employer is concerned only with profits. I seriously doubt that any of these operations are efficient and environmental. If these corporate farms where shown a farming system that saved dollars, was environmentally friendly, and was paid to build soil instead of destroying it, they would have no reason not to change.

Changes must be made. If Congress understood Nature, government-subsidized soil-building programs such as conservation tillage and organic farming could come into existence with the stroke of the pen. I don't think that all of our lawmakers are stupid. We need to vote the right people into office and support them with letters, phone calls and e-mails. Some say government should stay out of agriculture altogether. I will not argue either way. Nature doesn't care as long as it's done right.

Dedicated farmers would rather make money riding their tractors and working in the fields rather than accepting hand-outs from the government. Conservation tillage could give them the margin.

According to *National Corn Handbook* estimations comparing farms growing 1,000 acres of corn in equal environments — assuming diesel at $1.24 gallon and figuring all the tractor work each would require from start to finish — no-till would save $6,185, or approximately 5,000 gallons of fuel, compared to conventional tillage.

The savings might look small at 5 gallons per acre, but the real savings with no-till are environmental — for air, water, soil and our future, the savings are tremendous. Carbon dioxide and other greenhouse gases from crankcase and engine exhaust would be greatly reduced with no-till. Moisture and carbon loss from the soil would also be greatly reduced.

With no-till, all the plant material, crops and weeds are kept on top of the soil as mulch. This keeps the soil a more even temperature of 80 to 90 F during hot days instead the 120 F that I have measured in bare soil on a hot, sunny day. Mulch also stops "sandblasting" or blowing crops out on dry, windy days, which damages small plants and allows disease to set in, and many times means replanting.

Mulch is the perfect environment for earthworms and many other soil critters. Billions of microbes live in the moist, temperature-controlled environment. They all churn up, aerate, and build soil structure and fertility.

Heavy rains are held in place by mulch until it can soak into the churned-up, rich soil instead of causing runoff, erosion and floods that send the soil to the salty seas. We must never forget that, although 74 percent of the Earth is covered with water, it is all salty except for 3 percent — and between 80 and 90 percent of that small 3 percent is pumped onto the land for irrigation. No-till could greatly reduce this high percentage of water used to grow crops.

The annual rainfall average has gone up slightly for the last 125 years, but population growth, urban sprawl, higher standards of living and the demand for water by conventional farming is causing our water supply to run short. Neighbors and communities are already squabbling over this precious resource. The most urgent problem we face today is a water shortage. We need to concentrate on water conservation.

Conservation tillage — low- and no-till farming — is one of the most efficient and best methods of catching and storing fresh water. It is perhaps the most natural practice a farmer can adopt. Think about it: Nature never turns the soil over. When we stop plowing and exposing the soil, savings become tremendous. Production increases, eventually less fertilizer is needed, and insects and disease diminish.

Plowing, or any soil tillage, causes the soil to lose moisture and exposes it to damaging sun rays, in turn destroying billions of exposed microbes and fine root hairs. These small life forms then quickly oxidize to form CO_2, which escapes to an already overloaded atmosphere.

Conservation tillage is the best water-saving practice mankind has. Even the organic farmers who still plow could gain soil organic content faster and save the air from CO_2 pollution if they practiced no-till.

Strip-till, ridge-till and mulch-till are all methods of conservation tillage. No-till disturbs the soil the least. It is the best method to keep the carbon in the soil, and it increases the soil organic content the fastest without hauling in organic matter from an outside source. Applying compost, manure and other organic waste to farmland is an excellent method to build soil organic matter. Nature demands that all organics be recycled, but if conventional methods — with too much tilling, plowing, disking, cultivating — are continued, the soil carbon gained is eventually lost to create more air pollution. We need to think no-till and get rid of the plow mentality.

In some soil conditions aeration may periodically be necessary with conservation tillage, but it is not done by turning the soil upside down. A chisel or subsoiler is used when soil is fairly dry. If you cut the mulch in front of the chisel with a coulter (a giant, sharp, pizza-cutter-type attachment), you disturb the mulch very little. The chisel shatters the soil loose at the necessary depth without overexposing the soil.

Competing weeds always have and always will be and a problem in agriculture. With no-till, the cultivator for weed control isn't used. In our refined society, hand labor to hoe the weeds is impossible. There are enough people locked away in prisons who might enjoy using a hoe, but I don't see that happening.

In no-till farming, the major drawback is the need for herbicides in the early phases, and then periodically years later. Conventional tillage is always plowing some seeds in deeply and bringing others up from underground, meaning a continuous supply of weed seeds to sprout. Timely cultivating can do a fair job of controlling sprouting weed seeds, but if the weeds get too big because, for example, rain has delayed cultivation, your control choices are: let them grow, hand hoe, or use herbicide (obviously, the last is not an option for the organic grower).

No-till keeps all weed seeds on top of the soil, where you can eventually get rid of most of them — or if you wish, you can let them grow for additional mulch material. Decaying weeds builds soil fertility. It is a known fact that weeds become less and less of a problem as the health of the soil increases.

Glyphosate is the herbicide most widely used. If not used correctly — without a mist inhibitor or in wrong weather conditions or at the wrong time of day — it can drift to other locations, causing crop damage. It is toxic if inhaled or even through skin contact. However, all of this can be prevented if this chemical is handled properly. Nevertheless, as organic and sustainable enthusiasts, can we approve of using an herbicide?

When a well-known mycorrhizae specialist was asked, "Which is more damaging to the mycorrhizae, deep tilling or herbicide?" He explained that tillage kills the host plant and tears the mycorrhizal fungi to pieces. It destroys mycorrhizae before they get a chance to make spores (seed). With herbicides (glyphosate), the host plant is killed. As soon as the plant stops sending energy to the root, that is a signal for the mycorrhizae to quickly make seed so they can regrow on the next live plant root.

We also asked the above biologist and a biologist who specializes in the soil foodweb, "What happens to glyphosate in the soil?" They both agreed, "In a biologically healthy soil, there is a bacteria that feeds on glyphosate, in fact loves it, and quickly degrades it." Adding glyphosate to a dead soil is like taking it from one container and putting it into another, leaky one. Conservation tillage builds biologically healthy soil.

I have been an organic gardener and farmer since 1957. I have given hundreds of talks and presentations on doing things naturally. I have even written books on organics condemning chemicals. Something deep inside keeps telling me that I shouldn't OK a product designed by man to destroy. The plow and herbicides are both destroyers.

I wonder which Nature would approve? I doubt if she would approve of either.

Man created the mounting problems of our soil, water and air as well as the degrading conditions of our environment and our future. Man fouled up Mother Earth. Man, therefore, is stuck with making the decision.

Index

Acres U.S.A. — books are just the beginning!

Farmers and gardeners around the world are learning to grow bountiful crops profitably—without risking their own health and destroying the fertility of the soil. *Acres U.S.A.* can show you how. If you want to be on the cutting edge of organic and sustainable growing technologies, techniques, markets, news, analysis and trends, look to *Acres U.S.A.* For more than 30 years, we've been the independent voice for eco-agriculture. Each oversized monthly issue is packed with practical, hands-on information you can put to work on your farm, bringing solutions to your most pressing problems. Get the advice consultants charge thousands for . . .

- Fertility management
- Non-chemical weed & insect control
- Specialty crops & marketing
- Grazing, composting, natural veterinary care
- Soil's link to human & animal health

For a free sample copy or to subscribe, visit us online at

www.acresusa.com

or call toll-free in the U.S. and Canada

1-800-355-5313

Outside U.S. & Canada call (512) 892-4400

fax (512) 892-4448 • info@acresusa.com